THE MAHĀBHĀRATA

Selections from Sabhā Parva and Udyoga Parva

to

4516

kamla and anandi

THE MAHĀBHĀRATA

Selections from
Sabhā Parva and Udyoga Parva

Translated by

K. M. Ganguli

Edited by

Kanav Gupta and Meha Pande

WORLDVIEW
An Imprint of
Book Land Publishing Co.

WORLDVIEW PUBLICATIONS
An Imprint of Book Land Publishing Co.
Delhi: 58 U.B., Bungalow Road, Delhi-110007. India

ISBN: 978-93-82267-69-0

Typeset by Iluminati, Delhi-11000 7
Published by Sachin Rastogi for Book Land Publishing Co., Delhi-7 and
Printed at D.K. Fine Art Press (P) Ltd., Delhi.

Contents

APPENDIX

Publisher's Acknowledgements

The publisher wishes to thank the following for the permission to use copyright material:

Radhavallabh Tripathi, for the essay, 'Aesthetics of the *Mahābhārata*: Traditional Interpretations' from *Mahābhārata Now: Narration, Aesthetics, Ethics* edited by Arindam Chakrabarti and Sibaji Bandyopadhyay, 2014, pp. 85-94, reprinted by the permission of Indian Institute of Advanced Studies, Shimla; Sheldon Pollock, for the excerpt, 'Political Formations and Cultural Ethos' from *The Language of the Gods in the World of Men: Sanskrit, Culture, and Power in Premodern India*, 2006, pp. 223-237, reprinted by the permission of The Regeants of the University of California, Berkeley; Alf Hiltebeitel, for the excerpt, 'Draupadī's Question' from *Rethinking the Mahābhārata: A Reader's Guide to the Education of the Dharma King*, 2001, pp. 240-277, reprinted by the permission of University of Chicago Press, Illinois; Kevin McGrath, for excerpts from *The Sanskrit Hero: Karṇa in Epic Mahābhārata*, 2004, reprinted by the permission of the publisher Brill Academic Publisher; Angelika Malinar, for the essay, 'Arguments of a Queen: Draupadī's Views on Kingship' from *Gender and Narrative in the Mahābhārata*, edited by Simon Brodbeck and Brian Black, 2007, pp. 79-96, reprinted by the permission of the author; Yudhiṣṭhira-Yakṣa Dialogue from *The Mahābhārata Volume 2 Book 2:* The Book of Forest, reprinted by the permission of University of Chicago Press, Illinois; Iravati Karwe, for the essay, 'Krishna Vasudeva' from the book *Yuganta: End of an Epoch*, 159-182, 2006, reprinted by the permission of Orient Blackswan, Hyderabad.

Every effort has been made to trace the owners of copyrighted material, but if any have been inadvertently overlooked, the publishers will be pleased to make necessary arrangement at the first opportunity.

Preface

Bhāratiyajnanen kim prayojanam
What is the purpose of Indian knowledge?

Where knowledge finds relevance only in profitability, a classical text in a dead language should struggle to validate its existence. However, *classical knowledge* is often far more desirable because of the socio-political and cultural work it accomplishes. Societies often derive their identity from their sense of ancientness. Classical literatures supply precisely this ephemeral utility. In fact, even the market thrives on this sublimation. A lay reader is likely to know selected *shlokas*, episodes, and arguments received either as a part of their childhood moral training, or memorized for declamation contests, or imbibed via popular cultural forms. However, political rhetoric and insufficient reading often put twists on tales. The inability and unwillingness to distinguish a literary text from history leads to popular readings that serve strictly ideological motivations: for instance, Ashvatthāmā's apocalyptic violence is presented as proof of ancient nuclear weapons, or the *Bhagavadgitā* idea of the indestructibility of *ātmā* is read as evidence of Einstein°s theory before Einstein. Classical knowledge serves a purpose not always of its own accord.

However, the ubiquitous presence of classical knowledge in the quotidian life and its considered critical study in a classroom are different worlds. Classrooms are spaces where the metaphorical nature of texts, and the real, historical conditions of their production are differentiated and their relationship understood. In a humanities classroom, cultural texts are also studied through materials of their own producing: their reception-history. Here, even classical books emerge from their aura and meet us with their underlying human contingencies. To borrow from Eliot, these texts invite us to read and grapple with the *presentness* of the past, even as we contend with the *pastness* of our present. What end does the collective memory of cultural texts serve? Those who forget history are condemned to repeat it, but as Sheldon Pollock has insightfully quipped, 'those who remember history are condemned to repeat it too.'

* * *

This edition of the *Mahābhārata* includes the excerpts from the *Sabhā Parva* and *Udyoga Parva*, which are prescribed for the undergraduate students of Delhi University. In addition, a short and well-known section from the third book, the *Āraṇyaka Parva*—the 'Yaksha-Yudhishthira dialogue' has been included as an appendix, replicating how the epic is selectively excerpted in daily life for didactic purposes but we include this with a different objective, which is for students to see the way this epic synthesizes the large variety of existing discourses on some of its governing ideals. The prescribed translation by KM Ganguli has been used in this edition. To give the reader a glimpse into voluminous scholarly work on the epic, some representative essays relevant to the syllabus excerpts have also been included.

Radhavallabh Tripathi's essay gives a succinct appraisal of the *Mahābhārata* in *alankārashāstra*, or classical Sanskrit aesthetics. The essay flags the problematic of genre and proves that the problem is not new. Tripathi tests the *Mahābhārata* against various generic conventions, while reflecting on the complex relationship they bear to the rasa theory. Sheldon Pollock's essay 'Political Formations and Cultural Ethos' discusses the 'spatial logic' of the narrative in the *Mahābhārata* and its complex book history. His examination of the text for the 'circulatory space' of the various redactions offers insights into how the text helps in the creation of a supra-regional, geopolitical space that is founded on a deep understanding of the relationship of 'real power' to the power of a text. Alf Hiltebeitel, a prolific scholar of the *Mahābhārata* has at least six major books to his credit, none perhaps as significant as his study of Draupadi. So, we have included his exhaustive essay on Draupadi's tribulations and her question at the Kaurava sabha. Also included an excerpt from Kevin McGrath's work: his book on Karna, who he reads as 'the Sanskrit hero', a rich deliberation on the heroic code of the epic. Angelika Malinar's essay 'Arguments of a Queen' which layers the debates on Draupadi through her examination of gender and literary narration/representation in the epic. Malinar enquires into the Yudhishthira-Draupadi debate in the third book, to reflect on their conjugal relationship within their general responsibilities as the monarchical couple. To meet the changed syllabus, essay by Irawati Karve have been included in this updated edition. These essays offer nuanced and in-depth analysis of Krishna and his role in the epic. Finally, but at the beginning, is a short critical introduction, which aim to introduce some key plot-points and ideas around the text that will allow the readers to examine the excerpts.

K G
M P

Introduction

Kanav Gupta and Meha Pande

Many readers might be encountering the *Mahābhārata* text for the first time, but they could honestly believe that they do already know it. Italo Calvino has alerted us how classics are never read, always only *re-read.* This observation holds especially true for epics: we always re-encounter them, because the epic has usually already travelled through myriad channels and forms, and even without fully knowing how, we find ourselves familiarised with various versions of a seed story as well as the many myths that populate the epical universe. This basic familiarity with the text might be a good thing. However, because this familiarity generally remains at best sketchy it limits the possibility of an in-depth engagement with the world of the epic. To use Moritz Winternitz's words, "What the *Mahābhārata* means to the Indians" is quite different from what it means "to critical historians of literature".

"What the *Mahābhārata* means to the Indians" opens up interesting and important questions of its reception history, especially in the last two hundred years which saw its inevitable nationalisation in the anti-colonial period, its 'Hinduisation' in the decades after independence, and its embourgeoisement through film and television adaptations. Contrastingly, in an academic world, the *Mahābhārata* demands close and critical engagement with the 'original text' as well as the various academic questions raised within the text and in different historical periods of its production and consumption.

Various motifs and stories from the *Mahābhārata* have been dramatised as stage plays (Dharamvir Bharti's *Andhā Yuga,* 1954; Girish Karnad's *Yayāti,* 1961; Shaoli Mitra's *Nāthabati Anāthabat*), films (Shyam Benegal's *Kalyug,* 1980; Pratibha Ray's *Yajnaseni,* 1984;

Prakash Jha's *Raajneeti*, 2010), and television series (B.R. Chopra, Ramanand Sagar, Chandraprakash Dwivedi). Derivative literatures in numerous languages in the form of long poems (Dinkar's *Rashmirathi*, 1952; Subramanya Bharti's *Pānchāli Capatam*, 1914), novels (V.S. Khandekar's *Yayāti*, 1978; Chitra Banerjee Divakurni's *The Palace of Illusions*, 2008; Aditya Iyengar's *Thirteenth Day*, 2015), mythological fiction(Devdutt Pattanaik's *Jaya*, 2010; Carole Satyamurti's *Mahābhārata: A Retelling*, 2015), and even comic books (*Amar Chitra Katha*, 1988; *Epified*, 2015) all derive their narrative structure and content from the singular great resource of the *Mahābhārata*.

Besides this kaleidoscope of cultural afterlives, *Mahābhārata* continues to enjoy the stature of a Hindu 'scripture' as many didactic passages like the *Bhagavadgitā* are consumed regularly as a part of *kathā* (religious storytelling), *pravachana* (live commentary session) and *pāth* (ritual recitation) formats. However, exegetes often purpose the story of the Pāndavas to serve a didactic lesson, leading to a fair bit of misrepresentation leading to a scenario where many Hindu households refuse to keep a copy of the *Mahābhārata* to avoid bad luck and strife, even as the *Bhagavadgitā* is found in most believer households. Many characters from the epic have been acquiesced to fit within the perimeter of contemporary religious morality and bourgeois heroic standards through popular serialised television adaptations. In this scenario, a first-time reader of the original could well be caught off-guard discovering, for instance, the frequent exchange of thousands of slaves and "nubile girls" as gifts and tributes even among the Pāndavas and Krishna, the 'heroes'. That adaptations failed to even mention the significant detail of Draupadi's menstruation through her humiliations at āpura court adumbrates the threat that the female body exerts on fragile sensibilities of the bourgeois body-politic. But more than these excesses and omissions, the first reader is (hopefully) likely to identify the brittleness of moulds like 'victory-of-good-over-evil' into which the complexity of this text is habitually reduced.

What is the *Mahābhārata*?

Many a Western scholars in the have been left stunned by its sheer scale of the *Mahābhārata*, "faulting it for not being the *Iliad*" (Hiltebeitel 25, 1995) describing the text as a "literary un-thing" (Winternitz 272), a "monstrous chaos" (Oldenberg, cf. Fitzgerald 30).[1] In contrast, Indian scholars, far too many to mention, have gone the other distance in trying to establish historical dates of its production in order to invent an 'epic period' in Indian history.[2] In its final redaction, available to us today, the *Mahābhārata* touches a hundred thousand verses, and has often been held up as a matter of national achievement pride. The epic is frequently hailed for being three times the Homeric epics put together, and eight times the *Bible*.[3] Despite the diversity and motivation of approaches, scholars do agree on several crucial points, including the history of the various recensions and the need to separate extrapolative and religious readings. Even so, the near-invincible length of the epic poses the greatest challenge to its as analysis, but also makes the reward all the more valuable.

Close textual analysis and the evidence of available manuscripts has led scholars to postulate that the dates of *Mahābhārata's* composition should be between the period of 400 BC and 400 CE. The oldest extant written Sanskrit *Mahābhārata* was promulgated and stabilised around 300 and 450 CE in the Gupta period. That text, often called the 'Gupta version', effectively became the normative version for all future manuscripts. In his study of the two Sanskrit epics, John Brockington alludes to the scholarly debates on the *Mahābhārata* recensions and their chronology preceding the 'Gupta version'. There is general scholarly consensus that a

1 Such readings have also been regularly refuted by other Western scholars like J.A.B van Buitenen, Fitzgerald and (later) Hiltebeitel among others.

2 Regularly refuted by the likes of D.C. Sircar and Romila Thapar among other Indian scholars.

3 For many, length is a self-evident virtue. Never mind the fact that the *Mahābhārata* is also almost five times its predecessor epic, the *Rāmāyana*, a comparison which is not employed very commonly to establish its greatness!

precursor text of the Gupta version, which has been called *Bhārata,* began developing sometime after 400 BC.

Scholars also speculate that the *Mahābhārata* had an early Indo-Aryan provenance in oral bardic literature, possibly in even more ancient Indo-European bardic songs about warriors and wars. Franklin Edgerton's exhaustive research on the poetic meters and forms used in the *Mahābhārata* has found that the *'trishtubh'*, a minority verse form, as opposed to the loftier, Brahminical *shloka* constitutes about 11 percent of the 1,60,500 verses in the epic. Carroll Smith has demonstrated that 8,000 lines in this older, Vedic-style meter (*trishtubh)* constitute the 'core' of the *Bhārata* epic, reflecting an ancient, non-Brahminical "warrior society with close thematic ties to Homer and to *Beowulf*" (Fitzgerald 54). More recently, Arvind Sharma has argued that even the larger didactic portions of the epic have been composed in the *sūta* (court-bard) meter, the *anustubha.* All these formalist analyses point to a much shorter narrative 'core' developed after the Vedic age, to which over the next 800 years, didactic passages including the *Bhishma* and *Shanti parvas,* the *Bhagavadgitā,* numerous *ākhyānas* and *upākhyānas* (stories and substories) were added as it reached its final written form as *satsāhasree saṃhitā* (a collection of one hundred thousand verses) during the Gupta period. This has encouraged many scholars to read the *Mahābhārata* as two separate books: the 'real' epic comprising a narrative nucleus, surrounded by a voluminous didactic corpora. Edward Hopkins has separated from this didactic body from the 'real epic', calling it "the pseudo epic"[4] (Hopkins 362).

As opposed to this implicit or wilful severing of the didactic passages from the core narrative, many scholars has called reading the *Mahābhārata* as a unitary text. The argument is, best represented by van Buitenen who passionately argued for a 'design' in the final redaction, an argument he has made with more skepticism after its first fervent appearance in the introduction to the translation of the

4 Adam Bowles points out the eccentric reading where "Hopkins and others, imply and sometimes directly suggest that the didactic corpora were collated by more or less incompetent redactors" (Bowles 9).

first volume. VS Sukthankar has rebuked Hopkins and company as 'Western savants' who fail to grasp the fluidity of the oral tradition. Alf Hiltebeitel has regularly argued for the need to read the whole text, not corpora as the given unitary text instead of splitting it to along a core-periphery binary. Adam Bowles in his discussion of *āpaddharma*, points some problems of the core-periphery binary that both the schools have yet to address comprehensively. He observes:

> Yet, such studies are not concerned with the *Mahābhārata* as such; rather they utilise the *Mahābhārata* as a source text for historical data, standing alongside non-textual sources and other Indic texts, such as the *Upanishads* and the *Dharmashastras*, to reconstruct India's history, or the history of Indian ideas. Missing, however, are explorations that pose the question of the didactic corpora as constitutive features of the *Mahābhārata*: What is the relationship of the didactic corpora to the 'core' story of the fratricidal war? To the *Mahābhārata* as a whole? How do they tie into broader concerns evident elsewhere in the *Mahābhārata*? How can the didactic corpora be considered as properly constitutive of the *Mahābhārata*? (Bowles 17)

In one sense, the problem stems from the need for a stable text where familiar tools of scholarly and literary analyses can be comfortably used. An unstable text with multiple versions, the *Mahābhārata* is difficult to imagine as a stable book between two covers. Rather, it is more useful to imagine it as a collection of works with similar, integrative themes, or a library of books which are loosely held together on the basis of common themes and concerns. Y.V. Vassilkov offers a more organic imaginary to the question of genre by looking at the *Mahābhārata* as a continuous process of absorption and assimilation, which gives the epic its "uniqueness":

> The *Mahābhārata* went through the stage of the classical heroic epic and was partly transformed into a religious didactic épopée. But during this process, the Indian epic paradoxically retained some features typical of the epic folklore at the archaic stage. There is no other epic in the world which combines in the same way the features of all three main historical stages of development: archaic, classical and late. (255)

Vassilkov's threefold typology of archaic epics, classical epics, and religious/didactic epics allows for the convergence of the two schools which either follow or dismiss the 'narrative core-didactic periphery' model.

A more subtle and comprehensive way of reading the *Mahābhārata* was suggested by AK Ramanujan as he called for reading the text with a "native intuition", arguing for the need to grapple harder with and not dismiss its sheer expanse in order to understand its "structuring principle"(163). For instance, focusing on the patterns of paternity, divinity, plots, situations etc. — in the *Mahābhārata,* Ramanujan offered the device of 'repition' as a measure of 'progression' of its intelligible design. This also allowed for the inclusion of *upākhyānas* into the fold of the larger story, preparing ground for the examination of one idea in its myriad possibilities. Ramanujan also noted the performative nature of these tales, pointing to the danger of reading them as simplistic, explanatory interruptions to the 'main action'. "They too are acts", he argued persuasively, reading heroes' lives not as singular but representative of larger tendencies, the "tokens of a type" (169). Besides, he called for the need to incorporate the pervasive presence of the *Mahābhārata,* not simply another popular literary work but as a *tradition* of the Indian life.

The fecundity and the textual instability of the *Mahābhārata* are reflected in the disparate directions in which other creative and critical readings of the text have developed over the decades. Among the many sustained efforts to read the *Mahābhārata* as a unitary text, Biardeau's ideological readings, Matilal and Hiltebeitel's analyses of *Dharma* and gender, Fitzgerald's historicist reading of Brahmin renaissance against 'heathen religions like Jainism and Buddhism', McGrath's study of heroism and heroic codes, and more recently Bowles' exhaustive analysis of '*āpaddharma*', offer many fruitful ways of approaching this literary behemoth. Most of these texts use the Gupta redaction as a whole, best represented in the Poona Critical Edition (1919–1966) of the Bhandarkar Oriental Research Institute under the supervision Sukthankar, and later after his death, SK Belvalkar and PL Vaidya.[5] The very production of Poona CE itself stands testimony to the matrix of problems attending on the desire for a stable text. The edition was compiled and standardised after consulting numerous manuscripts, the oldest being only four hundred years, and by evening out the thousands and thousands of variations in the order of each *parva* and chapter.[6] Many additions were made to the vulgate versions and many passages, which were clearly interpolations, omitted to arrive at the standardised *Mahābhārata* that now comprises 80,000 verses. Clearly, the *Mahābhārata* continues to prove to be a formidable quarry of narrative materials for not just creative adaptations but also for various kinds of critical enquiries.

The Vyāsa Function

The 'pre-modern' can never be known fully, only intelligent speculations can be made about it. Even then, what can one say about the authorship of a book that reaches its final version — the only extant version — 800 years after its first signs? It is commonly held that the levirate father of Pāndu and Dhritrāshtra, Krishna Dvāipāyana Vyāsa, was also the 'author' of this epic and an entity no less than Ganesha was his scribe. As such, Vyāsa was both the literary

5 Despite the scholarly scepticism towards it, the Poona CE advances our understanding of the Sanskrit tradition immensely. The edition proves to be the starting point of all research work on the *Mahābhārata* in the West. A Japanese scholar called Muneo Tokunaga's massive efforts in 1996 led to the the digitization of the Poona edition. Later, John Smith reworked the Tokunaga text, significantly improving it, and is today available online for scholars to read.

6 Fitzgerald's comment on the numerous manuscripts and their standardisation, despite the decentralised nature of Indian cultural texts pursues the possibility of a normative written version at some moment: "But this process also revealed the striking fact that in the midst of all this variation, there was a remarkable degree of close agreement in readings line after line, in the order of verses, and in the contents of the parvans, agreement that can be explained only by postulating the existence of a normative written text at some point in the past and in some significant measure" (69).

and the biological progenitor of all the characters of the *Mahābhārata*. He is seen as a cosmic entity found across classical Sanskrit literature. Most significantly, he appears as the man who divides the *Veda* into four parts. Scholars agree that the literary meaning of the Sanskrit word 'Vyāsa' is 'a compiler', and given that the text is a series of recensions, this is a rather significant detail to bear in mind. In other words, because the character of the *Mahābhārata* as a text is not that of a stable book between covers, the nature of the author is not that of an identifiable individual either. An individual Vyāsa could not have possibly written the *Mahābhārata* all by themselves. Could they have written what has been called the narrative core? Who is to say, for no versions of the 'core' as distinct from the Gupta redaction survive. As has already been argued, the Gupta CE remains the first written redaction of the epic constituting the basis of both the 19th century Calcutta edition, as well as the 20th century Poona edition. The cumulative, palimpsestic nature of the text and its 'writing' is visible in its three -part frame-narrative structure, which Hiltebeitel insightfully classified as '*authorial*', '*generational*' and '*cosmological*'.

The innermost narrative begins with the *authorial* frame where Vyāsa recited the story to his five disciples, including his son Śuka. According to the *Bhagavata Purāna*, it is the intention of the author of the *Mahābhārata*, a key element in Vyāsa's "thought entire" to convey the message of the *Vedas* to those who were formally debarred from studying them, namely women and *sudras*. As an important character within the epic, Vyāsa's position raises — complex questions. Was an individual Vyāsa telling the saga of their progeny, or was this a metafictional device to suggest their authorship of the epic and it's characters? At one level, these are *faux* questions as authorship in a modern sense is extraneous to a 'pre-modern' epic. The answers are anyone's conjecture because the question of authorship seems extraneous to a pre-modern epic. As Vyāsa's scribe, Ganesha lends the project a divine fiat and a cosmic *gravitas*. Peter Brooks, in his celebrated international adaptation of the *Mahābhārata* (casting an African Bhima and a Japanese Dronacharya) among others — synthesised the literary and religious afterlives of the *Mahābhārata* by showing the figures of Vyāsa and Krishna cavorting together in a cosmic dance as creators of the world, and of the world of the epic. It is an intelligent and incisive dramatisation of the two Krishnas — Vāsudeva and Dwaipayana — as the authors of the word and the world, interdependent and interconnected.

What Hiltebeitel calls the *generational frame* is the second concentric circle, where Janmejaya, the great grandson of Pāndavas', attending the snake sacrifice ceremony, listens to the saga of his ancestors narrated by Vaiśampāyana, one of the four disciples who had learned it from Vyāsa in the first place. Scholars have noted the refrains of apocalyptic violence, revenge spirals and the motif of fresh creation throughout the epic. Janamejaya's *sarpa satra* should be read as one such gesture of annihilation and recreation. Vaiśampāyana's narrative frame centralises the Pāndavas as the protagonists in a cosmic project, ideologically directing the Kshatriyas to honour Brahmins and maintain the rule of *dharma*.

The outer *cosmological frame* narration takes place in the *Naimisa* forest, where the forest *rishis* hear the story from the bard Ugraśravas, who had in turn heard it at Janamejaya's snake-sacrifice. This frame has led many scholars to argue in favour of the aformentioned core-periphery binary by reinforcing the interpretation of the didactic passages as an instance of Brahminical ideology riding on the back of what was essentially Kshatriya war tales. The study of the didactic materials has led scholars to settle for two kinds of conclusions. One school has suggested that this material has been added while reimagining the epic as a counter-point to the anti-Brahminical momentum of 'heathen' religions in the Mauryan period. The didactic passages reinvigorate ideas like *karma*(action) and righteous violence in firm rebuttal of the pacifist Buddhist and Jain worldviews. The other school of thought holds that these additions cannot be attributed to a definitive political agenda, but must be read in the light of the flexible nature of the text that allows the absorption and assimilation of various discourses. This school, best represented by Hiltebeitel and more recently Bowles, argues that much of the didactic materials were already created and were simply added to the core narrative as sub-plots. In other words, they were not written specifically for the *Mahābhārata* with an ideological agenda in mind. *What* was the narrative?

The Story

That an epic of more than 75,000 shlokas can be summarised into a few paragraphs itself illustrates that it far exceeds the 'story'. As suggested above, the *Mahābhārata* has been read as comprising two severable parts:

i) 'the real epic,' or the nucleus comprising the plot and action and,
ii) the didactic corpora around the nucleus. A short summary of the story is provided for quick reference.

The nucleus story of the *Mahābhārata* is a succession feud in what is a large and complex joint family. The scion of the Bhārata dynasty, Sāntanu begot three sons; the first — and as such the legitimate heir — Devavrata, with the river goddess Ganga.[7] Later with Satyavati, an adopted daughter of a fisher tribe chieftan, Sāntanu had two sons, Chitrāngada and Vichitravirya, leading to the first round of succession complications. Satyavati and her father pre-empted these complications, bidding Devavrata to give up his right to the throne as Santanu's eldest son. Further to relinquishing his birthright, it is enjoined that he produced no children, for they could claim succession rights against Satyavati's grandsons in the future. Devavrata famously took the awe-inspiring vows to fulfil both conditions, on account of which he came to be known as 'Bhishma'. "Selling his birthright of succession for his father's privilege to indulge himself" (van Buitenen), Bhishma stemmed the first succession crisis. However, both the sons of Satyavati failed to produce any heirs of their own: while Chitrāngada died unmarried,

7. The story of Santanu and Ganga's marriage, Ganga's condition, their seven sons before Devavrata drowned by Ganga, and the eventual reunion betweeen the father and son are crucial subplots thar fit into the sublime spiral of causality that determines every human action in the epical universe. Familiarity with these episodes gives a fuller understanding of the predicament and premises that drive this section of the epic.

his younger brother Vichitravirya (literally 'of uncanny/queer virility') fathered no children despite marrying the two sisters, Ambika and Ambalika. Satyavati's hard bargain with Sāntanu seemed all in vain, an unexpectedly early extinction faced her line.

To remedy this prospect, Satyavati planned a levirate on Vichitravirya's widows with Bhishma, who, predictably, refused. Satyavati's pre-marital son following her brief encounter with the sage Parāshara, Krishna Dvāipāyana Vyāsa, is then called to service the two widows for offspring. Vyāsa fathered two leviratic sons: with the elder widow Ambika, the blind Dhritrāshtra, who by diminishing primogeniture rights, was the heir; and Pāndu, a boy of fragile health, with the younger Ambālika. Vyāsa also begot Vidura, a bastard son of the household with a handmaiden of Vichitravirya's widow called Parishrami. Dhritrāshtra's blindness complicates what would have been an automatic succession. Instead, Pāndu gets crowned as the king. However, he cannot sexually consummate his marriages, as it would result in his immediate death. Pāndu, renouncing the throne, retires to the forest. Coming true on his name, Dhritrāshtra ('he who holds the kingdom'), assumes the regency for the future king. In the forest, complicating the matters of paternity further, Kunti uses her childhood boons, and with divine intervention, begets three sons, while Mādri (Pāndu's second wife) produces two: the five brothers together come to be called the Pāndavas. Yudhishthira, the eldest, is born ahead of the blind regent Dhritrāshtra's eldest son, Duryodhana. While Dhritrāshtra recognised Yudhishthira's first right to the throne, he "does not commit himself to the cause of Yudhishthira's issue" (Hiltebeitel).

After the deaths of Pāndu and Mādri, the Pāndavas, accompanied by their mother Kunti, return to Hastināpura, triggering the succession crisis among Santanu's third generation. By now, Duryodhana had consolidated his designs on the Hastināpura throne and had attempted to remove the recognised claimants, his Pāndava cousins, first by assassination, and subsequently, through a scheme to burn them alive in a highly inflammable lacquer house. The scheme is discovered with Vidura's help and the Pāndavas escape unharmed. In the guise of young Brahmins, they reappear at the *swayamvara* of the princess Draupadi which her father, the Pānchala king Drupada had organised. Here, Arjuna wins Draupadi as common wife for the five brothers. The marriage alliance strenghtens the Pāndavas position to face Duryodhana, as Pānchala is a powerful kingdom. This alarms the Hastināpura Kauravas: the Pāndavas had not only survived the dastardly pyrotechnic plot, they had also secured a formidable ally. To worsen matters, Baladeva and Krishna Vāsudeva of Mathura stood in solidarity with the Pāndava cause. In the emergency council held at Hastināpura following these events, the great-uncle Bhishma advocated for the Pāndava rights. Nevertheless, the *de facto* king, Duryodhana, who is no longer amendable to the advice of the elders, presses for a precautionary war. Eventually, a compromise in the form of partition of the kingdom is suggested, whereby the Pāndavas are encouraged to accept a junior domain of the Bhārata kingdom in the uncultivated Khāndava forests to the southwest of Hastināpura on the banks of the Yamuna. Given Duryodhana's totalising ambitions, the division is hardly a lasting resolution. It proves to be a deferral to the great war as neither side was prepared to surrender the ultimate claim to full sovereignty.

The Pāndavas establish the glorious city of Indraprastha, violently clearing the Khāndava forests. They flourish and experience enough prosperity for Krishna Vāsudeva to suggest the performance of a *rājasūya*, a symbolic proclamation of independence from Hastināpura dominion. The imperial claims of full sovereignty reverberate afresh as the Pāndavas subjugate the known world through the *rājasūya*, securing enviable power and resources. Following this, Yudhishthira is duly anointed as the suzerain of suzerains, with prompt endorsement from Hastināpura. Duryodhana burns with envy seeing the Pāndava opulence on full display at Yudhishthira's consecration ceremony. With his maternal uncle Shakuni, Duryodhana schemes to assuage his imperial lust again, inviting the Pāndavas to Hastināpura for a friendly game of dice under the veneer of playful banter. Yudhishthira cannot ignore this challenge, since such a game was a concluding ritual of the consecration ceremony itself. At this game, he infamously gambles away his kingdom, his wealth, armies, and subjects to Duryodhana. Further he loses the freedom of his sons, his brothers, and eventually, himself. Spurred on, in a final throw that measures the immensity of his resignation, Yudhishthira stakes and loses Draupadi. Draupadi is consequently subjected to abominable humiliations, including disrobing and verbal sexual abuse in the hall occupied by the elders and sires of the kingdom. Driven to the limit, Draupadi raises a confounding question: considering, that his own liberty had already been gambled away, was Yudhishthira free to have staked his wife? In other words, did his husbandly right on his wife hold when he had himself been enslaved? The issue remains irresolute. Petrified by the wrath of the Pāndavas, Dhritrāshtra uses his kingly veto and annuls the entire game, restoring the status quo and urging that the Pāndavas returned home. However, for a variety of reasons, the game had to be played again. The Pāndavas are interrupted on their way back for one final, imperforate challenge: an all-or-nothing throw. They play their kingdom for the whole kingdom. Predictably, Duryodhana defeats Yudhishthira and the Pāndavas are forced into a thirteen-year expulsion from the kingdom, including a final year of exile incognito. After thirteen years, the Pāndavas re-emerge to stake their claim to Indraprastha, but are predictably snubbed by Duryodhana.

This is the short history of the strife that drove the two cousin clans to the inevitable threshold of the gruesome war. Both parties forged alliances and prepared for the battlefield. Krishna Vāsudeva was the Pāndava mentor and Dhrishtadyumna of Pānchala the military commander-in-chief. The great 'world' war continued for eighteen days resulting in the complete annihilation of the Kauravas. In the end, Ashvatthāmā's unmitigated, apocalyptic violence results in the murder of all Pāndavas sons — born or unborn, a dastardly act for which he is consigned to eternal hell by Krishna. Yudhishthira apathetically proclaims his victory with an *ashvamedha* ritual. Some years later, Krishna Vāsudeva's tribe commits suicide in a drunken brawl. The Pāndavas and Draupadi proceed on their last journey to heaven, to be reunited with the Kauravas who they had annihilated. The throne passes to Abhimanyu (Arjuna and Subhadrā's son) and

Uttarā's son Parikshit, and from Parikshit to Janamejaya, to whom the entire story is narrated by Vaiśampāyana on the violent occasion of the *sarpa satra* — the snake sacrifice. The short summary of the bare bones plot should point to the confounding complications that inform this epic and the continent and vacillating nature of ideals like good-over-evil, justice, and peace.

Very soon into the *Mahābhārata*, we realise that the story is merely infrastructural to its epical magnitude, however intricate and complex the infrastructure be. As mentioned, scholars generally agree that the standard version of the epic when it came to be known as "*satsāhasree saṃhitā* (a text comprising 1,00,000 verses) in the first millennium CE" (Bhate 29), was possibly the third major redaction upon the much shorter 'original', *Jaya* (possibly composed by the court bards, the *sūtas*). *Jaya* later developed into *Bhārata*, containing 24,000 verses. *Bhārata* assumed its later 'monstrosity' (Winternitz) after multiple redactions which added series of copious *upākhyānas* and voluminous didactic passages, a process that continued over many centuries until the epic reached the colossal six-figure number of verses in the 3rd or 4th century CE.

The *Sabhā Parva*

Ādi Parva, the first book of the *Mahābhārata*, ended in a rounded but tense resolution. After giving detailed stories of the origins of the universe, the various provenances and paternities of the numerous characters of the epic, and the consequent puzzling genealogy of the Bhāratas,[8] the first book took us through the episodes of early strife between the Kauravas and the Pāndavas which culminated, after the Pāndavas' alliance by marriage with the Pānchalas, in the division of the kingdom of Hastināpura. The Khāndava forest on the outskirts of Hastināpura was cleared by Krishna and Arjuna, and the city of Indraprastha was founded for the Pāndavas with the aid of an *asura* called Māyā. There is a semblance of peace as the truce advised by the elders meant that the Pāndavas ruled Indraprastha while Hastināpura became the

8 After Bhārata, the clan of which Sāntanu was the scion. Also called the Pauravas, from Puru.

uncontested, exclusive domain of the Kauravas. van Buitenen observes:

> *The Assembly Hall* makes all that went before just a beginning. Those were the pages of childhood and adolescence, in which the influence of elders was strong and decisive. Now [in book 2] the heroes are on their own and begin to act in their own right; and their natures are wilful.

The first stirring in the fragile and uneasy peace is experienced at the beginning of the *Sabhā Parva* with a visit of the celestial seer Nārada, who lectures Yudhishthira on *purushārtha*, statecraft, and the responsibilities of a king through a series of about one hundred questions. Nārada's un-commissioned visit should remind us of the outer frame of the narrative, which is its teleological investment in universal social reformation by elimination of the 'bad' *kshatras* at the hands of the 'good' (Brahminical) *kshatras*. Nārada prods Yudhishthira's desire to conduct the *rājasūya*, a Vedic ritual in order to legitimise and reinforce his kingly authority. However, the *rājasūya*, as noted by van Buitenen, was not simply a ceremonial ritual. It was, in fact, a sacrifice which proclaimed *universal suzerainty*: a king who performs the *rājasūya* establishes *sāmrājya* — suzerainty over suzerains, complete emperorship. He notes that the *rājasūya* is not simply the installation of a new king, but the "glorification of the king of kings". It is Krishna who had originally counselled Yudhishthira to celebrate the *rājasūya* presumably to mark independence from Hastināpura. Predictably, this went on to prove a major bone of contention between the two clans as Hastināpura was still the 'parent' kingdom. Although the *rājasūya* was performed by Yudhishthira, the entire Kaurava dynasty ('of Kuru' — includes the Pāndavas in this larger sense) became the suzerain dynasty.[9] Here it is important to note an understated motive that made the *rājasūya* a desideratum for establishing Pāndava authority. As is also implied in Nārada's rather forceful discourse on the duties of the king, Yudhishthira had done absolutely nothing in his years to

9 Later when Duryodhana wants to perform the *rājasūya*, he is duly told that there cannot be two suzerains in the same family.

stake his claim to rule as king. The adolescence of the Pāndavas was marked by a series of traps and escapes, all aided by some bad luck and some good. The Pāndavas were yet to fight any big or small wars to legitimise their authority; as mentioned, Yudhishthira is especially devoid of any personal accomplishments to stake his kingly claim. The Pāndavas are merely "prosperous princelings" (van Buitenen 3) at Indraprastha. Their alliance with the kingdom of Pānchala owes only to their marriage with the princess Draupadi. Indraprastha remains at most, a 'new home-base'— hardly a kingdom — that has been 'given' to them by the elders. As such, the *rājasūya* presents an inviolable means to settle the matter and establish the authority of the King, which Yudhishthira hitherto lacks entirely. It must be remembered that to perform the *rājasūya* itself requires no more accomplishments than the mere desire or intention to perform it. Yudhishthira performs the *rājasūya* successfully with generous help from their friend and cousin Krishna, who leads the expedition to kill the present *de facto* suzerain, Jarāsandha of Magadha.[10] He achieves *kshatrasampad* (unanimity of the Kshatriyas) at the behest of Krishna and the Pānchalas. The consecration and the ensuing celebrations at Indraprastha trigger the irreversible cycle of events that culminate in the great war.

The Tale of Two Assembly Halls

The *Sabhā Parva,* in contrast to the unbridled expanse of the *Ādi Parva,* represents a far tighter narrative structure with few extraneous digressions. The very name asks the reader to be attentive to the interior space of the assembly hall where most of the events of this

10 Killing Jarāsandha is crucial as he has defeated 84 of about 101 kshatriya kings and held them captive. Therefore, even in tactical terms, defeating Jarāsandha wins Yudhishthira the allegiance of 85 kings in one stroke. At the consecration ceremony of the *rājasūya,* Yudhishthira asks Krishna for permission, an oddity given that Krishna belongs to the Bhoja variety of kings. van Buitenen attributes this to the fact that Krishna was in charge for the battle with Jarāsandha, as such he is the one who ended the reign of the existing suzerain, apart from of course that 84 captive kings pledge their allegiance to him.

book unfold. The title resonates with significance from the inaugural passages itself. Nārada's aforementioned sermon on statecraft and *purushārtha* to Yudhishthira is reinforced by another fascinating side story. Clearly impressed with his new palace, Yudhishthira asks Nārada to tell him about the greatest palaces and kings of the universe. This pride in the palace adumbrates the growing Pāndava hubris, which finds its culmination in the consecration ceremonies at Indraprastha after the *digvijaya*[11] part of the *rājasūya*. Nārada places the Indraprastha (literally, 'the seat of Indra') palace at no less significance than one of the four ends of the cosmos,[12] diametrically opposite to the world of the highest God Brahma himself. van Buitenen observes:

> By the precise indication of its position in the configuration of the cosmos — and this in my view is the intention of the descriptions of the "worlds" of the World Guardians and Brahma — the palace is included in and made a structural component of cosmic space.

As such, Indraprastha, like numerous other seats of feudal power, is designated as the centre of the mortal world. This episode takes

11 *Digvijaya* comes from the word *dis*, or directions which in conjoined words becomes *dig*. After the *rājasūya* is decided to be performed, Yudhishthira sends his four brothers in the four directions — Arjuna in the North where he fights Bhāgadatt, the king of Assam, and heads further north to the Himalayas; Bheem goes East for Sisupāla of Chedi; Nakula goes West, as far as the Persian gulf, while Sahadeva goes South where he wins Agni, the fire god.

12 van Buitenen notes, "For us, if we give the matter any thought at all, the four compass points are surface directions, and we represent them somewhere on the horizon. The ancient Indians structured their space differently. Space was shaped like two pyramids joined at their bases. The four corners of the joint base represent the four points of the compass, the top of the upper pyramid the zenith, the top of the inverted, lower pyramid the nadir. At the zenith is the World of Brahma, 'on the roof beam of heaven', at the nadir, which is here on earth, is the hall of Yudhishthira. Each of these points is a *dis*, a direction, a word that therefore only in part corresponds with 'points of the compass'. Mention is frequently made of the 'ten *disās*', the four main points of the compass, the four intermediate ones, the zenith and nadir. These ten *disās* are synonymous with 'space'."

us back to the frame-narrative of the *Mahābhārata*'s history: namely, that it is the story of an epochal turn, an *avatārana* — a divinely commanded purge — of the 'bad *kshatras*', the armed men who had abandoned the ideals of *dharma* and socio-political morality. The more commonly understood meaning of *avatāra* is 'descent' of some deific power. However, the philosophical context of 'incarnation' is present in the literal meaning of '*avatāra*'— which is, 'a taking down' — in this context, of an oppressive burden of the people of the world.[13] Fitzgerald mentions how the periodic elimination of the bad *kshatras* at the hands of Rām Jāmadagneya (better known as the Kshatriya-slayer 'Parshuram') had become impossible because the troubled Brahmin ancestors had banished him. It fell upon the *devtās* to find a new solution to the problem of the bad *kshatras*. The entire *Mahābhārata* narrative therefore, especially the apocalyptic war, can be seen as an outsourced battle between the *devtās* and *asuras* in heaven. This is established by the narrative devices of incarnation, divine or semi-divine paternity, curses and boons, and regular direct or indirect participation of the immortals in the mortal world of the *Mahābhārata*. The new generation of demon Kshatriyas occupied the earth, led as they were by Duryodhana — the incarnation of *asura* Kali, or strife. Duryodhana and his ninety-nine brothers, all incarnations of demons have a contested and grotesque parentage, unlike the parentage of the Pāndavas, which though contested, was divine. Gandhari carried the hundred Kauravas for two years in her womb only to later abort the "grotesque fetal mass" (Fitzgerald 58). The levirate father of the fathers of the two clans, Krishna Dvāipāyana Vyāsa divides the mass into a hundred pots filled with *ghī*, an experiment which eventually leads to the birth of thoroughly wicked and strong young men, the Dhritrāshtra Kauravas. The one hundred Kauravas and their confederate Karna constitute the core targeted group of the 'avatāra mission' of the *devtās*. Nārada's description of the palace in effect reprises this cardinal responsibility upon the Pāndavas — the "war-party of the Gods" (Fitzgerald 56) — to lead the divine charge and

13 For an elaborate discussion on *avatāra*, see Fitzgerald, 'The *Mahābhārata*'.

expunge the demon *kshatras* from the face of the world.

The Indraprastha palace, placed in the august company of the *lokapālas* of the world, is one of the two halls where most of the action of the *Sabhā Parva* takes place. The Hastināpura palace contains the other fateful sabhā hall where the irreversible events of the dicing game and the shocking humiliations of Draupadi and the Pāṇdavas take place, engineering into motion the drama of complete destruction.

Indraprastha: 'The Palace of Illusions'

The story of the very construction of the Indraprastha palace makes for a significant and telling episode. When the Khāndava forest is destroyed in order to found the Pāndava capital, one of the inhabitants of the forest, an *asura* named Māyā asks Arjuna for asylum and is ultimately spared his life. Māyā introduces himself as a *Vishvakarman*[14] of the *asuras*. True to his name and upon the orders of Krishna to "build an assembly hall, where the designs of the Gods are laid out, and the designs of *asuras* and men", Māyā builds a spellbinding palace for the Pāndavas. van Buitenen has persistently, but unconvincingly, argued that the episode with Māyā and his architectural genius borrows from the Iranian and Zoroastrian architects who were transported to Chandragupta Maurya by the Seleucids. It has been mentioned before how the final redaction of the *Mahābhārata* into *satsāhasree saṃhitā* (a collection of a hundred thousand verses) happens around the Mauryan period. The Magadha empire of Chandragupta was touching the borders of Afghanistan after the peace treaty and marriage alliance with the Seleucids and a flow of Seleucid artisans and architects to Magadha is probable. van Buitenen quotes Mortimer Wheeler who finds strong hints of the architecture of Persepolis in the Mauryan capital of Pātaliputra. Māyā is described as an 'alien' who relates stories of 'ancient gods' of various places to the Pāndavas. Who are these ancient Gods, wonders van Buitenen, and speculates again that the suggestion is towards Māzda. Before building the palace,

14 The divine architect of the Gods.

Māyā asks Arjuna to leave in order to fetch jewels and "gem-encrusted sacrificial poles and golden altars have been set up there, for beauty's sake", which are to be found to the north of the *Mainaka* mountains near Lake *Bindu*, a mythical, unidentified site where all the ancient Gods "attend a sacrificial session every one thousand eons". Krishna Vāsudeva has himself donated "thousands and hundreds of thousands of golden-garlanded sacrificial pillars and most splendid altars." The bejewelled majesty of the assembly hall which takes Māyā and his 8000 *kinkara rākshasa* comrades about 14 days — a rather long time for an *asura* — to build, is spread over three acres. Here is a glimpse of the opulence of the palace:

> Radiant and divine, it had a superb color like the fire, or the sun, or the moon. Challenging as it were with its splendor the luminous splendor of the sun, it shone divinely forth, as though on fire,.with divine effulgence. It stood covering the sky like a mountain or monsoon cloud, long, wide, smooth, faultless, and dispelled fatigue. Made with the best materials, garlanded with gem-encrusted walls, filled with precious stones and treasures, it was built well by that Vishvakarma. Neither the *Sudharma* hall of the Dasarhas, nor the palace of Brahma possessed the matchless beauty that Maya imparted to it. . . . Inside the hall Maya built a peerless lotus pond, covered with beryl leaves and lotuses with gem-studded stalks, filled with lilies and water plants and inhabited by many flocks of fowl. Blossoming lotuses embellished it, and turtles and fishes adorned it. Steps descended gently into it; the water was not muddy and it was plentiful in all seasons; and the pearl-drop flowers that covered it were stirred by a breeze. Some kings who came there and saw it thick with precious stones and gems did not recognize it for a pond and fell into it. Around the hall stood tall trees that were always in bloom, lovely trees of many kinds that were dark and threw cool shade. Everywhere there were fragrant groves and lotus ponds made beautiful by wild geese, ducks, and *chakra* birds. The wind carried the fragrance of flowers on land or on water and fanned the Pāndavas with it.

The opulence of the palace notwithstanding, the above description also stresses its ephemerality. The repetition of the fire metaphor portends destruction. In general, the palace seems to supersede the quotidian laws of nature with its perennial and inexhaustible pools and trees. It is as if Nature has been mastered by Māyā's architectural genius. The overarching effect of the description is a kind of miasmic sensuality that seems to escape common faculties of comprehension, leading among other kings, Duryodhana, to fall into the ponds, which because of the gems encrusted on them, don't look like ponds. The Pāndava *hubris* is on full display as they slur and banish from the gates of the palace itself the kings who have not managed to pay appropriate tribute. These gifts and tributes are described in great detail, leaving an overall impression of excess. The palace, built as it is by 'Māyā' himself, seems to be a grandiloquent gesture of illusion: what seems present is really not, and vice versa. *Mahābhārata* frequently mentions its core idea of *karma* (action) and *dharma* (duty) as relevant to the perishable *samsaric* world. What the didactic passages of the *Mahābhārata* establish is that despite the *Samsara* being the avenue for human action, it is ephemeral and ever-vanishing. However, it is precisely its ephemerality which necessitates action. It is this ephemerality of the palace that will soon hit the Pāndavas who are about to gamble away their suzerainty over the known world on a dicing board.

Among other rituals and trifles, the episode involving Sisupāla, the king of Chedi, is significant for it rasps the celebrations somewhat. Moreover, it allows the Kauravas and some of their later allies a rallying point against the Pāndavas. Sisupāla of Chedi was Jarāsandha's deputy and was bitter with Krishna for manipulating Jarāsandha to a duel where he was killed. Both van Buitenen and Fitzgerald note that the Vedic rituals of the consecration proceedings also included the ritual of offering a portion of the unction water to the heir apparent. The unction water is collected from the seven holy rivers and is an important instrument to anoint the king with divinity. A portion of this 'divinity' is offered to the heir to establish his right to the throne after the King's death. However, there is no attempt in the consecration ceremony, in fact in the entire epic, to establish Yudhishthira's divinity. People who he rules over may look at him as their God, but there is no deification of the king as such. He is the ruler of the known world but what is celebrated is not his divinity or invincibility but only his material wealth. This is in sharp contrast to the other Dharma hero of the Sanskrit epic tradition, Rāma, who is apotheosised as a divine king in the

Rāmāyana.[15] In the case of *rājasūya* consecration as opposed to a simple consecration, since suzerainty is hardly hereditary, the unction water is given as gift to the next most powerful *Kshatriya* king present. As such, the relevance of the gift is not in its function but simply in its being an honour to whoever the suzerain deems is second only to him. In consultation with Bhishma, Yudhishthira decides to bestow this glory to Krishna. This does not go well with some kings on the grounds that Krishna is not a 'proper' Kshatriya, given his cowherd antecedents and his Bhoja-Kshatriya present. The same resentment is voiced in the form of an open rebellion by Sisupāla — a king who had otherwise helped Bhima on his conquests for Yudhishthira's *digvijaya.* Krishna, who by now has proved his martial might as well as political acumen in the epic, is belittled by Sisupāla in no uncertain terms. van Buitenen's suggestion is that perhaps the unction water ritual involving the heir apparent resonates with Sisupāla. Selecting Krishna for the honour means that the title might be bestowed upon him next — a position that in Sisupāla's mind might have belonged to himself, given that he was the general of the most powerful known king Jarāsandha, assassinated by Krishna for Yudhishthira's *rājasūya.* Sisupāla denigrates Bhishma and Yudhishthira and clamours that a cowherd is to be glorified ahead of an entire assembly of other more deserving, 'greater' kshatriyas. The episode ends with Krishna beheading Sisupāla with his discus. van Buitenen observes how the Sisupāla episode is a magnified and dramatized aspect of a minor ritual of the consecration: 'the chariot drive.'[16] This episode of the killing of Sisupāla by Krishna gives the Kauravas and some of their later *kshatriya* allies a rallying point.

15 Yudhishthira's 'lack' of divinity establishes him as a mortal king and this itself is a huge change in the post vedic political philosophy. The king is now a mortal, prone to mortal fragilities and excesses under the sway of which he can gamble away the wealth and freedom of his people.

16 van Buitenen gives the detail: 'The newly anointed king mounts a chariot, drives it off, and attacks a baron who has taken up a position somewhere to the east or north of the sacrificial compound. The king shoots arrows at the baron, makes the chariot turn right, and returns to his starting point.' (*Mbh* 61)

The Hastināpura Kauravas come to the *rājasūya* consecration of their elder cousin without any visible discord. The Pāndavas seek no tribute from them, just like they do not from Drupada Pānchala because of marriage and Krishna, out of friendship. However, when the Kauravas leave, it is clear that the sudden but matchless prosperity of the Pāndavas has managed to estrange Duryodhana further, which it can be argued, was also partly their objective. Duryodhana's raging envy at Yudhishthira's wealth and power is fuelled further by Draupadi's mockeries which injure his masculine pride. It is almost as if the fire-like dazzle of the Indraprastha palace singes the heart of Duryodhana and emblazons it with indelible envy.

Hastināpura: The Palace of Deceit

The word 'illusion' (*māyā*), which is often used to describe the Indraprastha palace, is near synonymous with the word used to describe the events at the Kaurava *sabhā* at Hastināpura: *chhal* (deceit). This is rather read not as a paradox but as an echo. What lends the idea of 'illusion' a positive cultural value is it's locatedness in the fundamental Vedic dualism between the body and the soul. Besides, the inevitable divesture of the physical world enforced by death lets the *post mortem* world emerge in contrast as an ideal and immortal space. While in its ultimate recension, the *Mahābhārata* seems to revise, even 'modernise' some moral codes and class values to emphasise the necessity of action (*karma*), it does so, not by dissolving but reinforcing, even perfecting this dualism. *Chhal* on the other hand, remains an irredeemable vice. Deceit does not find a place in the four means — *sāma* (arbitration), *dāma* (bribe), *danda* (punishment), *bheda* (division/manipulation) — which are accepted and recommended as strategic instruments in *niti*, or the Sanskrit traditions of political science. Whereas Duryodhana's maternal uncle Shakuni, invincible at the game of dice, had connived to defeat and deprive the Pāndavas on the premise of Yudhishthira's gambling addiction, there is no mention of this addiction in the voluminous first book. Even if we assume this puported addiction to be true, the price that Yudhishthira (literally, 'the one who holds firm in war') will pay for it is untenable. Why does Yudhishthira accept the invitation of the Kauravas to the game, despite Vidura's desperate counsel — besides his own astute assessment — against the same? What do we make of a man, newly anointed the king of the world, who could simply gamble it away along with his freedom, and the freedom of his people, his family, and his wife? Any hopes for Yudhishthira to have offered an explanation are thwarted as he maintained an agonising silence through the terrifying events of terrible Pāndava peripeteia.

van Buitenen offered an answer to the above questions, which despite being extraneous to the text, have attracted scholarly consideration. van Buitenen mounts Yudhishthira's defence in perusal of the consecration rituals themselves. There are many aspects of the Vedic *rājasūya* consecration, which — like any ritual — over time morphed into conventions and games. However, at the Kaurava sabhā, many such games associated with the Vedic consecration magnified dramatically, attaining a seriousness that exceeded van Buitenen's suggestion of their — ceremonial provenance. The example of Sisupāla's killing, for instance, must be read as an enlarged and reified performance of the ceremony where the new suzerain was offered a mock challenge or opposition by a guest, which he then symbolically vanquished in the same playful manner.[17] The game of dice constitutes a similarly spirited ritual to celebrate the successful accomplishment of the *rājasūya*. The new suzerain could not have refused any challenges, whether on the battlefield or on the dice board. In fact, given its unpredictable nature, the dice game allowed the *samrāt* to confirm and demonstrate his invincibility, even against the vicissitudes of *chance*. In this light, it was near-impossible for Yudhishthira to have refused an invitation to such a game, that too at his ancestral place, with his cousins, in the company of all his respected elders and cousins.

AK Ramanujan has offered a structuralist reading, arguing that the dicing as well as the sequel represent a progress of the

17 See van Buitenen for an elaborate discussion.

underlying design of the epic. As revealed later in the *Book of Forest* in the *Nalopākhyāna*, Yudhishthira's misery at the dicing game mirrors the misery of Nala, who had similarly gambled away his kingdom, lost his wife Damayanti in the forest, and got bitten by a snake, before the circle of fortune reunited him with Damayanti and their prosperity returned.[18] Yudhishthira's short-lived suzerainty had been established largely through the efforts of his brothers, and more importantly, on the advice of Krishna, who had also defeated Jarāsandha of Magadha. Magadha too had been conquered not through an actual war but through gamble not unlike the dicing itself. Resembling Yudhishthira's lack of political acumen and foresight, Jarāsandha accepts a one-on-one duel as the final settlement of Krishna's challenge to his throne. Both the rulers — Jarāsandha and Yudhishthira exhibit a strikingly similar hamartia as they abandon the teachings of *nitishāstras* for personal hubris, erring against the commands of *rājdharma* established at length by the political thinkers of the epic including Nārada, Vidura and Krishna. The repetitive design of the epic — for instance, Jarāsandha duel with Bhima lasted thirteen days, while the Pāndavas were forced on a thirteen year exile — compels comparative analyses. All the schemes and covert shortcuts that the Kauravas had undertaken to win the Hastināpura succession feud right from the *Book of Beginning* were all in vain, just as the Pāndava enterprise against Jarāsandha had failed. These connivances and strategems propel the two parties towards the inevitable great war. Besides, the question of succession by the logic of primogeniture remained unresolved even within the Pāndavas until Karna was living. As such, Yudhishthira's suzerainty would remain dubious — *it had to be* gambled away, for it was always, like the Indraprastha palace, ephemeral.

Another explanation to the events of the *Sabhā Parva* derives from the constant dialectic between *dharma* and *Daiva* (fate or

18 See Hiltebeitel's essay, anthologised here for a detailed discussion.

'arranger of fortune').[19] When intercepted midway for a second round of dicing despite the horrors of the first round, Yudhishthira says: "It is at the disposing of the arranger that creatures find good or ill. There is no averting of either, if we must play again." The inflexibility wrought on *dharma* by *daiva* abuts fatalism. It recalls more formalist idea of *dharma* perfected by the other great Sanskrit hero Rāma, and within the *Mahābhārata*, to a degree, by Bhishma. In these heroes, *dharma* is treated as a steadfast and unscrupulous adherence to or obedience of a formal code: for instance, of *pitri-dharma* in the case of Rāma. Yudhishthira echoes of Rāma when he says, "Although I may know that the challenge to the dicing at the old man's behest will bring ruin, I cannot disobey his word". Ramanujan divided epic protagonists into a two types: 'watchers' and 'actors'. This typology emerges from the differences in the relationship between *dharma* and *daiva*. Ramanujan's binary is expedient in reading the dicing sequence, as well as the action, and indeed, the inaction of various characters in the assembly hall. What is the blind king Dhritrāshtra, for instance — a 'watcher' or ironically because he does not 'see', an 'actor'? Is Yudhishthira a *watcher* of *daiva* conducting an inevitable reversal of fortunes, or is he an *actor*, a 'doer' who exercises agency, and who, consequently, could have averted the unbearable tribulations of his people by *not* participating in the game? The older model of *dharma* as a strict adherence to prescribed formal codes is decidedly revised, even supplanted in the *Mahābhārata* by a contingency-driven, interpretative model of *dharma*. With all its dramatic synapses, the *Mahābhārata* can arguably be read as a performance of this revision.

Two Games in One: Dice and Chance

It is clear from the beginning of the game that dicing is a metaphor

19 In his dissertation titled *Destiny and Human Initiative in the Mahābhārata*, Julian Woods notes, "Insofar as it is linked to the Divinity and to the seven worlds of epic cosmology, macrocosmic *Daiva* (distinguished with a capital D) is time (*kala*), an inexorable cyclic process of creation, manifestation and destruction of the cosmos" (34).

for the battlefield. As mentioned, it is one of the many stratagems deployed by the Kauravas to oust their cousins for a permanent and conclusive resolution to the Hastināpura throne. While 'chance' is theoretically equal for every player in a board game, the case of the Hastināpura sabha is considerably different. The exchange between Yudhishthira and Vidura at the moment of invitation to the game itself clarifies, that the two parties were destined to play two very different games on the same board.

Ramanujan's repetitive design mentioned earlier can be discerned in comparing Yudhishthira's victory over Jarāsandha and Duryodhana's victory over Yudhishthira in the dicing game. Just as Yudhishthira nominated his cunning political advisor Krishna, to win Magadha, Duryodhana deputed his maternal uncle, Shakuni, the master of the dice to play his sinister game. Yudhishthira's plays are the *throw of chance*. Shakuni's throws, however, are *throws of a cultivated skill*. It is an unequal game, for deploying Shakuni is like deploying a 'cheat-code', a guaranteed win because he had mastered the throw.

The rules of the game of *dyuta* are not known but its dramatisation seems to suggest that twenty throws were played in two sets of ten each. Two parties played, each with a representative who threw on their behalf. The similarity of Krishna's duel with Jarāsandha for the whole kingdom is all too conspicuous to be missed. After the tenth throw, Vidura tried to stop the Pāndavas' vilification with his pleas which were addressed not to the players, but to the blind king Dhritrāshtra, the supervising authority, suggesting, as van Buitenen has observed, that Yudhishthira was bound by law (of *rājasūya* ceremony) to continue playing. With Dhritrāshtra unwillingness to intervene, the game carried on into the next ten throws, all of which, expectedly, Yudhishthira lost. He lost all his wealth, cattle, and land by the thirteenth throw. In the fourteenth, he lost the sons of Draupadi by the five Pāndavas. In the next four throws, the freedom of each of his brothers is lost. In the nineteenth round, he is brought to staking and losing himself. Egged on to finish the twenty throws, Yudhishthira puts his wife, Draupadi on the line. To the terrified groans of the audience, Draupadi is lost. She is infamously summoned to the court, but the summoner returns with her question, a veritable riddle which dumbfounds the wisdom of the entire assembly: did Yudhishthira stake himself first, or Draupadi; and having lost himself, was he at liberty to stake her? The Kauravas will have nothing of it and Draupadi, menstruating and in a single cloth, is dragged by her hair into the sabhā and subjected to indignities that "shout for vengeance. She is disrobed but the power of her virtue replaces her skirt" (van Buitenen 30). She is called a whore by Karna, and is humiliated by a salacious Duryodhana consumed by Shakuni's triumps on his behalf.

A discussion follows on the point of legality raised by Draupadi's question. However, Draupadi's question has hit much deeper than its superficial enquiry of who was lost first. Vikarna (younger among the hundred Kauravas) interjects on Draupadi's behalf but finds himself snubbed by Karna stating the obvious double-defeat of Draupadi as the wife of a slave, for when Yudhishthira lost himself, he lost all of his possessions, including his wife. Draupadi's rhetorical enquiry really threatens the socio-political and philosophical organisation of the society because her question is truly *cosmic* in nature. By what decree do individuals possess/own other individuals — kinship, primogeniture, matrimony, feudal authority? Draupadi's wailing is followed by wrathful proclamations of Bhima and Arjuna and the howling of scavengers. Mortified by these omens, Dhritrāshtra finally intervenes with his king's veto annulling the entire game and, restoring status quo. However, far too much has already been lost. Draupadi has been dishonoured beyond forgiveness and time's wheel cannot be reversed by royal decree. In his belated appeasement efforts, Dhritrāshtra offers Draupadi three boons. Still holding firm onto *dharma,* Draupadi accepted the freedom of her husbands, and as a warning, their weapons, but firmly rejected the third boon. The Pāndavas, sent back with status quo restored, are intercepted midway for the *anudyuta,* or the sequel to dicing. All pretensions of friendliness are dropped, and the *anudyuta* is an all-or-nothing throw. Now under the beatitude of Dhritrāshtra's veto which saved them from enslavement, the Pāndavas return only to be defeated again. Further, they are ordered into a thirteen year exile, including the thirteenth year in disguise. Their discovery in the thirteenth would renew another period of exile. The Pāndavas leave Hastināpura in awful postures of doom: Yudhishthira cover his face with his shawl to avoid casting an evil eye on Hastināpura lest it is burnt by it; Bhima slouches spreading his arms wide, ready to use all his strength in war; Arjuna walks scattering sand, forecasting "the number of enemies that will burn with his arrows"; Sahadeva and Nakula smear their handsome faces and bodies with dust so as to avoid distraction from war. The bugles for the apocalyptic war have already been sounded. Most portentous among them is Draupadi who, "hiding her face in her dishevelled hair, cries, in her sole garment, wet and besmirched with blood". Dhaumya, the wise Pāndava family priest chants gruesome chants of death and Yama, holding the *kusa* grass in his hand. Both Draupadi and Dhaumya announce their apocalyptic prognostications which are part prophecy, part curse. Their ominous departure is followed by cosmic signs of destruction.

Hiltebeitel approaches his study of this momentous episode with the question of Krishna's inexplicable absence from this pivotal event in the life of the Pāndavas. There is the story of the Salva invasion of Dwarika which Krishna must immediately check. However, given his significance in the their lives, and his nuanced understanding of their relationship with the Kauravas, Krishna's absence continues to haunt the Pāndavas. van Buitenen and Ramanujan have found many parallels with the *upākhyānas* of Nala and the trial of king Prahlāda. A religious explanation takes us to the logic of incarnation. Krishna's absence is owing to his character as the incarnation of the preserver god Vishnu who cannot coexist in the same place as the god of destruction, Shiva. Where is Shiva in the entire episode, one may wonder. If Gods indeed 'kill us for their sport', Shiva's prefered sport is purported to be dice. As a destructive game, dice is seen as the symbol of the Shiva's cosmic destruction that is about to annihilate the Bhāratas. Apocalyptic destruction is also suggested in the disrobing of Draupadi, who is herself an incarnation of *Śri,* the consort of Vishnu. In her naked form, Śri is the goddess of destruction, *Kāli*. In his exhaustive study of Draupadi, Hiltebeitel has offered significant insights on the importance of Draupadi's menstruation, her open hair, and bloodied garment as foretokens of the total destruction of the Kauravas that unfolds in the successive parvas.

Dharma

Yatho dharma: tatho jayah
Where Dharma is, there is victory

But the question really is: where, after all, is *dharma*?

Dharma presents a particularly convoluted ideal around which the entire world of *Mahābhārata* revolves. *Dharma* continues to be a much peddled word to this day, despite being misunderstood, misinterpreted, even abused — both in religious and political discourse.[20] At its reductive, it signifies 'institutionalised religion.' However, conceived in Sanskrit literary history, *dharma* has had intricate but traceable history of its development before it came to mean the various profound things that it does in the *Mahābhārata*. Madeleine Biardeau, Alf Hiltebeitel, Wendy Doniger and more recently Adam Bowles have offered remarkable histories of *dharma* and its emergency version *āpaddharma*. As mentioned before, the word comes from the root verb √*dhṛ*,[21] which means to bear or sustain.[22] At its simplest, *dharma* connotes an individual code of conduct which is itself determined by the complex matrix of

20 In modern Indian political discourse, *dharma* gains momentum with Gandhi. However, in dogmatic right wing discourse, it also devolves into its 18th century usage where its purpose was to separate the 'Aryans from the *mlechh'*, as it did in 'traditional Indian xenology' (Halbfass 311). Significantly, Halbfass also reminds us that *Dharma* is the *Indian Constitution*'s 'official' term for 'religion', and the constitutional definition of the Indian Republic as a 'secular state' is translated as *dharmanirapekshya rājya*.

21 Paul Horsche, Cf. Bowles 84.

22 √*Dhṛ* also gives us the word *dharti,* which means the earth.

personal, social, political and religious/spiritual pressures that *make* the individual. Aditya Adarkar has observed that:

> Dharma is not law or religion which is distinct from nature or divine will. To conceive of dharma is to conceive the *entire universe as part of a single unified moral enterprise*: humans, gods, animals, plants, stones — any and every existent thing — all contribute to the upkeep, the sustenance, of the universe when it acts in accordance with dharma. (Emphasis added) (83)

A Brief Intellectual History of Dharma

The first instance of the word *Dharma* is to be found in the *Rigveda*. Sheldon Pollock (1990) has suggested that *dharma* originally belonged to the world of ritual, and hence that "the world outside of ritualism had originally little to do with dharma" (Pollock 1990, Cf. Bowles 83). Bowles notes that *dharma* comes from the verb *dharman*, a word that "expresses the function of a verb" (ibid.), which is to *do*. *Dharman* is the process of original cosmic creation as described in the *Rigveda*, according to which Varuna and Mitra, the Vedic Gods separate the sky and earth and cause the sun to come in between them, un-falling because of the act of *dharman*. The first cosmic sacrificial act performed by the gods after this is described as *sthāni dharmāni prathamāni*. Wilhelm Halbfass translates this phrase as "the first ritual laws." As such, the first laws replicate the first laws of creation itself,[23] placing a metaphorical cosmic onus on the followers of the laws, and the breakers. It also subtly points towards another derivative meaning of *dharma*, which is to

23 Bowles insightfully observes, "In the *Atharva Veda*, *dharman* is still found as the *instrument of a god*, in particular in its connection with Varuna". He observes that *dharman* is not so much a matter of fact cosmogonic event that follows creation but something that suggests a sort of an agency in the verb-noun 'creation'. He imagines *Dharman* as *a kind of a love charm*, love (smara) and intense burning are kindled in the man 'by the law of Varuna'". It is accurate perhaps that dharman is a "divine law", which, Bowles suggests, "can be invoked on the human plane in the *pursuance of a desired object*" (87).

separate, or qualify, or discern. At a xenological level, this leads to the fourfold *varna* system, where roles of the society are determined and fixed, in order that ultimate cosmic equilibrium be maintained. As such, in the Vedic period, *Dharma* implies the maintenance of social and cosmic order, but by performing Vedic rituals and sacrifices. Halbfass notes that *dharma* comes — after *dharman* — to connote the "principle of universal stability, the power which sustains, upholds, and maintains, the firmly established order" and later "the lawfulness and regularity, the harmony, the fundamental equilibrium, the norm which reigns in the cosmos, nature, society, and individual existence"(312).

Bowles traces the various literary canons where *dharma* underwent significant revision. In the literary digests on the *Vedas,* called the *brāhmanas,*[24] Dharma attained the character of law, and brought within its purview, social justice. This is the stage at which *dharma* began to be put into formal templates or directive principles, such as the *dharma* of the king, or *rājdharma,* a formal *prescription* distinctive from common *dharma* which any man or woman needed to follow for maintaining cosmic balance. In fact, passages in the *Mahābhārata* attentd to precisely this concept, with at least two capacious *parvas* — *Shānti* and *Anushāsana* (Books 12 and 13) — devoted entirely to expositions and commentaries on *rājdharma.* However, in the *brāhamanas, dharma* was only formalistic: it had attained the centrality that it did by the time of the *Mahābhārata.*

After the *brāhamanas, dharma* went through significant revision in the *Upanishads.* The *Varna* system had become entrenched both in law and heredity. So, in the *Upanishads,* the concept of *dharma* gained an emphatically Brahminical impetus. In order to expand and empower themselves, the Brahmins created the other three *Varnas* but to tackle the rather 'natural law' of 'might is right', they subdued the *kshatra* might by making *dharma* its governing principle, thereby putting a meta-barrier between the *kshatras* and themselves.

24 Not to be confused with the *varna. Brahāmanas* are post-Vedic collections of commentaries, legends and hymns pertaining to the *Vedas.* We have 19 extant *brahāmanas* in the present day.

To use a modern political expression, *dharma* at the *Upanishad* stage of its evolution is law promulgated for the *kshatra*, of the *kshatra*, by the Brahmin. It became charged with moral codes of truth and justice, allowing the Brahmins to keep the *kshatras* beholden while also deriving protection and patronage from them.[25] Bowles has noted the double benefit of this discursive masterstroke:

> *Dharma* [in the Upanishads] stands above the power of the king, and people can appeal to it for justice, just as one might appeal to the king. It is now independent of any other factor, yet clearly associated with the creation and separation of the four *varnas*. (95)

After *dharma* began to resemble an ideological apparatus in the *Upanishads*, in the *grhyasutras*,[26] it became a redundant collection of small rituals for the non-*kshatras*, thereby keeping them engaged and compliant. In the *grhyasutras*, a typology of *kuladharma* (clan rituals) and *grāmadharma* (village rituals) can be seen before it slowly ossified into a more regressive model, *jātidharma* (caste-specific ritualism).

However, it is with the *dharmasutras* which followed the *grhyasutras* that *dharma* started to gain the gravitas of social and individual morality. The comparative insignificance of *dharma* in the literatures before the *dharmasutras* is unsurprising as *dharma* was rooted in the practice of rituals. But the *dharmasutras* referred to the *Vedas* to reinvigorate the core concept of *dharma* as divine law that held the society and cosmos in balance. The *dharmasutra* thrust on the one hand, on a taxonomy of varna or gender-specific *dharmas*, and on the other, its insistence on social morality led to a two-fold intellectual development. Firstly, the highest *purushārtha* (human objective) was no longer seen as *svarga* (heaven), which in the *Vedas* could be obtained by a keen performance of sacrificial

25 Of course, for the purpose of the introduction, this extremely convoluted intellectual history is here all too neatly narrativised. Horsche, Halbfass and Bowles present exhaustive analyses of this history of ideas.

26 *Grhyasutras* along with *Saurtyasutras* and *Dharmasutras* are the codebooks dating to 500 BCE, which prescribed the various domestic rituals pertaining to birth till death as following from the *Vedas*.

rituals. Bowles has observed that *svarga* was "superseded by a new soteriological goal: the, liberation from the world into which one was continually reborn (*moksha*, or *nirvāna*)" (119). Secondly, this new principle which considered human life as affecting cosmic balance inevitably changed the nature of human *action*. The *karma kānda* or sacrificial rituals of the *Vedas* made way for the new ethical doctrine of *karma*, which enlarged human action to become a desideratum to the fatalistic cycle of moral causality. In other words, *dharma* became the yardstick of 'legitimacy' of human action (Bowles 112). The fourfold soteriological typology comprising *dharma*, *artha* (material), *kama* (desire), and *moksha* also gained significance and popularity among the lower *varnas* where *dharma* was the means to achieving the final objective of moksha, while fulfilling material, *sāmsāric* objectives. The individual who followed *dharma* realized the ideal of his own character and manifested the eternal lawfulness of the cosmos in himself. In this sense, *dharma* came to be constituted by a dialogue between both self-assertion and self-effacement.

Culminating in the doctrines of absolute *ahimsa* (non-violence) at any cost and *renunciation* of the false *sāmsāric* world of pain and death, Buddhist and *Ajivika* philosophies put the ultimate challenge to not just the socio-spiritual relevance of the Brahmins but even, the authority of the *Vedas*. To check this rising challenge, the idea of renunciation was reinterpreted in Brahminical literature to imply the renunciation of ritual.[27] The need to renounce the false material world led to the evolution of the *ashrama* system by which an individual life was divided into four stages, calibrating *dharma* according to age, as an eventual renunciation, while the *grhstyadharma* was the stage where as domestic fulfilment could be enjoyed without guilt.

The other challenge to Brahmanism was posed by Kautilya's *Arthashāstra*, a Mauryan period text that debunked Brahmanism frontally. Kautilya struck hard at the comfortable ideological manouvers of *rājdharma* which required the king's complete

27 One must keep in mind that the great war of *Mahābhārata* is repeatedly characterised a 'sacrifice' for dharma, or a *dharmayuddha*.

subservience to the Brahmins. The *Arthashāstra* promulgated *rājdharma* as perpetually in a state of exception, emergency or contingency, and therefore, free from any prescription that lay outside the King's personal discretion. The *Arthashāstra* punctured all codes of *varna* morality that were the mainstay of the *Manusmriti* and other similar Brahminical texts. Wendy Doniger has noted that Kautilya went so far as to say that the king must only appoint an amenable spiritual leader to important positions. The tables were quite fully turned as Kautilya brought home a spirit of Protestantism to polity and governance, making the early Mauryan period the *nemesis* of Brahmanism. This short intellectual history of *dharma* lays the grounds for a nuanced reading of *dharma* and its expostulated in the *Mahābhārata*.

Dharma in the Mahābhārata

At the very least, the *Mahābhārata* is a performative exploration of the complexities and problems of *dharma*. Unlike the *Vedas*, *samhitas* (collections), *sutras* (treatises or codebooks), or *shastras* (laws) which were prescriptive and didactic in nature, the *Mahābhārata* is a veritable laboratory where the *dharma* was examined in all the great variety of human life and contexts. Lingat goes so far as to call it a *dharma-smriti* (1970). Scholars like Biardeau and Fitzgerald argued that the valorised model of *dharma* in the *Mahābhārata* was essentially Brahminical revisions on Vedic codes promulgated in response to the growing threat of Jainism and Buddhism under Ashoka. Much didactic material was added around the Mauryan period to the core narrative of the *Bhārata*. Many didactic passages criticise and even express resentment against Ashoka's model of *dharma* as arrogant and hypocritical. Fitzgerald notes:

> Ashoka, who was a lay follower of the Buddha, did not subordinate himself to Brahmin guidance and even insulted Brahmanism by treating it as just one more religious elite among many elites that were all eligible for imperial support if they adopted the tolerant and pluralistic view of religions the emperor advocated. (59)

The *Mahābhārata* is replete with stories of Kshatriyas not recognising the purported dignity, and special contributions of the Brahmins. Ashoka's attitude towards Brahmins was only a more conspicuous example of the general rejection of the Brahmin philosophy in that society. Coming from the emperor, this cost them both wealth and socio-political power. The 'good Kshatriyas' who emerged as the winners were also, unsurprisingly the upholders of a particular version of *dharma* that was conducive to the writers of the *Mahābhārata*, the Brahmins. Unlike the Kauravas, the Pāndavas were great patrons of the Brahmins. Yudhishthira, son of Dharma himself, referred in the epic mostly as 'Dharma', bears a consistently 'unheroic' approach to material and martial glory. Yudhishthira's perennial distance from adventure since he was a child is itself Brahminical in a Vedic sense. His *rājasūya* ceremonies are a time for great porperity for the Brahmins:

> From every realm flocked in the brahmins, profound in all the fields of knowledge, learned in the *Vedas* and their branches. At the King Dharma's orders, carpenters by the thousands built cottages for each of them and his party, filled with many foods and beds, cottages with all the virtues of every season. There those brahmins dwelled, grandly hosted, telling many tales and watching dancers and players. And when those priests were feasting and talking, a loud din was incessantly heard from those great-spirited revelers. "Give, give!" and "Feast, feast!" were the exchanges that were heard constantly. The hundreds of thousands did the king give in cows, beds, gold, and women to each of them.
>
> (*Mahābhārata Vol.* 2, 88)

Jarāsandha was also a great patron of the Brahmins and the *snātakas* (junior Brahmins pursuing their studies). It is possible to read that Yudhishthira's generosity to the Brahmins is in propitiation of Magadha conquest. However, it must also be borne in mind that he does not gamble away the freedom and wealth of the Brahmins of his kingdom at the dice game. In the thirteenth year of *incognito* exile, he preferred the disguise of a Brahmin, an act at which he was most convincing. Nevertheless, to read the entire cornucopia of the discursive and narrative materials through only the frame of Brahminism is unpersuasive. The epic clearly differentiated between a king and a hero, both of whom must 'follow' and establish *dharma*.

No wonder many non-Brahminical *kshatras* managed to excel as heroes.[28] The heterodox perspectives of *dharma* found in the epic speak to its reimagination as a convergence point of value systems where various individualistic, social, and cosmic morals clashed and cooperated.

After their 34 years of post-war rule, the Pāndavas left for their final ascent to heaven. One by one, they all fall to their death. Only Yudhishthira managed to reach the gates of heaven, famously accompanied by his dog. There, when asked to abandon the dog, he refuses to enter without his companion. The dog turns out to be an incarnation of his father Dharma, who was putting his son to a final test right at the heaven's gates. This is the first of Yudhishthira's final tests. In heaven, when he sees the Kauravas but none of his brothers, he insists on being sent to hell where his brothers were. The veneer is removed to reveal that all the Pāndavas brothers are, in fact, together in heaven. This is Yudhishthira's final test. Thus ends the *Mahābhārata.*

Dharmrāj's Rājdharma, or, the Tests of Yudhishthira

The above story tells us something scary about Yudhishthira and the nature of the *dharma.* Through the course of the epic, both in the city and in exile, Yudhishthira faced regular tests. The final tests echo, for instance, the Yudhishthira-*Yaksha* dialogue in the *Aranyak Parva,* or the *Book of Forest.* The four younger Pāndava brothers, despite fierce warnings, consume forbidden water from a pond. Yudhishthira finds his brothers dead and finds that he must answer the questions of a *Yaksha* to resuscitate tem. This turns out to be a test that Yudhishthira passes and succeeds in reviving his brothers. The *Yaksha* is none other than Yudhishthira's father Dharmraj himself. Despite the death of his brothers on both these occasions, a debilitating prospect, Yudhishthira keeps his composure, tackling difficult questions. This is among the many tests

28 This also gives weight to the idea that *Mahābhārata* was largely composed by the *sūtas* (the charioteer court bards) and not the Brahmins — again a speculation that, however worthy, cannot be overstated.

that Yudhishthira faces, none more so dramatic or difficult as the apocalyptic war itself. This is the scary bit: what if Yudhishthira got a question wrong? Would he then suffer hell, despite lifelong travails and steadfastness in the *sāmsāric* world, and despite his natural affinity for renunciation? What was the value of the earlier tests when, theoretically, he was as far from heaven at its gates as he was in his childhood? Yudhishthira's life and character represent the idea of *dharma* being a constant negotiation, a subtle choice, a balance of the quotidian and the cosmic. Arguably, Yudhishthira's life allows numerous ideas and models of *dharma* from *Vedas* to *Arthshāstra* to emerge and undergo a synthesis. Here are some examples.

Nivrittidharma and Pravrittidharma

Yudhishthira's life and choices evoke the Vedic distinction between *Pravrittidharma* and *Nivrittidharma*. *Pravrittidharma* refers to the various rituals and codes that allow an individual to live his life fruitfully with the society in the *samsāra*.[29] Julian Woods has observed that *pravrittidharma* corresponds with the process of eternal creation and allows individuals to enjoy material and martial accomplishments in the mortal world. On the other hand, *nivrittidharma* is the disposition to renunciation, of material values and relationships, a concept that corresponds to ideas like *sanyāsa* and later to *ahimsa*. It might be useful to understand *pravrittidharma* as the Freudian *libido*, or the drive for life. Correspondingly, *nivrittidharma* can be imagined as *thanatos* or the death-drive. Post-Vedic literature, especially Buddhist philosophy, redefined *dharma* entirely in terms of what the *Vedas* call *nivrittidharma* with its final objective of *moksha* or *nirvāna*. From early on, Yudhishthira is favourably disposed towards the *nivrittidharma* while betraying a dislike for material or martial success, or *sāmsāric* accomplishments. Further, while a follower of *pravrittidharma* depended on Vedic ritual and sacrifices, the

29 *Pravrittidharma* derives from the Sanskrit root *pra*-*vrt* which means to go forth. *Pravritti* also comes to mean 'disposition' or an individual's 'nature'. *Nivritti* comes from *ni* which would roughly translate as 'non-return', with *āvritti* meaning 'to go back'. In this sense, Yudhishthira's *pravritti* is *nivritti*.

follower of *nivrittidharma* predominantly relied on knowledge.

Kingship was thrust onto Yudhishthira — like it had been on his father Pāndu — because he was the eldest son. In fact, he is not even the eldest — Karna is. Therefore, even primogeniture was thrust upon him, reinforcing the idea that he is an 'unnatural' king. Nārada's two visits — one at the founding of the Indraprastha palace, and the other after the destructive war — are aimed at teaching the '*dharmrāj*', the rules of *rājdharma*. Both the *rājasūya* and the destructive Kurukshetra war have been characterised as sacrificial rituals for the establishment of a more encompassing ideal.[30] The ritualistic violence of sacrifice at the *rājasūya yajna* becomes the righteous violence to restore the rule of dharma and the balance of the social and moral universe. Yudhishthira's reluctance against both the *rājasūya* and the war is justified in the end considering the sheer scale of annihilation. At the end of the war, he has no celebrations in him but only lament, which shall not be assuaged despite the sustained efforts of worthy interlocutors like Nārada, Bhishma and Krishna — three men who try to 'make a king out of Yudhishthira' by teaching him the hard-heartedness of *rājdharma*.[31] Not being soothed by either of these dharma spokespersons, unlike an Arjuna, elevates Yudhishthira as a 'knower' in the *nivritti* sense. As a man predisposed to his *nivritti*, the sacrificial rituals of both the *rājasūya* and the war are amenable to his nature. In Yudhishthira's personality, the decrees of the *Arthashāstra* negotiate with the oldest Vedic ideals as well as the new Buddhist ideals of unreserved *ahimsa* and *dharma*. At the level

30 The battlefield of Kurukshetra is called *dharmakshetra* (the land of dharma) and the war itself a *dharmayuddha*.

31 As it comes across in the *dharmashastras* and most specifically in Kautilya's *Arthashāstra*, *rājdharma* becomes associated with exceptional behavior, a certain relaxation of means in order that political stability and control of the emperor is ensured. *Rājdharma*, as such, is a step away from the logic of 'righteous violence'. The fact that this monarchical concept is peddled in contemporary democracies as ideal political behavior is a rather myopic and dangerous idea, especially if we go back into its intellectual antecedents.

of intellectual history, Yudhishthira's *dharma* amalgamates *brāhamana* literature with the *gryhasutras*. For instance, in the *Āranyakparva*, on being asked to renounce material desires completely by the seer Shaunaka, Yudhishthira gives him the following reply:

> I do not desire wealth out of a desire to enjoy it, but I wish for it in order to support the brahmins, not out of greed. For how, brahmin, can a man like me who is in the householder stage fail to support and preserve his followers? It is taught that one should share with all creatures; therefore, the householder must give to those who do not cook for themselves. In the houses of the good these four are never found lacking: straw, ground, water, and welcoming words. The sick deserve a bed, those tired of standing a seat, the thirsty water, the hungry food. One should lend one's eye and attention, speak the welcome, and rising to greet him meet the guest and honor him justly. (*Mahābhārata* III, 225)

Given his torn convictions before the commencement of war, Arjuna is often compared with another literary hero, Hamlet. A close reading of the *Mahābhārata* shows that even more than Arjuna, Yudhishthira is perennially in a Hamlet-like condition. Hesitation becomes Yudhishthira, pitching his personality in a tragicomic paradox with against his name — 'the one steady in war'. The *yuddha* (war) that Yudhishthira is skilled at is not fought in the battlefield, the one for which his brothers Bhima and Arjuna are better known. Unlike the war itself, Yudhishthira displays exemplary heroic patience and fortitude in the face of spiritual adversity. In other words, the *yuddha* where the eldest Pāndava is *sthira* (steady/ unwavering) is *ātmadvandva,* or the war within. *Dharma* is most visible when it is most vulnerable. This situation is called *dharmasankata,* or, the *dharma* conundrum. The *dharmasankat* of *Mahābhārata* differs from its treatment in the *Rāmāyana.* In the older Sanskrit epic, *dharma* was presented as a matter of choice between prescribed codes: as such, the intellectual model of *dharma* remained *Upanishadic.* The *Rāmāyana* imagined *dharma* as a simplistic but dogged straightforwardness of following a prescribed formal ideal with unflinching austerity. Rāma emerges as the hero precisely because he chooses fraternal duty, *pitrdharma,* which is the accomplishment of the word of the father without any *situational* exegesis. In the *Mahābhārata*, the *dharma* problematic can no longer be resolved through simple prioritisation between the prescribed codes, all of which appear to be correct and relevant but in a state of conflict with each other. As such, *dharma* becomes more interpretation-dependent, and *sūkshma* (subtle). The reason that Yudhishthira has been read as a Brahminical *kshatra*[32] is because he is so dogged and astute in the theoretical aspects of *dharma* that he passes each of the cosmic tests with flying colours. However, in terms of action, Yudhishthira is less memorable: he is neither an inspired warrior nor an enterprising king.

The character of Dronacharya's son Ashvathhāma mirrors Yudhishthira in that he is a *kshatriya* in a Brahmin's body. While *dharma* is about making the right choice, stepping into someone else's dharma can wreak havoc: "*paradharmo bhayavah*" (*Bhagavadgitā*). While this transgressive reversal of roles causes Ashvatthāma to bring the dastardly annihilation of even to the wombs of Pāndava wives, it leads the Brahminical Yudhishthira to much personal turmoil. The strong conflict between his *rājdharma* and *nivrittidharma* makes out of Yudhishthira the king, an existentialist escapist, a charge that is laid against him unsparingly by Draupadi.

In contrast to Yudhishthira's *nivrittidharma,* Draupadi represents an adherence to *pravrittidharma* . Born of the sacrificial fire, she is 'all-consuming'. She is the incarnation of *Śri,* the goddess of material prosperity. As such, it is no surprise that she is regularly projected in terms of her material accomplishments or sacrifices. Significantly, later in the epic, her single-minded desire for revenge distinguishes her from her husbands — except Bhima — and even Krishna. This should not be mistaken as ordinary greed, but a part of the same 'divine plan' by which the cosmic balance is maintained. Draupadi's knowledge of *dharma* is recognised and praised by Krishna himself. According to Bimal Matilal, Draupadi is one of the three Krishnas who protect the

32 Some versions refer to a story where Dronacharya observes that Yudhishthira is a Brahmin in a *kshatriya*'s body.

Pāndavas.[33] Her question about the propriety of the stake leads ultimately to the annulment of the dicing game and saves the husbands from life-long enslavement. Iravati Karve's speculative and narrow interpretation of Draupadi as a mere 'pretender' of *dharma* assumes the stability of *dharma* itself. Draupadi's riddle punctures the idea of a stable *dharma* while stalling the horrific events into an argumentative stalemate. In such a stalemate, the only recourse left was to cancel the game itself, a boyish resolution to what seemed to affect the entire cosmos.

Adam Bowles's exhaustive study of *āpaddharma* illustrates that *Mahābhārata*'s intellectual revision of *dharma* — following Kautilya's *Arthashāstra,* where all *rājdharma* is *āpaddharma* — gave birth to a new ideal which was contingency-prone and exceptional, not only in the life of a king but of every individual. This contingent *dharma* was far from a simplistic formal pursuit, making way for interpretation, where every situation of moral dilemma referred to the rule in a state of exception. This made interpretation the definitive aspect of *dharma.* The practitioners of the older, more inflexible, model of *dharma,* as per Shaunaka's words in the *Book of Forest,* were serving their own egos rather than the final cosmic balance. The awe-inspiring vows of celibacy and relinquishing the throne for a mock-reprise of Rāma's *pitridharma* serve only to give Bhishma, quite literally, a name. His abdication of the throne leads through various channels, to the destruction of the Bhāratas. He assumes the position of the 'egotistical sublime', but because his choices are self-serving, he is soundly rebuked by Krishna on his deathbed.

Dharma as *Praxis*

Among the various points of divergence between Karna and Arjuna is that Karna is a thinking hero while Arjuna is a more flamboyant warrior hero, so much so that even Krishna, and later Nārada are compelled to admire, in glowing terms, Karna's knowledge of *dharma* and his integrity in following it. He is a character who has

33 Krishna Dvāipāyana Vyāsa, Krishna Vāsudeva, and Krishnā Draupadi.

converted all his *daiviya* (of fate) challenges into his strengths. Being given away at birth to the waters, he earns the title of *dānvir* (alms-giver) Karna, his fortitude so unflinching that he let Indra dupe him of his divine, unbreachable *kavach* (armour). In this, Karna resembles Yudhishthira's hand at gambling, but also differs in that he adheres to the basic principle of charity, while Yudhishthira exhibits a fatalistic attitude to his predicament at the Kaurava sabhā. Karna is matched in every skill as a warrior with Arjuna, but he far exceeds him in his understanding of *dharma*. Arjuna, until his role in the war itself, is the prototypical blue-eyed boy of his clan and guru Dronāchārya (and even of the Gods) who not only trains him but also plots and schemes his ascent as 'the greatest archer'. Arjuna never faces exceptional moral conundrums and could therefore afford to hold on to his grandeur before the inevitable moral crisis hits him on the eve of war. On the other hand, Karna displays poise and acumen in balancing his *dharma* and his actions — his *pravritti* and *nivritti*. Arjuna's crisis is not so much characterised as a tussle between *pravritti* and *nivritti*, as one between *shreyas* (that which is best) and *preyas* (that which is loved). Insofar as that, Arjuna's battlefield quandary is not unlike any ordinary person's moral dilemmas.

Arjuna finds himself incapable of tussling with the intricacies of prescriptive or interpretative *dharma*. Even so, his great skill as an archer is the strongest foot of the Pāndavas. How would a reluctant Arjuna fulfill the great providence that was upon him, which included the killing of the grandfathers who had borne him as a child and the teachers who had made him what he was? The answers are all given by Krishna in what has become the most reproduced, the most translated and the most well-known part of the *Mahābhārata*, the *Bhagavadgitā*.[34] The *Bhagavadgitā* stands evidence to Krishna's deep knowledge of the intellectual history of

34 While some scholars argue that the *Bhagavadgitā* is an interpolation, the issue is settled when one chooses to abandon the core-periphery speculative model (as discussed before) and consider the 'Gupta redaction' as a single literary unit.

dharma and his skill at interpreting and manoeuvring it for its practical deployment and 'application'. However, Arjuna is not to be convinced by the various available meanings of *dharma* that are offered to him by Krishna. Therefore, in motivating him to act, and while perfecting the *interpretative* essence of *dharma*, Krishna offers his great alternative version of dharma as pure action, or *Karma*. *Karma* makes a dazzling re-entry into the intellectual world from the *Vedas* where it meant the performance of sacrificial rituals, after experiencing a long period of dormancy which allowed *ahimsa* to become the *paramdharma* (highest dharma). The *dharmayuddha* of the *Mahābhārata* needed to characterise and legitimise itself as perfunctory violence, which was mandatory for the establishment of a larger socio-politico-cosmic justice and order.[35] As Georges Dumezil has observed, both the king and the warrior on the Pāndava side — Yudhishthira and Arjuna — on the eve of the war remain unconvinced of its importance, and there are chances that they would withdraw.

As mentioned, Arjuna can be convinced to war not through ideals of *dharma* but something that renders his mind free from all consideration of the impact of his actions. Krishna promulgates the theory of *Karma* or action without the expectation of results or consequences. This is a remarkable semantic shift from the Vedic interpretation of karma as prescribed rituals with the final goal of *svarga*. In post-*Vedic* literature, action is important but subsumed within *dharma* with its ultimate goal being the attainment of *moksha*. In this sense, karma had always been the determinant of fate. The *karma* theory in the *Bhagavadgitā* was an ideological instrument of freedom to act. *Dharma* is *sūkshma* and confusing, therefore instead of getting into its hair-splitting intricacies, one might as well abandon the responsibility of the results of 'doing' onto God or providence and simply perform the *karma*. The welding of fate and karma in a relationship of mutual determinism freed the agent from the troubles of *dharma*. The Gita could easily be dismissed as

35 In historical readings, this has been understood as the reestablishment of a Brahminical regime.

cosmic moonshine by which Krishna brainwashed Arjuna and egged him on to act. However, what grounds *karma* in *goodness* is the significant change that Krishna promulgated in the relationship between man and god, and between the mortal and cosmic worlds. The relationship, which was sacrificial in the time of the *Vedas,* changed in post-*Vedic* literature to an intellectual negotiation (epitomised in the rather equal relationship between Yudhishthira and his father Dharma). When intellectual negotiation becomes unsustainable, the way of relating to God changes to *bhakti. Dharma* is effectively replaced by *bhakti* as the moral rudder of action in the *Bhagavadgitā.* The incapacity for knowledge is not to be met with reason and wisdom, but with good faith and dependence. *Bhakti* derives from the Sanskrit root noun *bhāg* which literally means 'to divide' or 'to share'. The *Bhagavadgitā* also alters the way in which earth related to the cosmos. Earlier the actions of the Gods are seen as mirrored on earth. Now however, earth was seen to partake of the cosmos. The *Nar-Nārāyana* binary of the *Vedas* was re-invoked by Krishna to reimagine the relationship between man and God. While the 'knowing man', Yudhishthira can never really look at Krishna as God, Arjuna, the non-knower, can only find comfort in a benevolent God who will take care of the fruits and retribution of his actions. The *Mahābhārata* then paved the way for the eighteen *Purānas* which consolidated the idea of *bhakti,* presenting it as the moral alternative to the numerous problems of *dharma,* action and purpose.

A Note on the Cover

The painting unambiguously positions Draupadi as its protagonist, with her unending white garment forming a continuum with both the time and space that fall outside the frame. Her eyes are closed in supplication or terror, reflecting the pathos of her situation. Her unbraided hair follow the spiral flow of her robe, which suggests both the spiral of revenge as well as the vacillating continuum of time.

The five Pāndavas sit in surrender while Duhshasana pulls one end of Draupadi's robe. His stance suggests neither lust nor aggression, as if subdued by the robe's endlessness and his inability to strip her of it. Except Bhima, the brothers are identical, anonymised figures with closed eyes. Only Bhima's eyes are open, but they look nowhere. Draupadi's robe — passes tenderly over Bhima's knee, a token of solidarity.

The pathetic figures of Dhritrāshtra and Gandhari, sit near Draupadi. Gandhari and Draupadi present contrasting studies in wifehood: Draupadi prods her husbands to action, while Gandhari effectively blinds her husband further. Blindfolded as a mark of devotion to her husband, she only reinforces his literal and moral blindness.

Dhritrāshtra sits particularly mortified, holding his two hands between his legs, paradoxically inert for a king. His face carries the pallor of doom that is to descend on his clan as a result of his inaction.

The various shades of fire consume the painting's empty spaces: there is the golden yellow which reminds us of the Indraprastha palace's golden blazon. The orange and deep reds suggest both blood and fire, both symbols of rage. The blue also accentuates the fire and the heat. Listless figures look from behind these colours, a veritable pointer to the large number of the Kaurava sabhā audiences that are about to be consumed by the sacrificial fire, the *dharmayuddha* of Kurukshetra. A crow sits in the scene a redoubtable symbol of death sprung from within the fire, hovering over the heads of the king and queen.

The Mahābhārata

TRANSLATED BY K M GANGULI

The Dicing and the Sequel to the Dicing

Selections from the Sabhā Parva

Book 2 Section XLV-LXXX

(Dyuta Parva)

The Dicing and the Sequel to Dicing

Section XLV (45)

Vaisampayana said,—"When that foremost of sacrifices, the Rajasuya so difficult of accomplishment, wascompleted, Vyasa surrounded by his disciples presented himself before Yudhishthira. And Yudhishthira, uponbeholding him quickly rose from his seat, surrounded by his brothers, and worshipped the Rishi who was hisgrand-father, with water to wash his feet and the offer of a seat. The illustrious one having taken his seat on acostly carpet inlaid with gold, addressed king Yudhishthira the just and said.—'Take your seat'. And after the kinghad taken his seat surrounded by his brothers, the illustriousVyasa, truthful in speech said,—'O son of Kunti, you grow from good fortune. You have obtained imperial sway so difficult ofacquisition. And O perpetuator of the Kuru race, all the Kauravas have prospered in consequence ofyou. O Emperor, I have been duly worshipped. I desire now to go with your leave! King Yudhishthira the just, thus addressed by the *Rishi* of dark hue, saluted (him) his grandfather and touching hisfeet said,—'O chief of men, a doubt difficult of being dispelled, has risen within me. O bull among regenerateones, save you there is none to remove it. The illustrious *Rishi* Narada said that (as a consequence ofthe Rajasuya sacrifice) three kinds of portents, viz., celestial, atmospherical and terrestrial ones happen. O grandsire, have those portents been ended by the fall of the king of the Chedis?"

Vaisampayana continued,—"Hearing these words of the king, the exalted son of Parasara, the island-born Vyasa of dark hue, spoke these words,—'For thirteen years, O king, those portents will bear mighty consequences ending in destruction, O king of kings, of all the Kshatriyas. In course of time, O bull of the Bharata race, making you the sole cause, the assembled Kshatriyas of the world will be destroyed, O Bharata, for the sins of Duryodhana andthrough the might of Bhima and Arjuna. In your dream, O king of kings you will behold towards theend of this night the blue throated Bhava, the slayer of Tripura, ever absorbed in meditation, having thebull for his mark, drinking off the human skull, and fierce and terrible, that lord of all creatures, thatgod of gods, the husband of Uma, otherwise called Hara and Sarva, and Vrisha, armed with the tridentand the bow called Pinaka, and attired in tiger skin. And you will behold Siva, tall and white as the Kailasa cliff and seated on his bull, gazing unceasingly towards the direction (south) presided over bythe king of the *Pitris*. Even this will be the dream you will dream today, O king of kings. Do not grieve for dreaming such a dream. None can rise superior to the influence of Time. Blessed be thou! I will now proceed towards the Kailasa mountain. Rule thou the earth with vigilance and steadiness, patiently bearing every privation!'"

Vaisampayana continued,—"Having said this, the illustrious and island-born Vyasa of dark hue, accompanied byhis disciples ever following the dictates of the Vedas, proceeded towards Kailasa. And after the grand-father hadthus gone away, the king afflicted with anxiety and grief, began to think continuously upon what the Rishi hassaid. And he said to himself, 'Indeed, what the Rishi has said must come to pass. We will succeed in warding off the fates by exertion alone?' Then Yudhishthira endued with great energy addressing all his brothers, said, 'Ye tigers among men, ye have heard what the island-born *Rishi* has told me. Having heard thewords of the *Rishi*, I have arrived at this firm resolution viz., that I should die, as I am ordained to bethe cause of the destruction of all Kshatriyas. You my dear ones, if Time has intended so what need isthere for me to live?' Hearing these words of the king, Arjuna replied, 'O king, yield not yourself to this terrible depression that is destructive of reason. Mustering fortitude, O great king, do what would be beneficial.' Yudhishthira then, firm in truth, thinking all the while of Dwaipayana's words answered his brothers thus,—'Blessed be you. Listen to my vow from this day. For thirteen years, what ever purpose have I to live for.

I shall not speak a hard word to my brothers or to any of the kings of the earth. Living under thecommand of my relatives, I shall practise virtue, exemplifying my vow. If I live in this way, making no distinction between my own children and others, there will be no disagreement (between me and others). It is disagreement that is the cause of war in the world. Keeping war at a distance, and everdoing what is agreeable to others, evil reputation will not be mine in the world, you bulls among men. Hearing these words of their eldest brother, the Pandavas, always engaged in doing what was agreeable to him, approved of them. And Yudhishthira the just, having pledged so, along with his brothers in the midst of that assembly, gratified his priests as also the gods with due ceremonies. And, O bull of the Bharata race, after all the monarchs had gone away, Yudhishthira along with his brothers, having performed the usual auspicious rites, accompanied by his ministers entered his own palace. And, O ruler of men, king Duryodhana and Sakuni, the son of Suvala, continued to dwell in that delightful assembly house.

Section XLVI (46)

Vaisampayana said, — "That bull among men, Duryodhana, continued to dwell in that, assembly house (of the Pandavas). And with Sakuni, the Kuru prince slowly examined the whole of that mansion, and the Kuru prince beheld in it many celestial designs, which he had never seen before in the city called after the elephant (Hastinapore). And one day king Duryodhana in going round that mansion came upon a crystal surface. And the king, from ignorance, mistaking it for a pool of water, drew up his clothes. And afterwards finding out his mistake the king wandered about the mansion in great sorrow. And sometime after, the king, mistaking a lake of crystal water adorned with lotuses of crystal petals for land, fell into it with all his clothes on. Beholding Duryodhana fallen into the lake, the mighty Bhima laughed aloud as also the menials of the palace. And the servants, at the command of the king, soon brought him dry and handsome clothes. Beholding the plight of Duryodhana, the mighty Bhima and Arjuna and both the twins—all laughed aloud. Being unused to putting up with insults,

Duryodhana could not bear that laugh of theirs. Concealing his emotions he even did not cast his looks on them. And beholding the monarch once more draw up his clothes to cross a piece of dry land which he had mistaken for water, they all laughed again. And the king sometime after mistook a closed door made of crystal as open. And as he was about to pass through it his head struck against it, and he stood with his brain reeling. And mistaking as closed another door made of crystal that was really open, the king in attempting to open it with stretched hands, tumbled down. And coming upon another door that was really open, the king thinking it as closed, went away from it. And, O monarch, king Duryodhana beholding that vast wealth in the Rajasuya sacrifice and having become the victim of those numerous errors within the assembly house at last returned, with the leave of the Pandavas, to Hastinapore.

And the heart of king Duryodhana, afflicted at sight of the prosperity of the Pandavas, became inclined to sin, as he proceeded towards his city reflecting on all he had seen and suffered. And beholding the Pandavas happy and all the kings of the earth paying homage to them, as also everybody, young and old, engaged in doing good unto them, and reflecting also on the splendour and prosperity of the illustrious sons of Pandu, Duryodhana, the son of Dhritarashtra, became pale. In proceeding (to his city) with an efflicted heart, the prince thought of nothing else but that assembly house and that unrivalled prosperity of the wise Yudhishthira. And Duryodhana, the son of Dhritarashtra, was so taken up with his thought then that he spoke not a word to Suvala's son even though the latter addressed him repeatedly. And Sakuni, beholding him absent-minded, said,—'O Duryodhana, why art thou proceeding thus'?

"Duryodhana replied,—O uncle, beholding this whole earth owning the sway of Yudhishthira in consequence of the might of the illustrious Arjuna's weapons and beholding also that sacrifice of the son of Pritha like unto the sacrifice of Sakra himself of great glory among the celestials, I, being filled with jealousy and burning day and night, am being dried up like a shallow tank in the summer season. Behold, when Sisupala was slain by the chief of the Satwatas, there was no man to take the side of Sisupala. Consumed by the fire of the Pandava, they all forgave that offence; otherwise who is there that could forgive it? That highly improper act of grave consequence done by Vasudeva succeeded in consequence of the power of the illustrious son of Pandu. And so many monarchs also brought with them various kinds of wealth for king Yudhishthira, the son of Kunti, like tribute-paying Vaisyas! Beholding Yudhishthira's prosperity of such splendour, my heart burneth, efflicted with jealously, although it behoveth me not to be jealous.'

"Having reflected in this way, Duryodhana, as if burnt by fire, addressed the king of Gandhara again and said,—'I shall throw myself upon a flaming fire or swallow poison or drown myself in water. I cannot live. What man is there in the world possessed of vigour who can bear to see his foes in the enjoyment of prosperity and himself in destitution? Therefore I who bear to see that accession of prosperity and fortune (in my foes) am neither a woman nor one that is not a woman, neither also a man nor one that is not a man. Beholding their sovereignty over the world and vast affluence, as also that sacrifice, who is there like me that would not smart under all that? Alone I am incapable of acquiring such royal prosperity; nor do I behold allies that could help me in the matter. It is for this that I am thinking of self-destruction. Beholding that great and serene prosperity of the son of Kunti, I regard Fate as supreme and exertions fruitless. O son of Suvala, formerly I strove to compass his destruction. But baffling all my efforts he hath grown in prosperity even like the lotus from within a pool of water. It is for this that I regard Fate as supreme and exertions fruitless. Behold, the sons of Dhritarashtra are decaying and the sons of Pritha are growing day by day. Beholding that prosperity of the Pandavas, and that assembly house of theirs, and those menials laughing at me, my heart burneth as if it were on fire. Therefore, O uncle, know me now as deeply grieved and filled with jealousy, and speak of it to Dhritarashtra.

Section XLVII (47)

"Sakuni said.—'O Duryodhana, thou shouldst not be jealous of Yudhishthira. The sons of Pandu are enjoying what they deserve in consequence of their own good fortune. O slayer of foes, O great king, thou couldst not destroy them by repeatedly devising numberless plans, many of which thou hadst even put to practice. Those tigers among men out of sheer luck escaped all those machinations. They have obtained Draupadi for wife and Drupada with his sons as also Vasudeva of great prowess as allies, capable of helping them in subjugating the whole world. And O king, having inherited the paternal share of the kingdom without being deprived of it they have grown in consequence of their own energy. What is there to make thee sorry for this? Having gratified Hustasana, Dhananjaya hath obtained the bow Gandiva and the couple of inexhaustible quivers and many celestial weapons. With that unique bow and by the strength of his own arms also he hath brought all the kings of the world under his sway. What is there to make thee sorry for this? Having saved the *Asura* Maya from a conflagration, Arjuna, that slayer of foes, using both his hands with equal skill, caused him to build that assembly house. And it is for this also that commanded by Maya, those grim *Rakshasas* called *Kinkaras* supported that assembly house. What is there in this to make thee sorry? Thou hast said, O king, that thou art without allies. This, O Bharata, is not true. These thy brothers are obedient to thee. Drona of great prowess and wielding the large bow along with his son, Radha's son Karna, the great warrior Gautama (Kripa), myself with my brothers and king Saumadatti—these are thy allies. Uniting thyself with these, conquer thou the whole of the earth.'

"Duryodhana said,—'O king, with thee, as also with these great warriors, I shall subjugate the Pandavas, if it pleases thee. If I can now subjugate them, the world will be mine and all the monarchs, and that assembly house so full of wealth.'

"Sakuni replied,—'Dhananjaya and Vasudeva, Bhimasena and Yudhishthira, Nakula and Sahadeva and Drupada with his sons,—these cannot be vanquished in battle by even the celestials, for they are all great warriors wielding the largest bows, accomplished in weapons, and delighting in battle. But, O king, I know the means by which Yudhishthira himself may be vanquished. Listen to me and adopt it.'

"Duryodhana said,—'without danger to our friends and other

illustrious men, O uncle, tell me if there is any way by which I may vanquish him.'

"Sakuni said,—'The son of Kunti is very fond of dice-play although he doth not know how to play. That king if asked to play, is ill able to refuse. I am skillful at dice. There is none equal to me in this respect on earth, no, not even in the three worlds, O son of Kuru. Therefore, ask him to play at dice. Skilled at dice, I will win his kingdom, and that splendid prosperity of his for thee, O bull among men. But, O Duryodhana, represent all this unto the king (Dhritarashtra). Commanded by thy father I will win without doubt the whole of Yudhishthira's possessions.'

"Duryodhana said 'O son of Suvala, thou thyself represent properly all this to Dhritarashtra, the chief of the Kurus. I shall not be able to do so.

Section XLVIII (48)

Vaisampayana said—"O king, impressed with the great Rajasuya sacrifice of king Yudhishthira, Sakuni, the son of Suvala, having learnt before the intentions of Duryodhana, while accompanying him in the way from the assembly house, and desirous of saying what was agreeable to him, approached Dhritarashtra endued with great wisdom, and finding the monarch deprived of his eye seated (in his throne), told him these words,—'Know, O great king, O bull of the Bharata race, that Duryodhana, having lost colour, hath become pale and emaciated and depressed and a prey to anxiety. Why dost thou not, after due enquiry, ascertain the grief that is in the heart of thy eldest son. the grief that is caused by the foe?'

"Dhritarashtra said,—'Duryodhana, what is the reason of thy great affliction. O son of the Kuru race? If it is fit for me to hear it, then tell me the reason. This Sakuni here says that thou hast lost colour, become pale and emaciated, and a prey to anxiety. I do not know what can be the reason of the sorrow. This vast wealth of mine is at thy control. Thy brothers and all our relations never do anything that is disagreeable to thee. Thou wearest the best apparel and eatest the best food that is prepared with meat. The best of horse carries thee. What it is, therefore, that hath made thee pale and emaciated? Costly beds, beautiful damsels, mansions decked with excellent furniture, and sport of the delightful kind, without doubt these all wait but at thy command, as in the case of the gods themselves. Therefore, O proud one, why dost thou grieve, O son, as if thou wert destitute.'

"Duryodhana said,— 'I eat and dress myself like a wretch and pass my time all the while a prey to fierce jealousy. He indeed is a man, who incapable of bearing the pride of the foe, liveth having vanquished that foe with the desire of liberating his own subjects from the tyranny of the foe. Contentment, as also pride, O Bharata, are destructive of prosperity; and those other two qualities also, *viz.*, compassion and fear. One who acteth under the influence of these, never obtaineth anything high. Having beheld Yudhishthira's prosperity, whatever I enjoy brings me no gratification. The prosperity of Kunti's son that is possessed of such splendour maketh me pale. Knowing the affluence of the foe and my own destitution, even though that affluence is not before me, I yet see it before me. Therefore, have I lost colour and become melancholy, pale and emaciated. Yudhishthira supporteth eighty-eight thousand Snataka Brahmanas leading domestic lives, giving unto each of them thirty slave-girls. Beside this, thousand other Brahmanas daily eat at his palace the best of food on golden plates. The king of Kambhoja sent unto him (as tribute) innumerable skins, black, darkish, and red, of the deer Kadali, as also numberless blankets of excellent textures. And hundreds and thousands and thousands of she-elephants and thirty thousand she-camels wander within the palace, for the kings of the earth brought them all as tribute to the capital of the Pandavas. And, O lord of earth, the kings also brought unto this foremost of sacrifices heaps upon heaps of jewels and gems for the son of Kunti. Never before did I see or hear of such enormous wealth as was brought unto the sacrifice of the intelligent sons of Pandu. And, O king, beholding that enormous collection of wealth belonging to the foe, I can not enjoy peace of mind. Hundreds of Brahmanas supported by the grants that Yudhishthira hath given them and possessing wealth of kine, waited at the palace gate with three thousands of millions of tribute but were prevented by the keepers from entering the mansion. Bringing with them clarified butter in handsome *Kamandalus* made of gold, they did not obtain admission into the palace, and Ocean himself brought unto him in vessels of white copper the nectar that is generated within his waters and which is much superior to that which flowers and annual plants produce for Sakra. And Vasudeva (at the conclusion of the sacrifice) having brought an excellent conch bathed the Sun of Pritha with sea water brought in thousand jars of gold, all well adorned with numerous gems. Beholding all this I became feverish with jealousy. Those jars had been taken to the Eastern and the Southern oceans. And they had also been taken on the shoulders of men to the Western ocean, O bull among men. And, o father, although none but birds only can go to the Northern region, Arjuna, having gone thither, exacted as tribute a vast quantity of wealth. There is another wonderful incident also which I will relate to thee. O listen to me. When a hundred thousand Brahmanas were fed, it had been arranged that to notify this act every day conches would be blown in a chorus. But, O Bharata, I continually heard conches blown there almost repeatedly. And hearing those notes my hair stood on end. And, O great king, that palatial compound, filled with innumerable monarchs that came there as spectators, looked exceedingly handsome like the cloudless firmament with stars. And, O king of men, the monarchs came into that sacrifice of the wise son of Pandu bringing with them every kind of wealth. And the kings that came there became like Vaisyas the distributors of food unto the Brahmanas that were fed. And O king, the prosperity that I beheld of Yudhishthira was such that neither the chief himself of the celestials, nor Yama or Varuna, nor the lord of the Guhyakas owneth the same. And beholding that great prosperity of the son of Pandu, my heart burneth and I cannot enjoy peace.

"Hearing these words of Duryodhana, Sakuni replied,—'Hear how thou mayest obtain this unrivalled prosperity that thou beholdest in the son of Pandu, O thou that hast truth for thy prowess. O Bharata, I am an adept at dice, superior to all in the world. I can ascertain the success or otherwise of every throw, and when to stake and when not. I have special knowledge of the game. The Son of Kunti also is fond of dice playing though he possesseth little skill in it. Summoned to play or battle, he is sure to come forward, and I will defeat him repeatedly at every throw by practising deception. I promise to win all that wealth of his, and thou, O Duryodhana, shalt then enjoy the same.'

Vaisampayana continued,— "King Duryodhana, thus addressed by Sakuni, without allowing a moment to elapse, said unto Dhritarashtra,— 'This, Sakuni, an adept at dice, is ready to win at dice, O king, the wealth of the sons of Pandu. It behoveth thee to grant him permission to do so."

"Dhritarashtra replied,—'I always follow the counsels of Kshatta, my minister possessed of great wisdom. Having consulted with him, I will inform thee what my judgment is in respect of this affair. Endued with great foresight, he will, keeping morality before his eyes, tell us what is good and what is proper for both parties, and what should be done in this matter.'

"Duryodhana said,—'If thou consultest with Kshatta, he will make thee desist. And if thou desist, O king, I will certainly kill myself. And when I am dead, O king, thou wilt become happy with Vidura. Thou wilt then enjoy the whole earth; what need hast thou with me?'"

Vaisampayana continued,—"Dhritarashtra, hearing these words of affliction uttered by Duryodhana from mixed feeling, himself ready to what Duryodhana had dictated, commanded his servant, saying,— 'Let artificers be employed to erect without delay a delightful and handsome and spacious palace with an hundred doors and a thousand columns. And having brought carpenters and joiners, set ye jewels and precious stones all over the walls. And making it handsome and easy of access, report to me when everything is complete.' And, O monarch, king Dhritarashtra having made this resolution for the pacification of Duryodhana, sent messengers unto Vidura for summoning him. For without taking counsel with Vidura never did the monarch form any resolution. But as regards the matter at hand, the king although he knew the evils of gambling, was yet attracted towards it. The intelligent Vidura, however, as soon as he heard of it, knew that the arrival of Kali was at hand. And seeing that the way to destruction was about to open, he quickly came to Dhritarashtra. And Vidura approaching his illustrious eldest brother and bowing down unto his feet, said these words:

'O exalted king, I do not approve of this resolution that thou hast formed. It behave thee, O king, to act in such a way that no dispute may arise between thy children on account of this gambling match.'

Dhritarashtra replied,— 'O Kshatta, if the gods be merciful unto us, assuredly no dispute will ever arise amongst my sons. Therefore, auspicious or otherwise, beneficial or otherwise, let this friendly challenge at dice proceed. Even this without doubt is what fate hath ordained for us. And, O son of the Bharata race, when I am near, and Drona and Bhishma and thou too, nothing evil that even Fate might have ordained is likely to happen. Therefore, go thou on a car yoking thereto horses endued with the speed of the wind, so that thou mayest reach Khandavaprastha even today and bring thou Yudhishthira with thee. And, O Vidura, I tell that even this is my resolution. Tell me nothing. I regard Fate as supreme which bringeth all this.' Hearing these words of Dhritarashtra and concluding that his race was doomed, Vidura in great sorrow went unto Bhishma with great wisdom."

Section XLIX (49)

Janamejaya said,—"O thou foremost of all conversant with the Vedas, how did that game at dice take place, fraught with such evil to the cousins and through which my grand-sires, the son of Pandu, were plunged into such sorrow? What kings also were present in that assembly, and who amongst them approved of the gambling match and who amongst them forbade it? O sinless one, O chief of regenerate ones, I desire thee to recite in detail all about this, which, indeed, was the cause of the destruction of the world."

Santi said,—"Thus addressed by the king, the disciple of Vyasa, endued with great energy and conversant with the entire *Vedas*, narrated everything that had happened."

Vaisampayana said,—"O best of the Bharatas, O great king, if thou desirest to hear, then listen to me as I narrate to thee everything again in detail.

"Ascertaining the opinion of Vidura, Dhritarashtra the son of Amvika, calling Duryodhana told him again in private—O son of Gandhari, have nothing to do with dice. Vidura doth not speak well of it. Possessed of great wisdom, he will never give me advice that is not for my good. I also regard what Vidura sayeth as exceedingly beneficial for me. Do that, O son, for I regard it all as for thy good also. Indeed, Vidura knoweth with all its mysteries the science (of political morality) that the illustrious and learned and wise Vrihaspati, the celestial *Rishi* who is the spiritual guide of Vasava—had unfolded unto the wise chief of the immortals. And O son, I always accept what Vidura adviseth. O king, as the wise Uddhava is ever regarded amongst the Vrishnis, so is Vidura possessed of great intelligence esteemed as the foremost of the Kurus. Therefore, O son, have nothing to do with dice. It is evident that dice soweth dissensions. And dissensions are the ruin of the kingdom. Therefore, O son, abandon this idea of gambling. O son, thou hast obtained from us what, it hath been ordained, a father and a mother should give unto their son, viz., ancestral rank and possessions. Thou art educated and clever in every branch of knowledge, and hast been brought up with affection in thy paternal dwelling. Born the eldest among all thy brothers, living within thy own kingdom, why regardest thou thyself as unhappy? O thou of mighty arms, thou obtainest food and attire of the very best kind and which is not obtainable by ordinary men. Why dost thou grieve yet. O son, O mighty-armed one, ruling thy large ancestral kingdom swelling with people and wealth, thou shinest as splendidly as the chief of the celestials in heaven. Thou art possessed of wisdom. It behoveth thee to tell me what can be the root of this grief that hath made thee so melancholy.

"Duryodhana replied,— 'I am a sinful wretch, O king, because I eat and dress beholding (the prosperity of the foes). It hath been said that man is a wretch who is not filled with jealousy at the sight of his enemy's prosperity. O exalted one, this kind of prosperity of mine doth not gratify me. Beholding that blazing prosperity of the son of Kunti, I am very much pained. I tell thee strong must be my vitality, in as much as I am living even at the sight of the whole earth owning the sway of Yudhishthira. The Nipas, the Chitrakas, the Kukkuras, the Karaskaras, and the Lauha-janghas are living in the palace of Yudhishthira like bondsmen. The Himavat, the ocean, the regions on the sea-shore, and the numberless other regions that yield jewels and gems, have all acknowledged superiority of the mansion of Yudhishthira in respect of wealth it containeth. And, O Monarch, regarding me as the eldest and entitled to respect, Yudhishthira having received me respectfully, appointed me in receiving the jewels and gems (that were brought as tribute). O Bharata, the limit and the like of the excellent and invaluable jewels that were brought there have not been seen. And O king, my hands were fatigued in receiving that wealth. And when I was tired, they that brought those valuable articles from distant regions used to wait till I was able to resume my labour. Bringing jewels from the lake Vindu, the *Asura* architect Maya constructed (for the Pandavas) a lake-like surface made of crystal. Beholding the (artificial) lotuses with which it was filled, I mistook it, O king for water. And seeing me draw up my clothes (while about to cross it), Vrikodara (Bhima) laughed at me, regarding me as wanting in jewels and having lost my head at the sight of the affluence of my enemy. If I had the ability, I would, O king, without the loss of a moment, slay Vrikodara for that. But, O monarch, if we endeavour to slay Bhima now, without doubt, ours will be the fate of Sisupala. O Bharata, that insult by the foe burneth me. Once again, O king, beholding a similar lake that is really full of water but which I mistook for a crystal surface, I fell into it. At that, Bhima with Arjuna once more laughed derisively, and Draupadi also accompanied by other females joined in the laughter. That paineth my heart exceedingly. My apparel having been wet, the menials at the command of the king gave me other clothes. That also is my great sorrow. And O king, hear now of another mistake that I speak of. In attempting to pass through what is exactly of the shape of a door but through which there was really no passage, I struck my forehead against stone and injured myself. The twins Nakula and Sahadeva beholding from a distance that I was so hit at the head came and supported me in their arms, expressing great concern for me. And Sahadeva repeatedly told me, as if with a smile,—'This O king, is the door. Go this way!' And Bhimasena, laughing aloud, addressed me and said,—'O son of Dhritarashtra, this is the door'. And, O king I had not even heard of the names of those gems that I saw in that mansion. And it is for these reasons that my heart so acheth."

Section L (50)

Duryodhana said,—'Listen now, O Bharata, about all the most costly articles I saw, belonging unto the sons of Pandu, and brought one after another by the kings of the earth. Beholding that wealth of the foe, I lost my reason and scarcely knew myself. And, O Bharata, listen as I describe that wealth consisting of both manufactures and the produce of the land. The king of Kamboja gave innumerable skins of the best king, and blankets made of wool, of the soft fur of rodents and other burroughers, and of the hair of cats,—all inlaid with threads of gold. And he also gave three hundred horses of the Titteti and the Kalmasha species possessing noses like parrots. And he also gave three hundred camels and an equal number of she-asses, all fattened with the olives and the *Pilusha*. And innumerable Brahmanas engaged in rearing cattle and occupied in low offices for the gratification of the illustrious king Yudhishthira the just waited at the gate with three hundred millions of tribute but they were denied admission into the palace. And hundred upon hundreds of Brahmanas possessing wealth of kine and living upon the lands that Yudhishthira had given them, came there with their handsome golden *Kamandalus* filled with clarified butter. And though they had brought such tribute, they were refused admission into the palace. And the Sudra kings that dwelt in the regions on the seacoast, brought with them, O king, hundred thousands of serving girls of the Karpasika country, all of beautiful features and slender waist and luxuriant hair and decked in golden ornaments; and also many skins of the *Ranku* deer worthy even of Brahmanas as tribute unto king Yudhishthira. And the tribes Vairamas, Paradas, Tungas, with the Kitavas who lived upon crops that depended on water from the sky or of the river and also they who were born in regions on the sea-shore, in woodlands, or countries on the other side of the ocean waited at the gate, being refused permission to enter, with goats and kine and asses and camels and vegetable, honey and blankets and jewels and gems of various kinds. And that great warrior king Bhagadatta, the brave ruler of Pragjyotisha and the mighty sovereign of the *mlechchas*, at the head of a large number of Yavanas waited at the gate unable to enter, with a considerable tribute comprising of horses of the best breed and possessing the speed of the wind. And king Bhagadatta (beholding the concourse) had to go away from the gate, making over a number of swords with handles made of the purest ivory and well-adorned with diamonds and every kind of gems. And many tribes coming from different regions, of whom some possess two eyes, some three and some had eyes on their foreheads, and those also called *Aushmikas*, and Nishadas, and Romakas, some cannibals and many possessing only one leg. I say, O king, standing at the gate, being refused permission to enter. And these diverse rulers brought as tribute ten thousand asses of diverse hues and black necks and huge bodies and great speed and much docility and celebrated all over the world. And these asses were all of goodly size and delightful colour. And they were all bred on the coast of Vankhu. And there were many kings that gave unto Yudhishthira much gold and silver. And having given much tribute they obtained admission into the palace of Yudhishthira. The people that came there possessing only one leg gave unto Yudhishthira many wild horses, some of which were as red as the cochineal, and some white, and some possessing the hues of the rainbow and some looking like evening clouds, and some that were of variegated colour. And they were all endued with the speed of the mind. And they also gave unto the king enough gold of superior quality. I also saw numberless Chins and Sakas and Uddras and many barbarous tribes living in the woods, and many Vrishnis and Harahunas, and dusky tribes of the Himavat, and many Nipas and people residing in regions on the sea-coast, waiting at the gate being refused permission to enter. And the people of Valhika gave unto him as tribute ten thousand asses, of goodly size and black necks and daily running two hundred miles, And those asses were of many shapes. And they were well-trained and celebrated all over the world. And possessed of symmetrical proportion and excellent colour, their skins were pleasant to the touch. And the Valhikas also presented numerous blankets of woollen texture manufactured in Chin and numerous skins of the Ranku deer, and clothes manufactured from jute, and others woven with the threads spun by insects. And they also gave thousands of other clothes not made of cotton, possessing the colour of the lotus. And these were all of smooth texture. And they also gave soft sheep-skins by thousands. And they also gave many sharp and long swords and scimitars, and hatchets and fine-edged battle-axes manufactured in the western countries. And having presented perfumes and jewels and gems of various kinds by thousands as tribute, they waited at the gate, being refused admission into the palace. And the Sakas and Tukhatas and Tukharas and Kankas and Romakas and men with horns bringing with them as tribute numerous large elephants and ten thousand horses, and hundreds and hundreds of millions of gold waited at the gate, being refused permission to enter. And the kings of the eastern countries having presented numerous valuable articles including many costly carpets and vehicles and beds, and armours of diverse hues decked with jewels and gold and ivory, and weapons of various kinds, and cars of various shapes and handsome make and adorned with gold, with well-trained horses trimmed with tiger skins, and rich and variegated blankets for caprisoning elephants, and various kinds of jewels and gems, arrows long and short and various other kinds of weapons, obtained permission to enter the sacrificial palace of the illustrious Pandava!'"

Section LI (51)

Duryodhana said,—'O sinless one, listen to me as I describe that large mass of wealth consisting of various kinds of tribute presented unto Yudhishthira by the kings of the earth. They that dwell by the side of the river Sailoda flowing between the mountains of Mer and Mandara, and enjoy the delicious shade of topes of the *Kichaka* bamboo, *viz.*, the Khashas, Ekasanas, the Arhas, the Pradaras, the Dirghavenus, the Paradas, the Kulindas, the Tanganas, and the other Tanganas, brought as tribute heaps of gold measured in *dronas* (jars) and raised from underneath the earth by ants and therefore called after these creatures. The mountain tribes endued with great strength having brought as tribute numerous *Chamaras* (long brushes) soft and black and others white as moon-beam and sweet honey extracted from the flowers growing on the Himavat as also from the *Mishali champaka* and garlands of flowers brought from the region of the northern Kurus, and diverse kinds of plants from the north even from Kailasa, waited with their heads bent down at the gate of king Yudhishthira, being refused permission to enter. I also beheld there numberless chiefs of the Kiratas armed with cruel weapons and ever engaged in cruel deeds, eating of fruits and roots and attired in skins and living on the northern slopes of the Himavat and on the mountain from behind which the sun rises and in the region of Karusha on the sea-coast and on both sides of the Lohitya mountains. And, O king, having brought with them as tribute loads upon loads of sandal and aloe as also black aloe, and heaps upon heaps of valuable skins and gold and perfumes, and ten thousand serving-girls of their own race, and many beautiful animals and birds of remote countries, and much gold of great splendour procured from mountains, the Kiratas waited at the gate, being refused permission to enter. The Kairatas, the Daradas, the Darvas, the Suras, the Vaiamakas, the Audumvaras, the Durvibhagas, the Kumaras, the Paradas along with the Vahlikas, the Kashmiras, the Ghorakas, the Hansakayanas, the Sivis, the Trigartas, the Yauddheyas, the ruler of Madras and the Kaikeyas, the Amvashtas, the Kaukuras, the Tarkshyas, the Vastrapas along with the Palhavas, the Vashatayas, the Mauleyas along with the Kshudrakas, and the Malavas, the Paundrayas, the Kukkuras, the Sakas, the Angas, the Vangas, the Punras, the Sanavatyas, and the Gayas—these good and well-born Kshatriyas distributed into regular clans and trained to the use of arms, brought tribute unto king Yudhishthira by hundreds and thousands. And the Vangas, the Kalingas, the Magadhas, the Tamraliptas, the Supundrakas, the Dauvalikas, the Sagarakas, the Patrornas, the Saisavas, and innumerable Karnapravaranas, who presented themselves at the gate, were told by the gate-keepers at the command of the king, that if they could wait and bring good tribute they could obtain admission. Then the kings of those nations each gave a thousand elephants furnished with tusks like unto the shafts of ploughs and decked with girdles made of gold, and covered with fine blankets and therefore, resembling the lotus in hue. And they were all darkish as rocks and always musty, and procured from the sides of the Kamyaka lake, and covered with defensive armour. And they were also exceedingly patient and of the best breed. And having made these presents, those kings were permitted to enter. O king, these and many others, coming from various regions, and numberless other illustrious kings, brought jewels and gems unto this sacrifice. And Chitraratha, also the king of Gandharvas, the friend of Indra, gave four hundred horses gifted with the speed of the wind. And the *Gandharva* Tumvuru gladly gave a hundred horses of the colour of mango leaf and decked in gold. And, O thou of the Kuru race, the celebrated king of the *Mlechcha* tribe, called the Sukaras, gave many hundreds of excellent elephants. And Virata, the king of Matsya, gave as tribute two thousand elephants decked in gold. And king Vasudana from the kingdom of Pansu presented unto the son of Pandu six and twenty elephants and two thousand horses. O king, all decked in gold and endued with speed and strength and in full vigour of youth, and diverse other kinds of wealth. And Yajnasena presented unto the sons of Pandu for the sacrifice, fourteen thousand serving-girls and ten thousand serving-men with their wives, many hundreds of excellent elephants, six and twenty cars with elephants yoked unto them, and also his whole kingdom. And Vasudeva of the Vrishni race, in order to enhance the dignity of Arjuna, gave fourteen thousands of excellent elephants. Indeed, Krishna is the soul of Arjuna and Arjuna is the soul of Krishna, and whatever Arjuna may say Krishna is certain to accomplish. And Krishna is capable of abandoning heaven itself for the sake of Arjuna. and Arjuna also is capable of sacrificing his life for the sake of Krishna. And the Kings of Chola and Pandya, though they brought numberless jars of gold filled with fragrant sandal juice from the hills of Malaya, and loads of sandal and aloe wood from the Dardduras hills, and many gems of great brilliancy and fine cloths inlaid with gold, did not obtain permission (to enter). And the king of the Singhalas gave those best of sea-born gems called the *lapis lazuli*, and heaps of pearls also, and hundreds of coverlets for elephants. And numberless dark-coloured men with the ends of their, eyes red as copper, attired in clothes decked with gems, waited at the gate with those presents. And numberless Brahmanas and Kshatriyas who had been vanquished, and Vaisyas and serving Sudras, from love of Yudhishthira, brought tribute unto the son of Pandu. And even all the *Mlechchas*, from love and respect, came unto Yudhishthira. And all orders of men, good, indifferent and low, belonging to numberless races, coming from diverse lands made Yudhishthira's habitation the epitome of the world.

"And beholding the kings of the earth to present unto the foes such excellent and valuable presents, I wished for death out of grief. And O king, I will now tell thee of the servants of the Pandavas, people for whom Yudhishthira supplieth food, both cooked and uncooked. There are a hundred thousand billions of mounted elephants and cavalry and a hundred millions of cars and countless foot soldiers. At one place raw provisions are being measured out; at another they are being cooked; and at another place the foods are being distributed. And the notes of festivity are being heard everywhere. And amongst men of all orders I beheld not a single one in the mansion of Yudhishthira that had not food and drink and ornaments. And eighty-eight thousands of Snataka Brahmanas leading domestic lives, all supported by Yudhishthira, with thirty serving-girls given unto each, gratified by the king, always pray with complacent hearts for the destruction of his foes. And ten thousands of other ascetics with vital seed drawn up, daily eat of golden plates in Yudhishthira's palace. And, O king, Yajnaseni, without having eaten herself, daily seeth whether everybody, including even the deformed and the dwarfs, hath eaten or not. And, O Bharata, only two do not pay tribute unto the son of Kunti, viz., the Panchalas in consequence of their relationship by marriage, and the Andhakas and Vrishnis in consequence of their friendship.

Section LII (52)

Duryodhana said,—"Those king that are revered over all the world, who are devoted to truth and who are pledged to the observance of rigid vows, who are possessed of great learning and eloquence, who are fully conversant with the *Vedas* and their branches as also with sacrifices, who have piety and modesty, whose souls are devoted to virtue, who possess fame, and who have enjoyed the grand rites of coronation, all wait upon and worship Yudhishthira. And, O king, I beheld there many thousands of wild kine with as many vessels of white copper for milking them, brought thither by the kings of the earth as sacrificial presents to be given away by Yudhishthira unto the Brahmana. And, O Bharata, for bathing Yudhishthira at the conclusion of the sacrifice, many kings with the greatest alacrity, themselves brought there in a state of purity many excellent jars (containing water). And king Vahlika brought there a car decked with pure gold. And king Sudakshina himself yoked thereto four white horses of Kamboja breed, and Sunitha of great might fitted the lower pole and the ruler of Chedi with his own hands took up and fitted the flag-staff. And the king of the Southern country stood ready with the coat of mail; the ruler of Magadha, with garlands of flowers and the head-gear; the great warrior Vasudana with a sixty years old elephant, the king of Matsya, with the side-fittings of the car, all encased in gold; king Ekalavya, with the shoes; the king of Avanti, with diverse kinds of water for the final bath; king Chekitana, with the quiver; the king of Kasi, with the bow; and Salya; with a sword whose hilt and straps were adorned with gold. Then Dhaumya and Vyasa, of great ascetic merit, with Narada and Asita's son Devala, standing before performed the ceremony of sprinkling the sacred water over the king. And the great *Rishis* with cheerful hearts sat where the sprinkling ceremony was performed. And other illustrious *Rishis* conversant with the *Vedas*, with Jamadagni's son among them, approached Yudhishthira, the giver of large sacrificial presents, uttering *mantras* all the while, like the seven *Rishis*, approaching the great India in heaven. And Satyaki of unbaffled prowess held the umbrella (over the king's head). And Dhananjaya and Bhima were engaged in tanning the king; while the twins held a couple of chamaras in their hands. And the Ocean himself brought in a sling that big conch of Varuna which the celestial artificer Viswakarman had constructed with a thousand *Nishkas* of gold, and which Prajapati had in a former *Kalpa*, presented unto India. It was with that conch that Krishna bathed Yudhishthira after the conclusion of the sacrifice, and beholding it, I swooned away. People go to the Eastern or the Western seas and also to the Southern one. But, O father, none except birds can ever go to the Northern sea. But the Pandavas have spread their dominion even there, for I heard hundreds of conches that had been brought thence blown (in the sacrificial mansion) indicative of auspicious rejoicing. And while those conches blew simultaneously, my hair stood on end. And those among the kings, who were weak in strength fell down. And Dhrishtadyumna and Satyaki and the sons of Pandu and Kesava,—those eight, endued with strength and prowess and handsome in person, beholding the kings deprived of consciousness and myself in that plight, laughed outright. Then Vibhatsu (Arjuna) with a cheerful heart gave, O Bharata, unto the principal Brahmanas five hundred bullocks with horns plated with gold. And king Yudhishthira, the son of Kunti, having completed the Rajasuya sacrifice, obtained like the exalted Harishchandra such prosperity that neither Rantideva nor Nabhaga, nor Jauvanaswa, nor Manu, nor king Prithu the son of Vena, nor Bhagiratha, Yayati, nor Nahusha, had obtained its like. And beholding, O exalted one, such prosperity, in the son of Pritha which is even like that which Harishchandra had, I do not see the least good in continuing to live, O Bharata! O ruler of men, a yoke that is tied (to the bullock's shoulders) by a blind man becomes loosened. Even such is the case with us. The younger ones are growing while the elder ones are decaying. And beholding all this, O chief of the Kurus, I cannot enjoy peace even with the aid of reflection. And it is for this, O king, that I am plunged into grief and becoming pale and emaciated."

Section LIII (53)

"Dhritrashtra said,—'Thou art my eldest son and born also of my eldest wife. Therefore, O son, be not jealous of the Pandavas. He that is jealous is always unhappy and suffereth the pangs of death. O bull of the Bharata race, Yudhishthira knoweth not deception, possesseth wealth equal unto thine, hath thy friends for his, and is not jealous of thee. Why shouldst thou, therefore, be jealous of him? O king, in respect of friends and allies thou art equal unto Yudhishthira. Why shouldst thou, therefore, covet, from folly, the property of thy brother? Be not so. Cease to be jealous. Do not grieve. O bull of the Bharata race, it thou covetest the dignity attaching to the performance of a sacrifice, let the priests arrange for thee the great sacrifice, called the

Saptatantu. The kings of the earth will then, cheerfully and with great respect, bring for thee also much wealth and gems and ornaments. O child, coveting other's possessions is exceedingly mean. He, on the other hand, enjoyeth happiness, who is content with his own being engaged in the practices of his own order. Never striving to obtain the wealth of others, persevering in one's own affairs, and protecting what hath been earned,—these are the indications of true greatness. He that is unmoved in calamity, skilled in his own business, ever exerting vigilant and humble, always beholdeth prosperity. The sons of Pandu are as thy arms. Do not lop off those arms of thine. Plunge not into internal dissensions for the sake of that wealth of thy brothers. O king, be not jealous of the sons of Pandu. Thy wealth is equal unto that of thy brothers in his entirety. There is great sin in quarrelling with friends. They that are thy grandsires are theirs also. Give away in charity on occasions of sacrifices, gratify every dear object of thy desire, disport in the company of women freely, and enjoy thou peace.'"

Section LIV (54)

"Duryodhana said,—'He that is devoid of intellect but hath merely heard of many things, can scarcely understand the real import of the scriptures, like the spoon that hath no perception of the taste of the soup it toucheth. Thou knowest everything, but yet confoundest me. Like a boat fastened to another, thou and I are tied to each other. Art thou unmindful of thy own interests? Or, dost thou entertain hostile feeling towards me? These thy sons and allies are doomed to destruction, inasmuch as they have thee for their ruler, for thou describest as attainable in the future what is to be done at the present moment. He often trippeth whose guide acts under the instructions of others. How then can his followers expect to come across a right path? O king, thou art of mature wisdom; thou hast the opportunity to listen to the words of old, and thy senses also are under thy control. It behoveth thee not to confound us who are ready to seek our own interests. Vrihaspati hath said that the usage of kings are different from those of common people. Therefore kings should always attend to their own interests with vigilance. The attainment of success is the sole criterion that should guide the conduct of a Kshatriya. Whether, therefore, the means is virtuous or sinful, what scruples can there be in the duties of one's own order? He that is desirous of snatching the blazing prosperity of his foe, should, O bull of the Bharata race, bring every direction under his subjection like the charioteer taming the steeds with his whip. Those used to handling weapons say that, a weapon is not simply an instrument that cuts but is a means, whether covert or overt, that can defeat a foe. Who is to be reckoned a foe and who a friend, doth not depend on one's figure or dimensions. He that paineth another is, O king, to be regarded a foe by him that is pained. Discontent is the root of prosperity. Therefore, O king, I desire to be discontented. He that striveth after the acquisition of prosperity is, O king, a truly politic person. Nobody should be attached to wealth and affluence, for the wealth that hath been earned and hoarded may be plundered. The usages of kings are even such. It was during a period of peace that Sakra cut off the head of Namuchi after having given a pledge to the contrary, and it was because he approved of this eternal usage towards the enemy that he did so. Like a snake that swalloweth up frogs and other creatures living in holes, the earth swalloweth up a king that is peaceful and a Brahmana that stirreth not out of home. O king, none can by nature be any person's foe. He is one's foe, and not anybody else, who hath common pursuits with one. He that from folly neglecteth a growing foe, hath his vitals cut off as by a disease that he cherished without treatment. A foe, however insignificant, if suffered to grow in prowess, swalloweth one like the white ants at the root of a tree eating off the tree itself. O Bharata, O Ajamida, let not the prosperity of the foe be acceptable to thee. This policy (of neglecting the foe) should always be borne on their heads by the wise even like a load. He that always wisheth for the increase of his wealth, ever groweth in the midst of his relatives even like the body naturally growing from the moment of birth. Prowess conferreth speedy growth. Coveting as I do the prosperity of the Pandavas. I have not yet made it my own. At present I am a prey to doubts in respect of my ability. I am determined to resolve those doubts of mine. I will either obtain that prosperity of theirs, or lie down having perished in battle. O king when the state of my mind is such, what do I care now for life, for the Pandavas are daily growing while our possessions know no increase?'"

Section LV (55)

"Sakuni said,—O thou foremost of victorious persons, I will snatch (for thee) this prosperity of Yudhishthira, the son of Pandu, at the sight of which thou grievest so. Therefore, O king, let Yudhishthira the son of Kunti be summoned. By throwing dice a skilful man, himself uninjured, may vanquish one that hath no skill. Know, O Bharata, that betting is my bow, the dice are my arrows, the marks on them my bow-string, and the dice-board my car.

"Duryodhana said,—'This Sukuni skilled at dice, is ready, O king, to snatch the prosperity of the son of Pandu by means of dice. It behoveth thee to give him permission.

"Dhritarashtra said,—'I am obedient to the counsels of my brother, the illustrious Vidura. Consulting with him, I shall tell what should be done in this matter.

"Duryodhana said,—'Vidura is always engaged in doing good to the sons of Pandu. O Kaurava, his feelings towards us are otherwise. He will, therefore, without doubt, withdraw thy heart from the proposed act. No man should set himself to any task depending upon the counsels of another, for, O son of Kuru's race, the minds of two persons seldom agree in any particular act. The fool that liveth shunning all causes of fear wasteth himself like an insect in the rainy season. Neither sickness nor Yama waiteth till one is in prosperity. So long, therefore, as there is life and health, one should (without waiting for prosperity) accomplish his purpose.'

"Dhritarashtra said,—'O son, hostility with those that are strong, is what never recommendeth itself to me. Hostility bringeth about a change of feelings, and that itself is a weapon though not made of steel. Thou regardest, O Prince, as a great blessing what will bring in its train the terrible consequences of war, what is really fraught with mischief. If once it beginneth, it will create sharp swords and pointed arrows.'

"Duryodhana replied,—'Men of the most ancient times invented the use of dice. There is no destruction in it, nor is there any striking with weapons. Let the words of Sakuni, therefore, be acceptable to thee, and let thy command be issued for the speedy construction of the assembly house. The door of heaven, leading us to such happiness, will be opened to us by gambling. Indeed, they that betake to gambling (with such aid) deserve such good fortune. The Pandavas then will become thy equals (instead of, as now, superiors); therefore, gamble thou with the Pandavas.

"Dhritarashtra said,—'The words uttered by thee do not recommend themselves to me. Do what may be agreeable to thee, O ruler of men. But thou shall have to repent for acting according to these words; for, words that are fraught with such immorality can never bring prosperity in the future. Even this was foreseen by the learned Vidura ever treading the path of truth and wisdom. Even the great calamity, destructive of the lives of the Kshatriyas, cometh as destined by fate.'"

Vaisampayana continued—"Having said this, the weak-minded Dhritarashtra regarded fate as supreme and unavoidable. And the king deprived of reason by Fate, and obedient to the counsels of his son, commanded his men in loud voice, saying—'Carefully construct, without loss of time, an assembly house of the most beautiful description, to be called the crystal-arched palace with a thousand columns, decked with gold and *lapis lazuli*, furnished with a hundred gates, and full two miles in length and in breadth the same.' Hearing those words of his, thousands of artificers endued with intelligence and skill soon erected the palace with the greatest alacrity, and having erected it brought thither every kind of article. And soon after they cheerfully represented unto the king that the palace had been finished, and that it as delightful and handsome and furnished with every kind of gems and covered with many-coloured carpets inlaid with gold. Then king Dhritarashtra, possessed of learning, summoning Vidura the chief of his ministers, said,—'Repairing (to Khandavaprastha), bring prince Yudhishthira here without loss of time. Let him come hither with his brothers, and behold this handsome assembly house of mine, furnished with countless jewels and gems, and costly beds and carpets, and let a friendly match at dice commence here.'"

Section LVI (56)

Vaisampayana said,—"King Dhritarashtra, ascertaining the inclinations of his son and knowing that Fate is inevitable, did what I have said. Vidura, however, that foremost of intelligent men, approved not his brother's words and spoke thus, 'I approve not, O king, of this command of thine. Do not act so. I fear, this will bring about the destruction of our race. When thy sons lose their unity, dissension will certainly ensue amongst them. This I apprehend, O king, from this match at dice.'

"Dhritarashtra said,—'If Fate be not hostile, this quarrel will not certainly grieve me. The whole universe moveth at the will of its Creator, under the controlling influence of Fate. It is not free. Therefore, O Vidura, going unto king Yudhishthira at my command, bring thou soon that invincible son of Kunti.'"

Section LVII (57)

Vaisampayana said,—"Vidura then, thus commanded against his will by king Dhritarashtra, set out, with the help of horses of high mettle and endued with great speed and strength, and quiet and patient, for the abode of the wise sons of Pandu. Possessed of great intelligence, Vidura proceeded by the way leading to the capital of the Pandavas. And having arrived at the city of king Yudhishthira, he entered it and proceeded towards the palace, worshipped by numberless Brahmanas. And coming to the palace which was even like unto the mansion of Kuvera himself, the virtuous Vidura approached Yudhishthira, the son of Dharma. Then the illustrious Ajamida devoted to truth and having no enemy on earth, reverentially saluted Vidura, and asked him about Dhritarashtra and his sons. And Yudhishthira said,'O Kshatta, thy mind seemeth to be cheerless. Dost thou come here in happiness and peace? The sons of Dhritarashtra, I hope, are obedient to their old father. The people also, I hope, are obedient to Dhritarashtra's rule.'

"Vidura said,—'The illustrious king, with his sons, is well and happy, and surrounded by his relatives he reigneth even like Indra himself. The king is happy with his sons who are all obedient to him and hath no grief. The illustrious monarch is bent on his own aggrandisement. The king of the Kurus hath commanded me to enquire after thy peace and prosperity, and to ask thee to repair to Hastinapore with thy brothers and to say, after beholding king Dhritarashtra's newly erected palace, whether that one is equal to thy own. Repairing thither, O son of Pritha, with thy brothers, enjoy ye in that mansion and sit to a friendly match at dice. We shall be glad if thou goest, as the Kurus have already arrived there. And thou wilt see there those gamblers and cheats that the illustrious king Dhritarashtra hath already brought thither. It is for this, O king, that I have come hither. Let the king's command be approved by thee.

"Yudhishthira said,—'O Kshatta, if we sit to a match at dice, we may quarrel. What man is there, who knowing all this, will consent to gamble? What dost thou think fit for us? We all are obedient to thy counsels.'

"Vidura said,—'I know that gambling is the root of misery, and I strove to dissuade the king from it. The king, however, hath sent me to thee. Having known all this, O learned one, do what is beneficial.

"Yudhishthira said,—'Besides the sons of Dhritarashtra what other dishonest gamblers are there ready for play? Tell us, O Vidura, who they are and with whom we shall have to play, staking hundreds upon hundreds of our possessions.'

"Vidura said,—'O monarch, Sakuni, the king of Gandhara, an adept at dice, having great skill of hand and desperate in stakes, Vivingati, king Chitrasena, Satyavrata, Purumitra and Jaya, these,—O king, are there.'

"Yudhishthira said,—'It would seem then that some of the most desperate and terrible gamblers always depending upon deceit are there. This whole universe, however, is at the will of its Maker, under the control of fate. It is not free. O learned one, I do not desire, at the command of king Dhritarashtra to engage myself in gambling. The father always wisheth to benefit his son. Thou art our master, O Vidura. Tell me what is proper for us. Unwilling as I am to gamble, I will not do so, if the wicked Sakuni doth not summon me to it in the *Sabha*? If, however, he challengeth me, I will never refuse. For that, as settled, is my eternal vow."

Vaiṣampayana continued,—"King Yudhishthira the just having said this unto Vidura, commanded that preparations for his journey might be made without loss of time. And the next day, the king accompanied by his relatives and attendants and taking with him also the women of the household with Draupadi in their midst, set out for the capital of the Kurus. '*Like some brilliant body falling before the eyes, Fate depriveth us of reason, and man, tied as it were with a cord, submitteth to the sway of Providence,*' saying this, king Yudhishthira, that chastiser of the foe, set out with Kshatta, without deliberating upon that summons from Dhritarashtra. And that slayer of hostile heroes, the son of Pandu and Pritha, riding upon the car that had been given him by the king of Valhika, and attired also in royal robes, set out with his brothers. And the king, blazing as it were with royal splendour, with Brahmanas walking before him, set out from his city, summoned by Dhritarashtra and impelled by what hath been ordained by Kala (Time). And arriving at Hastinapore he went to the palace of Dhritarashtra. And going there, the son of Pandu approached the king. And the exalted one then approached Bhishma and Drona and Karna, and Kripa, and the son of Drona, and embraced and was embraced by them all. And the mighty-armed one, endued with great prowess, then approached Somadatta, and then Duryodhana and Salya, and the son of Suvala, and those other kings also that had arrived there before him. The king then went to the brave Dusshasana and then to all his (other) brothers and then to Jayadratha and next to all the Kurus one after another. And the mighty-armed one, then surrounded by all his brothers, entered the apartment of the wise king Dhritarashtra. And then Yudhishthira beheld the reverend Gandhari, ever obedient to her lord, and surrounded by her daughters-in-law like Rohini by the stars. And saluting Gandhari and blessed by her in return, the king then beheld his old uncle, that illustrious monarch whose wisdom was his eye. King Dhritarashtra then, O monarch, smelt his head as also the heads of those four other princes of the Kuru race, viz., the sons of Pandu with Bhimasena as their eldest. And, O king, beholding—the handsome Pandava those tigers among men, all the Kurus became exceedingly glad. And commanded by the king, the

Pandavas then retired to the chambers allotted to them and which were all furnished with jewels and gems. And when they had retired into the chambers, the women of Dhritarashtra's household with Dussala taking the lead visited them. And the daughters-in-law of Dhritarashtra beholding the blazing and splendid beauty and prosperity of Yajnaseni, became cheerless and filled with jealousy. And those tigers among men, having conversed with the ladies went through their daily physical exercises and then performed the religious rites of the day. And having finished their daily devotions, they decked their persons with sandal paste of the most fragrant kind. And desiring to secure good luck and prosperity they caused (by gifts) the Brahmanas to utter benedictions. And then eating food that was of the best taste they retired to their chambers for the night. And those bulls among the Kurus then were put to sleep with music by handsome females. And obtaining from them what came in due succession, those subjugators of hostile towns passed with cheerful hearts that delightful night in pleasure and sport. And waked by the bards with sweet music, they rose from their beds, and having passed the night thus in happiness, they rose at dawn and having gone through the usual rites, they entered into the assembly house and were saluted by those that were ready there for gambling."

Section LVIII (58)

Vaisampayana said,—"The sons of Pritha with Yudhishthira at their head, having entered that assembly house, approached all the kings that were present there. And worshipping all those that deserved to be worshipped, and saluting others as each deserved according to age, they seated themselves on seats that were clean and furnished with costly carpets. After they had taken their seats, as also all the kings, Sakuni the son of Suvala addressed Yudhishthira and said, 'O king, the assembly is full. All had been waiting for thee. Let, therefore, the dice be cast and the rules of play be fixed, O Yudhishthira.'

"Yudhishthira replied, 'Deceitful gambling is sinful. There is no Kshatriya prowess in it. There is certainly no morality in it. Why, then, O king, dost thou praise gambling so? The wise applaud not the pride that gamesters feel in deceitful play. O Sakuni, vanquish us, not like a wretch, by deceitful means.'

Sakuni said,—"That high-souled player who knoweth the secrets of winning and losing, who is skilled in baffling the deceitful arts of his *confrere*, who is united in all the diverse operations of which gambling consisteth, truly knoweth the play, and he suffereth all in course of it. O son of Pritha, it is the staking at dice, which may be lost or won that may injure us. And it is for that reason that gambling is regarded as a fault. Let us, therefore, O king, begin the play. Fear not. Let the stakes be fixed. Delay not!'

"Yudhishthira said,—"That best of *Munis*, Devala, the son of Asita, who always instructeth us about all those acts that may lead to heaven, hell, or the other regions, hath said, that it is sinful to play deceitfully with a gamester. To obtain victory in battle without cunning or stratagem is the best sport. Gambling, however, as a sport, is not so. Those that are respectable never use the language of the *Mlechchas*, nor do they adopt deceitfulness in their behaviour. War carried on without crookedness and cunning, this is the act of men that are honest. Do not, O Sakuni, playing desperately, win of us that wealth with which according to our abilities, we strive to learn how to benefit the Brahmanas. Even enemies should not be vanquished by desperate stakes in deceitful play. I do not desire either happiness or wealth by means of cunning. The conduct of one that is a gamester, even if it be without deceitfulness, should not be applauded.'

"Sakuni said,—'O Yudhishthira, it is from a desire of winning, which is not a very honest motive, that one high-born person approacheth another (in a contest of race superiority). So also it is from a desire of defeating, which is not a very honest motive, that one learned person approacheth another (in a contest of learning). Such motives, however, are scarcely regarded as really dishonest. So also, O Yudhishthira, a person skilled at dice approacheth one that is not so skilled from a desire of vanquishing him. One also who is conversant with the truths of science approacheth another that is not from desire of victory, which is scarcely an honest motive. But (as I have already said) such a motive is not really dishonest. And, O Yudhishthira, so also one that is skilled in weapons approacheth one that is not so skilled; the strong approacheth the weak. This is the practice in every contest. The motive is victory, O Yudhishthira. If, therefore, thou, in approaching me, regardest me to be actuated by motives that are dishonest, if thou art under any fear, desist then from play.'

"Yudhishthira said,—'Summoned, I do not withdraw. This is my established vow. And, O king, Fate is all powerful. We all are under the control of Destiny. With whom in this assembly am I to play? Who is there that can stake equally with me? Let the play begin.'

"Duryodhana said,—'O monarch, I shall supply jewels and gems and every kind of wealth. And it is for me that this Sakuni, my uncle, will play.'

"Yudhishthira said,—'Gambling for one's sake by the agency of another seemeth to me to be contrary to rule. Thou also, O learned one, will admit this. If, however, thou art still bent on it, let the play begin.'"

Section LIX (59)

Vaisampayana said,—"When the play commenced, all those kings with Dhritarashtra at their head took their seats in that assembly. And, O Bharata, Bhishma and Drona and Kripa and the high-souled Vidura with cheerless hearts sat behind. And those kings with leonine necks and endued with great energy took their seats separately and in pairs upon many elevated seats of beautiful make and colour. And, O king, that mansion looked resplendent with those assembled kings like heaven itself with a conclave of the celestials of great good fortune. And they were all conversant with the Vedas and brave and of resplendent countenances. And, O great king, the friendly match at dice then commenced.

Yudhishthira said,—"O king, this excellent wealth of pearls of great value, procured from the ocean by churning it (of old), so beautiful and decked with pure gold, this, O king, is my stake. What is thy counter stake, O great king,—the wealth with which thou wishest to play with me?"

"Duryodhana said,—'I have many jewels and much wealth. But I am not vain of them. Win thou this stake.'

Vaisampayana continued,—"Then Sakuni, well-skilled at dice, took up the dice and (casting them) said unto Yudhishthira, 'Lo, I have won!'"

Section LX (60)

Yudhishthira said,—'Thou hast won this stake of me by unfair means. But be not so proud, O Sakuni. Let us play staking thousands upon thousands. I have many beautiful jars each full of a thousand *Nishkas* in my treasury, inexhaustible gold, and much silver and other minerals. This, O king, is the wealth with which I will stake with thee!'"

Vaisampayana continued,—'Thus addressed, Sakuni said unto the chief of the perpetuators of the Kuru race, the eldest of the sons of Pandu, king Yudhishthira, of glory incapable of sustaining any diminution. 'Lo, I have won!'"

Yudhishthira said,—'This my sacred and victorious and royal car which gladdeneth the heart and hath carried us hither, which is equal unto a thousand cars, which is of symmetrical proportions and covered with tiger-skin, and furnished with excellent wheels and flag-staffs which is handsome, and decked with strings of little bells, whose clatter is even like the roar of the clouds or of the ocean, and which is drawn by eight noble steeds known all over the kingdom and which are white as the moon-beam and from whose hoofs no terrestrial creature can escape—this, O king, is my wealth with which I will stake with thee!'"

Vaisampayana continued,—'Hearing these words, Sakuni ready with the dice, and adopting unfair means, said unto Yudhishthira, 'Lo, I have won!'

"Yudhishthira said,—'I have a hundred thousand serving-girls, all young, and decked with golden bracelets on their wrists and upper arms, and with *nishkas* round their necks and other ornaments, adorned with costly garlands and attired in rich robes, daubed with the sandal paste, wearing jewels and gold, and well-skilled in the four and sixty elegant arts, especially versed in dancing and singing, and who wait upon and serve at my command the celestials, the Snataka Brahmanas, and kings. With this wealth, O king, I will stake with thee!'"

Vaisampayana continued,—'Hearing these words, Sakuni ready with the dice, adopting unfair means, said unto Yudhishthira. 'Lo, I have won!'

Yudhishthira said,—'I have thousands of serving-men, skilled in waiting upon guests, always attired in silken robes, endued with wisdom and intelligence, their senses under control though young, and decked with ear-rings, and who serve all guests night and day with plates and dishes in hand. With this wealth, O king, I will stake with thee!'"

Vaisampayana continued,—'Hearing these words, Sakuni, ready with the dice, adopting unfair means said unto Yudhishthira, 'Lo, I have won!'

"Yudhishthira said,—'I have, O son of Suvala, one thousand musty elephants with golden girdles, decked with ornaments, with the mark of the lotus on their temples and necks and other parts, adorned with golden garlands, with fine white tusks long and thick as plough-shafts, worthy of carrying kings on their backs, capable of bearing every kind of noise on the field of battle, with huge bodies, capable of battering down the walls of hostile towns, of the colour of new-formed clouds, and each possessing eight she-elephants. With this wealth, O king, I will stake with thee.'"

Vaisampayana continued,—'Unto Yudhishthira who had said so, Sakuni, the son of Suvala, laughingly said, 'Lo, I have won it!'

Yudhishthira said,—'I have as many cars as elephants, all furnished with golden poles and flag-staffs and well-trained horses and warriors that fight wonderfully and each of whom receiveth a thousand coins as his monthly pay whether he fighteth or not. With this wealth, O king, I will stake with thee!'"

Vaisampayana continued,—"When these words had been spoken, the wretch Sakuni, pledged to enmity, said unto Yudhishthira, 'Lo, I have won it.'

Yudhishthira said.—'The steeds of the *Tittiri, Kalmasha,* and *Gandharva* breeds, decked with ornaments, which Chitraratha having been vanquished in battle and subdued cheerfully gave unto Arjuna, the wielder of the Gandiva. With this wealth, O king, I will stake with thee."

Vaisampayana continued, "Hearing this, Sakuni, ready at dice, adopting unfair means, said unto Yudhishthira: 'Lo, I have won!'

Yudhishthira said,—'I have ten thousand cars and vehicles unto which are yoked draught animals of the foremost breed. And I have also sixty thousand warriors picked from each order by thousands, who are all brave and endued with prowess like heroes, who drink milk and eat good rice, and all of whom have broad chests. With this wealth, O king, I will stake with thee.'

Vaisampayana continued,—"Hearing this, Sakuni ready at dice, adopting unfair means said unto Yudhishthira, 'Lo, I have won!'

Yudhishthira said,—'I have four hundred *Nidis* (jewels of great value) encased in sheets of copper and iron. Each one of them is equal to five *draunikas* of the costliest and purest leaf gold of the *Jatarupa* kind. With this wealth, O king, I will stake with thee.'"

Vaisampayana continued,—"Hearing this, Sakuni ready at dice, adopting foul means, said unto Yudhishthira, 'Lo, I have won it!'"

Section LXI (61)

Vaisampayana said,—"During the course of this gambling, certain to bring about utter ruin (on Yudhishthira), Vidura, that dispeller of all doubts, (addressing Dhritarashtra) said, 'O great king, O thou of the Bharata race, attend to what I say, although my words may not be agreeable to thee, like medicine to one that is ill and about to breathe his last. When this Duryodhana of sinful mind had, immediately after his birth, cried discordantly like a jackal, it was well known that he had been ordained to bring about the destruction of the Bharata race. Know, O king, that he will be the cause of death of ye all. A jackal is living in thy house, O king, in the form of Duryodhana. Thou knowest it not in consequence of thy folly. Listen now to the words of the Poet (Sukra) which I will quote. They that collect honey (in mountains), having received what they seek, do not notice that they are about to fall. Ascending dangerous heights, abstracted in the pursuit of what they seek, they fall down and meet with destruction. This Duryodhana also, maddened with the play at dice, like the collector of honey, abstracted in what he seeketh, marketh not the consequences. Making enemies of these great warriors, he beholdeth not the fall that is before him. It is known to thee, O thou of great wisdom, that amongst the Bhojas, they abandoned, for the good of the citizens a son that was unworthy of their race. The Andhakas, the Yadavas, and the Bhojas uniting together, abandoned Kansa. And afterwards, when at the command of the whole tribe, the same Kansa had been slain by Krishna that slayer of foes, all the men of the tribe became exceedingly happy for a hundred years. So at thy command, let Arjuna slay this Suyodhana. And in consequence of the slaying of this wretch, let the Kurus be glad and pass their days in happiness. In exchange of a crow, O great king, buy these peacocks—the Pandavas; and in exchange of a jackal, buy these tigers. For the sake of a family a member may be sacrificed; for the sake of a village a family may be sacrificed, for the sake of a province a village may be sacrificed and for the sake of one's own soul the whole earth may be sacrificed. Even this was what the omniscient Kavya himself, acquainted with the thoughts of every creature, and a source of terror unto all foes, said unto the great Asuras to induce them to abandon Jambha at the moment of his birth. It is said that a certain king, having caused a number of wild birds that vomited gold to take up their quarters in his own house, afterwards killed them from temptation. O slayer of foes, blinded by temptation and the desire of enjoyment, for the sake of gold, the king destroyed at the same time both his present and future gains. Therefore, O king, prosecute not the Pandavas from desire of profit, even like the king in story. For then, blinded by folly thou wilt have to repent afterwards, even like the person that killed the birds. Like a flower-seller that plucketh (many flowers) in the garden from trees that he cherisheth with affection from day to day, continue, O Bharata, to pluck flowers day by day from the Pandavas. Do not scorch them to their roots like a fire-producing breeze that reduceth everything to black charcoal. Go not, O king, unto the region of Yama, with thy sons and troops, for who is there that is capable of fighting with the sons of Pritha, together? Not to speak of others, is the chief of the celestials at the head of the celestials themselves, capable of doing so?"

Section LXII (62)

"Vidura said,—"Gambling is the root of dissensions. It bringeth about disunion. Its consequences are frightful. Yet having recourse to this, Dhritarashtra's son Duryodhana createth for himself fierce enmity. The descendants of Pratipa and Santanu, with their fierce troops and their allies the Vahlikas, will, for the sins of Duryodhana meet with destruction. Duryodhana, in consequence of this intoxication, forcibly driveth away luck and prosperity from his kingdom, even like an infuriate bull breaking his own horns himself. That brave and learned person who disregarding his own foresight, followeth, O king, (the bent of) another man's heart, sinketh in terrible affliction even like one that goeth into the sea in a boat guided by a child. Duryodhana is gambling with the son of Pandu, and thou art in raptures that he is winning. And it is such success that begeteth war, which endeth in the destruction of men. This fascination (of gambling) that thou has well-devised only leadeth to dire results. Thus hast thou simply brought on by these counsels great affliction to thy heart. And this thy quarrel with Yudhishthira, who is so closely related to thee, even if thou hadst not foreseen it, is still approved by thee. Listen, ye sons of Santanu, ye descendants of Pratipa, who are now in this assembly of the Kauravas, to these words of wisdom. Enter ye not into the terrible fire that hath blazed forth following the wretch. When Ajatasatru, the son of Pandu, intoxicated with dice, giveth way to his wrath, and Vrikodara and Arjuna and the twins (do the same), who, in that hour of confusion, will prove your refuge? O great king, thou art thyself a mine of wealth. Thou canst earn (by other means) as much wealth as thou seekest to earn by gambling. What dost thou gain by winning from the Pandavas their vast wealth? Win the Pandavas themselves, who will be to thee more than all the wealth they have. We all know the skill of Suvala in play. This hill-king knoweth many nefarious methods in gambling. Let Sakuni return whence he came. War not, O Bharata, with the sons of Pandu!'

Section LXIII (63)

Duryodhana said,—'O Kshatta, thou art always boasting of the fame of our enemies, deprecating the sons of Dhritarashtra. We know, O Vidura, of whom thou art really fond. Thou always disregardest us as children. That man standeth confest, who wisheth for success unto those that are near to him and defeat unto those that are not his favourites. His praise and blame are applied accordingly. Thy tongue and mind betray thy heart. But the hostility thou showeth in speech is even greater than what is in thy heart. Thou hast been cherished by us like a serpent on our lap. Like a cat thou wishest evil unto him that cherisheth thee. The wise have said that there is no sin graver than that of injuring one's master. How is it, O Kshatta, that thou dost not fear this sin? Having vanquished our enemies we have obtained great advantages. Use not harsh words in respect of us. Thou art always willing to make peace with the foes. And it is for this reason that thou hatest us always. A man becometh a foe by speaking words that are unpardonable. Then again in praising the enemy, the secrets of one's own party should not be divulged. (Thou however, transgressest this rule). Therefore, O thou parasite, why dost thou obstruct us so? Thou sayest whatever thou wishest. Insult us not. We know thy mind. Go and learn sitting at the feet of the old. Keen up the reputation that thou hast won. Meddle not with the affairs of other men. Do not imagine that thou art our chief. Tell us not harsh words always, O Vidura. We do not ask thee what is for our good. Cease, irritate not those that have already borne too much at thy hands. There is only one Controller, no second. He controlleth even the child that is in the mother's womb. I am controlled by Him. Like water that always floweth in a downward course, I am acting precisely in the way in which He is directing me. He that breaketh his head against a stone-wall, and he that feedeth a serpent, are guided in those acts of theirs by their own intellect. (Therefore, in this matter I am guided by my own intelligence). He becometh a foe who seeketh to control others by force. When advice, however, is offered in a friendly spirit, the learned bear with it. He again that hath set fire to such a highly inflammable object as camphor, beholdeth not its ashes. If he runneth immediately to extinguish it. One should not give shelter to another who is the friend of his foes, or to another who is ever jealous of his protector or to another who is evil-minded. Therefore, O Vidura, go whither-so-ever thou pleasest. A wife that is unchaste, however well-treated, forsaketh her husband yet.'

"Vidura addressing Dhritarashtra, said, 'O monarch, tell us (impartially) like a witness what thou thinkest of the conduct of those who abandon their serving-men thus for giving instruction to them. The hearts of kings are, indeed, very fickle. Granting protection at first, they strike with clubs at last. O prince (Duryodhana), thou regardest thyself as mature in intellect, and, O thou of bad heart, thou regardest me as a child. But consider that he is a child who having first accepted one for a friend, subsequently findeth fault with him. An evil-hearted man can never be brought to the path of rectitude, like an unchaste wife in the house of a well-born person. Assuredly, instruction is not agreeable to this bull of the Bharata race like a husband of sixty years to a damsel that is young. After this, O king, if thou wishest to hear words that are agreeable to thee, in respect of all acts good or bad, ask thou women and idiots and cripples or persons of that description. A sinful man speaking words that are agreeable may be had in this world. But a speaker of words that are disagreeable though sound as regimen, or a hearer of the same, is very rare. He indeed, is a king's true ally who disregarding what is agreeable or disagreeable to his master beareth himself virtuously and uttereth what may be disagreeable but necessary as regimen. O great king, drink thou that which the honest drink and the dishonest shun, even humility, which is like a medicine that is bitter, pungent, burning, unintoxicating, disagreeable, and revolting. And drinking it, O king, regain thou thy sobriety. I always wish Dhritarashtra and his sons affluence and fame. Happen what may unto thee, here I bow to thee (and take my leave). Let the Brahmanas wish me well. O son of Kuru, this is the lesson I carefully inculcate, that the wise should never enrage such as adders as have venom in their very glances!"

Section LXIV (64)

"Sakuni said,—'Thou hast, O Yudhishthira, lost much wealth of the Pandavas. If thou hast still anything that thou hast not yet lost to us, O son of Kunti, tell us what it is!"

"Yudhishthira said,—O son of Suvala, I know that I have untold wealth. But why is it, O Sakuni, that thou askest me of my wealth? Let tens of thousands and millions and millions and tens of millions and hundreds of millions and tens of billions and hundreds of billions and trillions and tens of trillions and hundreds of trillions and tens of quadrillions and hundreds of quadrillions and even more wealth be staked by thee. I have as much. With that wealth, O king, I will play with thee."

Vaisampayana said,—"Hearing this, Sakuni, ready with the dice, adopting unfair means, said unto Yudhishthira, 'Lo, I have won!'

'Yudhishthira said,—'I have, O son of Suvala, immeasurable kine and horses and milch cows with calves and goats and sheep in the country extending from the Parnasa to the eastern bank of the Sindu. With this wealth, O king, I will play with thee.

Vaisampayana said,—"Hearing this Sakuni, ready with the dice, adopting unfair means, said unto Yudhishthira, 'Lo, I have won!'

Yudhishthira said,—'I have my city, the country, land, the wealth of all dwelling therein except of the Brahmanas, and all those persons themselves except Brahmanas still remaining to me. With this wealth, O king, I will play with thee.'

Vaisampayana said,—"Hearing this, Sakuni, ready with the dice, adopting foul means, said unto Yudhishthira, 'Lo! I have won.'

"Yudhishthira said,—These princes here, O king, who look resplendent in their ornaments and their earrings and *Nishkas* and all the royal ornaments on their persons are now my wealth. With this wealth, O king, I play with thee.

Vaisampayana said,—"Hearing this, Sakuni, ready with his dice, adopting foul means, said unto Yudhishthira, 'Lo! I have won them.'

"Yudhishthira said,—'This Nakula here, of mighty arms and leonine neck, of red eyes and endued with youth, is now my one stake. Know that he is my wealth.'

Sakuni said,—'O king Yudhishthira, prince Nakula is dear to thee. He is already under our subjection. With whom (as stake) wilt thou now play?"

Vaisampayana said,—"Saying this, Sakuni cast those dice, and said unto Yudhishthira, 'Lo! He hath been won by us.'

Yudhishthira said,—"This Sahadeva administereth justice. He hath also acquired a reputation for learning in this world. However undeserving he may be to be staked in play, with him as stake I will play, with such a dear object as it, indeed, he were not so!'

Vaisampayana said,—"Hearing this, Sakuni, ready with the dice, adopting foul means, said unto Yudhishthira, 'Lo! I have won.'

"Sakuni continued,—'O king, the sons of Madri, dear unto thee, have both been won by me. It would seem, however, that Bhimasena and Dhananjaya are regarded very much by thee.'

"Yudhishthira said,—'Wretch! thou actest sinfully in thus seeking to create disunion amongst us who are all of one heart, disregarding morality.'

"Sakuni said,—'One that is intoxicated falleth into a pit (hell) and stayeth there deprived of the power of motion. Thou art, O king, senior to us in age, and possessed of the highest accomplishments. O bull of the Bharata race, I (beg my pardon and) bow to thee. Thou knowest, O Yudhishthira, that gamesters, while excited with play, utter such ravings that they never indulge in the like of them in their waking moments nor even in dream.'

"Yudhishthira said,—He that taketh us like a boat to the other shore of the sea of battle, he that is ever victorious over foes, the prince who is endued with great activity, he who is the one hero in this world, (is here). With that Falguna as stake, however, undeserving of being made so, I will now play with thee.'"

Vaisampayana said,—"Hearing this, Sakuni, ready with the dice, adopting foul means, said unto Yudhishthira, 'Lo! I have won.'

"Sakuni continued,—'This foremost of all wielders of the bow, this son of Pandu capable of using both his hands with equal activity hath now been won by me. O play now with the wealth that is still left unto thee, even with Bhima thy dear brother, as thy stake, O son of Pandu.

"Yudhishthira said,—'O king, however, undeserving he may be of being made a stake, I will now play with thee by staking Bhimasena, that prince who is our leader, who is the foremost in fight,—even like the wielder of the thunder-bolt—the one enemy of the Danavas,—the high-souled one with leonine neck and arched eye-brows and eyes looking askance, who is incapable of putting up with an insult, who hath no equal in might in the world, who is the foremost of all wielders of the mace, and who grindeth all foes.'"

"Vaisampayana said,—"Hearing this, Sakuni, ready with the dice adopting foul means, said unto Yudhishthira. 'Lo! I have won.'

Sakuni continued,—Thou hast, O son of Kunti, lost much wealth, horses and elephants and thy brothers as well. Say, if thou hast anything which thou hast not lost.'

Yudhishthira, said—'I alone, the eldest of all my brothers and dear unto them, am still unwon. Won by thee, I will do what he that is won will have to do.'"

Vaisampayana said,—"Hearing this Sakuni, ready with the dice, adopting foul means, said unto Yudhishthira, 'Lo! I have won.'

Sakuni continued,—'Thou hast permitted thyself to be won. This is very sinful. There is wealth still left to thee, O king. Therefore, thy having lost thyself is certainly sinful.'"

Vaisampayana continued,—"Having said this, Sakuni, well-skilled at dice, spoke unto all the brave kings present there of his having won, one after another, all the Pandavas. The son of Suvala then, addressing Yudhishthira said,—'O king, there is still one stake dear to thee that is still unwon. Stake thou Krishna, the princess of Panchala. By her, win thyself back.'

"Yudhishthira said,—'With Draupadi as stake, who is neither short nor tall, neither spare nor corpulent, and who is possessed of blue curly locks, I will now play with thee. Possessed of eyes like the leaves of the autumn lotus, and fragrant also as the autumn lotus, equal in beauty unto her (Lakshmi) who delighteth in autumn lotuses, and unto Sree herself in symmetry and every grace she is such a woman as a man may desire for wife in respect of softness of heart, and wealth of beauty and of virtues. Possessed of every accomplishment and compassionate and sweet-speeched, she is such a woman as a man may desire for wife in respect of her fitness for the acquisition of virtue and pleasure and wealth. Retiring to bed last and waking up first, she looketh after all down to the cowherds and the shepherds. Her face too, when covered with sweat, looketh as the lotus or the jasmine. Of slender waist like that of the wasp, of long flowing locks, of red lips, and body without down, is the princess of Panchala. O king, making the slender-waisted Draupadi, who is even such as my stake, I will play with thee, O son of Suvala.'"

Vaisampayana continued,—'When the intelligent king Yudhishthira the just has spoken thus,—'*Fie*!' '*Fie*!' were the words that were uttered by all the aged persons that were in the assembly. And the whole conclave was agitated, and the kings who were present there all gave way to grief. And Bhishma and Drona and Kripa were covered with perspiration. And Vidura holding his head between his hands sat like one that had lost his reason. He sat with face downwards giving way to his reflections and sighing like a snake. But Dhritarashtra glad at heart, asked repeatedly, 'Hath the stake been won?' 'Hath the stake been won?' and could not conceal his emotions. Karna with Dussassana and others laughed aloud, while tears began to flow from the eyes of all other present in the assembly. And the son of Suvala, proud of success and flurried with excitement and repeating. 'Thou hast one stake, dear to thee', etc. said,—'Lo! I have won' and took up the dice that had been cast."

Section LXV (65)

Duryodhana said,—'Come, Kshatta, bring hither Draupadi the dear and loved wife of the Pandavas. Let her sweep the chambers, force her thereto, and let the unfortunate one stay where our serving-women are.'

"Vidura said,—'Dost thou not know, O wretch, that by uttering such harsh words thou art tying thyself with cords? Dost thou not understand that thou art hanging on the edge of a precipice? Dost thou not know that being a deer thou provokest so many tigers to rage? Snakes of deadly venom, provoked to ire, are on thy head! Wretch, do not further provoke them lest thou goest to the region of

Yama. In my judgement, slavery does not attach to Krishna, in as much as she was staked by the King after he had lost himself and ceased to be his own master. Like the bamboo that beareth fruit only when it is about to die, the son of Dhritarashtra winneth this treasure at play. Intoxicated, he perceiveth nor in these his last moments that dice bring about enmity and frightful terrors. No man should utter harsh speeches and pierce the hearts of the others. No man should subjugate his enemies by dice and such other foul means. No one should utter such words as are disapproved by the *Vedas* and lead to hell and annoy others. Some one uttereth from his lips words that are harsh. Stung by them another burneth day and night. These words pierce the very heart of another. The learned, therefore, should never utter them, pointing them at others. A goat had once swallowed a hook, and when it was pierced with it, the hunter placing the head of the animal on the ground tore its throat frightfully in drawing it out. Therefore, O Duryodhana, swallow not the wealth of the Pandavas. Make them not thy enemies. The sons of Pritha never use words such as these. It is only low men that are like dogs who use harsh words towards all classes of people, *viz.*, those that have retired to the woods, those leading domestic lives, those employed in ascetic devotions and those that are of great learning. Alas! the son of Dhritarashtra knoweth not that dishonesty is one of the frightful doors of hell. Alas! many of the Kurus with Dussasana amongst them have followed him in the path of dishonesty in the matter of this play at dice. Even gourds may sink and stones may float, and boats also may always sink in water, still this foolish king, the son of Dhritarashtra, listeneth not to my words that are even as regimen unto him. Without doubt, he will be the cause of the destruction of the Kurus. When the words of wisdom spoken by friends and which are even as fit regimen are not listened to, but on the other hand temptation is on the increase, a frightful and universal destruction is sure to overtake all the Kurus."

Section LXVI (66)

Vaisampayana said,— "Intoxicated with pride, the son of Dhritarashtra spake,—'Fie on Kshatta! and casting his eyes upon the *Pratikamin* in attendance, commanded him, in the midst of all those reverend seniors, saying,—'Go *Pratikamin*, and bring thou Draupadi hither. Thou hast no fear from the sons of Pandu. It is Vidura alone that raveth in fear. Besides, he never wisheth our prosperity!'"

Vaisampayana continued,—"Thus commanded, the *Pratikamin*, who was of the *Suta* caste, hearing the words of the king, proceeded with haste, and entering the abode of the Pandavas, like a dog in a lion's den, approached the queen of the sons of Pandu. And he said,—'Yudhishthira having been intoxicated with dice, Duryodhana, O Draupadi, hath won thee. Come now, therefore, to the abode of Dhritarashtra. I will take thee, O Yajnaseni, and put thee in some menial work.'

Draupadi said,—'Why, O *Pratikamin*, dost thou say so? What prince is there who playeth staking his wife? The king was certainly intoxicated with dice. Else, could he not find any other object to stake?'

"The Pratikamin said,'When he had nothing else to stake, it was then that Ajatasatru, the son of Pandu, staked thee. The king had first staked his brothers, then himself, and then thee, O princess.'

"Draupadi said,—'O son of the *Suta* race, go, and ask that gambler present in the assembly, whom he hath lost first, himself, or me. Ascertaining this, come hither, and then take me with thee, O son of the *Suta* race.'

Vaisampayana continued,—"The messenger coming back to the assembly told all present the words of Draupadi. And he spoke unto Yudhishthira sitting in the midst of the kings, these words,—Draupadi hath asked thee, Whose lord wert thou at the time thou lost me in play? Didst thou lose thyself first or me? Yudhishthira, however sat there like one demented and deprived of reason and gave no answer good or ill to the *Suta*.

"Duryodhana then said,—'Let the princess of Panchala come hither and put her question. Let every one hear in this assembly the words that pass between her and Yudhishthira.'

Vaisampayana continued,—"The messenger, obedient to the command of Duryodhana, going once again to the palace, himself much distressed, said unto Draupadi,—'O princess, they that are in the assembly are summoning thee. It seemeth that the end of the Kauravas is at hand. When Duryodhana, O princess, is for taking thee before the assembly, this weak-brained king will no longer be able to protect his prosperity.'

"Draupadi said,—'The great ordainer of the world hath, indeed, ordained so. Happiness and misery pay their court to both the wise and unwise. Morality, however, it hath been said, is the one highest object in the world. If cherished, that will certainly dispense blessings to us. Let not that morality now abandon the Kauravas. Going back to those that are present in that assembly, repeat these my words consonant with morality. I am ready to do what those elderly and virtuous persons conversant with morality will definitely tell me.

Vaisampayana continued,—"The *Suta*, hearing these words of Yajnaseni, came back to the assembly and repeated the words of Draupadi. But all sat with faces downwards, uttering not a word, knowing the eagerness and resolution of Dhritarashtra's son.

"Yudhishthira, however, O bull of the Bharata race, hearing of Duryodhana's intentions, sent a trusted messenger unto Draupadi, directing that although she was attired in one piece of cloth with her navel itself exposed, in consequence of her season having come, she should come before her father-in-law weeping bitterly. And that intelligent messenger, O king, having gone to Draupadi's abode with speed, informed her of the intentions of Yudhishthira. The illustrious Pandavas, meanwhile, distressed and sorrowful, and bound by promise, could not settle what they should do. And casting his eyes upon them, king Duryodhana, glad at heart, addressed the Suta and said,—'O *Pratikamin*, bring her hither. Let the Kauravas answer her question before her face.' The *Suta*, then, obedient to his commands, but terrified at the (possible) wrath of the daughter of Drupada, disregarding his reputation for intelligence, once again said to those that were in the assembly,—'What shall I say unto Krishna?'

"Duryodhana, hearing this, said,—'O Dussasana, this son of my *Suta*, of little intelligence, feareth Vrikodara. Therefore, go thou thyself and forcibly bring hither the daughter of Yajnasena. Our enemies at present are dependent on our will. What can they do thee?' Hearing the command of his brother, prince Dussasana rose with blood-red eyes, and entering the abode of those great warriors, spake these words unto the princess, 'Come, come, O Krishna, princess of Panchala, thou hast been won by us. And O thou of eyes large as lotus leaves, come now and accept the Kurus for thy lords. Thou hast been won virtuously, come to the assembly.' At these words, Draupadi, rising up in great affliction, rubbed her pale face with her hands, and distressed she ran to the place where the ladies of Dhritarashtra's household were. At this, Dussasana roaring in anger, ran after her and seized the queen by her locks, so long and blue and wavy. Alas! those locks that had been sprinkled with water sanctified with *mantras* in the great Rajasuya sacrifice, were now forcibly seized by the son of Dhritarashtra disregarding the prowess of the Pandavas. And Dussasana dragging Krishna of long long locks unto the presence of the assembly—as if she were helpless though having powerful protectors—and pulling at her, made her tremble like the banana plant in a storm. And dragged by him, with body bent, she faintly cried—'Wretch! it ill behoveth thee to take me before the assembly. My season hath come, and I am now clad in one piece of attire.' But Dussasana dragging Draupadi forcibly by her black locks while she was praying piteously unto Krishna and Vishnu who were Narayana and Nara (on earth), said unto her—'Whether thy season hath come or not, whether thou art attired in one piece of cloth or entirely naked, when thou hast been won at dice and made our slave, thou art to live amongst our serving-women as thou pleasest."

Vaisampayana continued,—"With hair dishevelled and half her attire loosened, all the while dragged by Dussasana, the modest Krishna consumed with anger, faintly said—"In this assembly are persons conversant with all the branches of learning devoted to the performance of sacrifices and other rites, and all equal unto Indra, persons some of whom are really my superiors and others who deserve to be respected as such. I can not stay before them in this state. O wretch! O thou of cruel deeds, drag me not so. Uncover me not so. The princes (my lords) will not pardon thee, even if thou hast the gods themselves with Indra as thy allies. The illustrious son of Dharma is now bound by the obligations of morality. Morality, however, is subtle. Those only that are possessed of great clearness of vision can ascertain it. In speech even I am unwilling to admit an atom of fault in my lord forgetting his virtues. Thou draggest me who am in my season before these Kuru heroes. This is truly an unworthy act. But no one here rebuketh thee. Assuredly, all these are of the same mind with thee. O fie! Truly hath the virtue of the Bharata gone! Truly also hath the usage of those acquainted with the Kshatriya practice disappeared! Else these Kurus in this assembly would never have looked silently on this act that transgresseth the limits of their practices. Oh! both Drona and Bhishma have lost their energy, and so also hath the high-souled Kshatta, and so also this king. Else, why do these foremost of the Kuru elders look silently on this great crime?"

Vaisampayana continued,—"Thus did Krishna of slender waist cry in distress in that assembly. And casting a glance upon her enraged lords—the Pandavas—who were filled with terrible wrath, she inflamed them further with that glance of hers. And they were not so distressed at having been robbed of their kingdom, of their wealth, of their costliest gems, as with that glance of Krishna moved by modesty and anger. And Dussasana, beholding Krishna looking at her helpless lords, dragging her still more forcibly, and addressed her, 'Slave, Slave' and laughed aloud. And at those words Karna became very glad and approved of them by laughing aloud. And Sakuni, the son of Suvala, the Gandhara king, similarly applauded Dussasana. And amongst all those that were in the assembly except these three and Duryodhana, every one was filled with sorrow at beholding Krishna thus dragged in sight of that assembly. And beholding it all, Bhishma said, 'O blessed one, morality is subtle. I therefore am unable to duly decide this point that thou hast put, beholding that on the one hand one that hath no wealth cannot stake the wealth belonging to others, while on the other hand wives are always under the orders and at the disposal of their lords. Yudhishthira can abandon the whole world full of wealth, but he will never sacrifice morality. The son of Pandu hath said—'I am won.' Therefore, I am unable to decide this matter. Sakuni hath not his equal among men at dice-play. The son of Kunti still voluntarily staked with him. The illustrious Yudhishthira doth not himself regard that Sakuni hath played with him deceitfully. Therefore, I can not decide this point."

"Draupadi said,—"The king was summoned to this assembly and though possessing no skill at dice, he was made to play with skilful, wicked, deceitful and desperate gamblers. How can he said then to have staked voluntarily? The chief of the Pandavas was deprived of his senses by wretches of deceitful conduct and unholy instincts, acting together, and then vanquished. He could not understand their tricks, but he hath now done so. Here, in this assembly, there are Kurus who are the lords of both their sons and their daughters-in-law! Let all of them, reflecting well upon my words, duly decide the point that I have put.

Vaisampayana continued,—'Unto Krishna who was thus weeping and crying piteously, looking at times upon her helpless lord, Dussasana spake many disagreeable and harsh words. And beholding her who was then in her season thus dragged, and her upper garments loosened, beholding her in that condition which she little deserved, Vrikodara afflicted beyond endurance, his eyes fixed upon Yudhishthira, gave way to wrath."

Section LXVI (67)

"Bhima said,—'O Yudhishthira, gamblers have in their houses many women of loose character. They do not yet stake those women having kindness for them even. Whatever wealth and other excellent articles the king of Kasi gave, whatever, gems, animals, wealth, coats of mail and weapons that other kings of the earth gave, our kingdom, thyself and ourselves, have all been won by the foes. At all this my wrath was not excited for thou art our lord. This, however, I regard as a highly improper act—this act of staking Draupadi. This innocent girl deserveth not this treatment. Having obtained the Pandavas as her lords, it is for thee alone that she is being thus persecuted by the low, despicable, cruel, and mean-minded Kauravas. It is for her sake, O king, that my anger falleth on thee. I shall burn those hands of thine. Sahadeva, bring some fire.' "

"Arjuna hearing this, said,—'Thou hast never, O Bhimasena, before this uttered such words as these. Assuredly thy high morality hath been destroyed by these cruel foes. Thou shouldst not fulfil the wishes of the enemy. Practise thou the highest morality. Whom doth it behave to transgress his virtuous eldest brother? The king was summoned by the foe, and remembering the usage of the Kshatriyas, he played at dice against his will. That is certainly conducive to our great fame.'

Bhima said,—'If I had not known, O Dhananjaya, that the king had acted according to Kshatriya usage, then I would have, taking his hands together by sheer force, burnt them in a blazing fire.' "

Vaisampayana continued,—"Beholding the Pandavas thus distressed and the princess of Panchala also thus afflicted, Vikarna the son of Dhritarashtra said—'Ye kings, answer ye the question that hath been asked by Yajnaseni. If we do not judge a matter referred to us, all of us will assuredly have to go to hell without delay. How is that Bhishma and Dhritarashtra, both of whom are the oldest of the Kurus, as also the high-souled Vidura, do not say anything! The son of Bharadwaja who is the preceptor of us, as also Kripa, is here. Why do not these best of regenerate ones answer the question? Let also those other kings assembled here from all directions answer according to their judgment this question, leaving aside all motives of gain and anger. Ye kings, answer ye the question that hath been asked by this blessed daughter of king Drupada, and declare after reflection on which side each of ye is.' Thus did Vikarna repeatedly appeal to those that were in that assembly. But those kings answered him not one word, good or ill. And Vikarna having repeatedly appealed to all the kings began to rub his hands and sigh like a snake. And at last the prince said—'Ye kings of the earth, ye Kauravas, whether ye answer this question or not, I will say what I regard as just and proper. Ye foremost of men, it hath been said that hunting, drinking, gambling, and too much enjoyment of women, are the four vices of kings. The man, that is addicted to these, liveth forsaking virtue. And people do not regard the acts done by a person who is thus improperly engaged, as of any authority. This son of Pandu, while deeply engaged in one of these vicious acts, urged thereto by deceitful gamblers, made Draupadi a stake. The innocent Draupadi is, besides, the common wife of all the sons of Pandu. And the king, having first lost himself offered her as a stake. And Suvala himself desirous of a stake, indeed prevailed upon the king to stake this Krishna. Reflecting upon all these circumstances, I regard Draupadi as not won."

"Hearing these words, a loud uproar rose from among those present in that assembly. And they all applauded Vikarna and censured the son of Suvala. And at that sound, the son of Radha, deprived of his senses by anger, waving his well-shaped arms, said these words,—'O Vikarna, many opposite and inconsistent conditions are noticeable in this assembly. Like fire produced from a faggot, consuming the faggot itself, this thy ire will consume thee. These personages here, though urged by Krishna, have not uttered a word. They all regard the daughter of Drupada to have been properly won. Thou alone, O son of Dhritarashtra in consequence of thy immature years, art bursting with wrath, for though but a boy thou speakest in the assembly as if thou wert old. O younger brother of Duryodhana, thou dost not know what morality truly is, for thou sayest like a fool that this Krishna who hath been (justly) won as not won at all. O son of Dhritarashtra, how dost thou regard Krishna as not won, when the eldest of the Pandavas before this assembly staked all his possessions? O bull of the Bharata race, Draupadi is included in all the possessions (of Yudhishthira). Therefore, why regardest thou Krishna who hath been justly won as not won? Draupadi had been mentioned (by Suvala) and approved of as a stake by the Pandavas. For what reason then dost thou yet regard her as not won? Or, if thou thinkest that bringing her hither attired in a single piece of cloth, is an action of impropriety, listen to certain excellent reasons I will give. O son of the Kuru race, the gods have ordained only one husband for one woman. This Draupadi, however, hath many husbands. Therefore, certain it is that she is an unchaste woman. To bring her, therefore, into this assembly attired though she be in one piece of cloth—even to uncover her is not at all an act that may cause surprise. Whatever wealth the Pandavas had—she herself and these Pandavas themselves,—have all been justly won by the son of Suvala. O Dussasana, this Vikarna speaking words of (apparent) wisdom is but a boy. Take off the robes of the Pandavas as also the attire off Draupadi. Hearing these words the Pandavas, O Bharata, took of their upper garments and throwing them down sat in that assembly. Then Dussasana, O king, forcibly seizing Draupadi's attire before the eyes of all, began to drag it off her person."

Vaisampayana continued,—"When the attire of Draupadi was being thus dragged, the thought of Hari, (And she herself cried aloud, saying), 'O Govinda, O thou who dwellest in Dwaraka, O Krishna, O thou who art fond of cow-herdesses (of Vrindavana). O Kesava, seest thou not that the Kauravas are humiliating me. O Lord, O husband of Lakshmi, O Lord of Vraja (Vrindavana), O destroyer of all afflictions, O Janarddana, rescue me who am sinking in the Kaurava Ocean. O Krishna, O Krishna, O thou great yogin, thou soul of the universe, Thou creator of all things, O Govinda, save me who am distressed,—who am losing my senses in the midst of the Kurus.' Thus did that afflicted lady resplendent still in her beauty, O king, covering her face cried aloud, thinking of Krishna, of Hari, of the lord of the three worlds. Hearing the words of Draupadi, Krishna was deeply moved. And leaving his seat, the benevolent one, from compassion, arrived there on foot. And while Yajnaseni was crying aloud to Krishna, also called Vishnu and Hari and Nara for protection, the illustrious Dharma, remaining unseen, covered her with excellent clothes of many hues. And, O monarch as the attire of Draupadi was being dragged, after one was taken off, another of the same kind, appeared covering her. And thus did it continue till many clothes were seen. And, O exalted one, owing to the protection of Dharma, hundreds upon hundreds of robes of many hues came off Draupadi's person. And there arose then a deep uproar of many many voices. And the kings present in that assembly beholding that most extraordinary of all sights in the world, began to applaud Draupadi and censure the son of Dhritarashtra. And Bhima then, squeezing his hands, with lips quivering in rage, swore in the midst of all those kings a terrible oath in a loud voice.

"And Bhima said,—'Hear these words of mine, ye Kshatriyas of the world. Words such as these were never before uttered by other men, nor will anybody in the future ever utter them. Ye lords of earth, if having spoken these words I do not accomplish them hereafter, let me not obtain the region of my deceased ancestors. Tearing open in battle, by sheer force, the breast of this wretch, this wicked-minded scoundrel of the Bharata race, if I do not drink his life-blood, let me not obtain the region of my ancestors."

Vaisampayana continued,—"Hearing these terrible words of Bhima that made the down of the auditors to stand on end, everybody present there applauded him and censured the son of Dhritarashtra. And when a mass of clothes had been gathered in that assembly, all dragged from the person of Draupadi, Dussasana, tired and ashamed, sat down. And beholding the sons of Kunti in that state, the persons—those gods among men—that were in that assembly all uttered the word 'Fie!' (on the son of Dhritarashtra). And the united voices of all became so loud that they made the down of anybody who heard them stand on end. And all the honest men that were in that assembly began to say,—'Alas! the Kauravas answer not the question that hath been put to them by Draupadi.' And all censuring Dhritarashtra together, made a loud clamour. Then Vidura, that master of the science of morality, waving his hands and silencing every one, spake these words;—'Ye that are in this assembly, Draupadi having put her question is weeping helplessly. Ye are not answering her. Virtue and morality are being persecuted by such conduct. An afflicted person approacheth an assembly of good men, like one that is being consumed by fire. They that are in the assembly quench that fire and cool him by means of truth and morality. The afflicted person asketh the assembly about his rights, as sanctioned by morality. They that are in the assembly should, unmoved by interest and anger, answer the question. Ye kings, Vikarna hath answered the question, according to his own knowledge and judgment. Ye should also answer it as ye think proper. Knowing the rules of morality, and having attended an assembly, he that doth not answer a query that is put, incurreth half the demerit that attacheth to a lie. He, on the other hand, who, knowing the rules of morality and having joined an assembly answereth falsely, assuredly incurreth the sin of a lie. The learned quote as an example in this connection the old history of Prahlada and the son of Angirasa.

"There was of old a chief of the Daityas of the name Prahlada. He had a son named Virochana. And Virochana, for the sake of obtaining a bride, quarrelled with Sudhanwan, the son of Angiras. It hath been heard by us that they mutually wagered their lives, saying—I am superior,—I am superior,—for the sake of obtaining a bride. And after they had thus quarrelled with each other, they both made Prahlada the arbitrator to decide between them. And they asked him, saying;—'Who amongst us is superior (to the other)? Answer this question. Speak not falsely.' Frightened at this quarrel, Prahlada cast his eyes upon Sudhanwan. And Sudhanwan in rage, burning like unto the mace of Yama, told him,—'If thou answerest falsely, or dost not answer at all thy head will then be split into a hundred pieces by the wielder of the thunderbolt with that bolt of his.—Thus addressed by Sudhanwan, the Daitya, trembling like a leaf of the fig tree, went to Kasyapa of great energy, for taking counsel with him. And Prahlada said,—'Thou art, O illustrious and exalted one, fully conversant with the rules of morality that should guide both the gods and the Asuras and the Brahmanas as well. Here, however, is a situation of great difficulty in respect of duty. Tell me, I ask thee, what regions are obtainable by them who upon being asked a question, answer it not, or answer it falsely.' Kasyapa thus asked answered.—'He that knoweth, but answereth not a question from temptation, anger or fear, casteth upon himself a thousand nooses of Varuna. And the person who, cited as a witness with respect to any matter of ocular or auricular knowledge, speaketh carelessly, casteth a thousand nooses of Varuna upon his own person. On the completion of one full year, one such noose is loosened. Therefore, he that knoweth, should speak the truth without concealment. If virtue, pierced by sin, repaireth to an assembly (for aid), it is the duty of every body in the assembly to take off the dart, otherwise they themselves would be pierced with it. In an assembly where a truly censurable act is not rebuked, half the demerit of that act attacheth to the head of that assembly, a fourth to the person acting censurably and a fourth unto those others that are there. In that assembly, on the other hand, when he that deserveth censure is rebuked, the head of the assembly becometh freed from all sins, and the other members also incur none. It is only the perpetrator himself of the act that becometh responsible for it. O Prahlada, they who answer falsely those that ask them about morality destroy the meritorious acts of their seven upper and seven lower generations. The grief of one who hath lost all his wealth, of one who hath lost a son, of one who is in debt, of one who is separated from his companions, of a woman who hath lost her husband, of one that hath lost his all in consequence of the king's demand, of a woman who is sterile, of one who hath been devoured by a tiger (during his last struggles in the tiger's claws), of one who is a co-wife, and of one who hath been deprived of his property by false witnesses, have been said by the gods to be uniform in degree. These different sorts of grief are his who speaketh false. A person becometh a witness in consequence of his having seen, heard, and understood a thing. Therefore, a witness should always tell the truth. A truth-telling witness never loseth his religious merits and earthly possessions also.' Hearing these words of Kasyapa, Prahlada told his son, 'Sudhanwan is superior to thee, as indeed, (his father) Angiras is superior to me. The mother also of Sudhanwan is superior to thy mother. Therefore, O Virochana, this Sudhanwan is now the lord of the life.' At these words of Prahlada, Sudhanwan said, "Since unmoved by affection for thy child, thou hast adhered to virtue, I command, let this son of thine live for a hundred years.'

"Vidura continued,—'Let all the persons, therefore, present in this assembly hearing these high truths of morality, reflect upon what should be the answer to the question asked by Draupadi'".

Vaisampayana continued,—"The kings that were there hearing these words of Vidura, answered not a word, yet Karna alone spoke unto Dussasana, telling him, 'Take away this serving-woman Krishna into the inner apartments. And thereupon Dussasana began to drag before all the spectators the helpless and modest Draupadi, trembling and crying piteously unto the Pandavas her lords."

Section LXVIII (68)

Draupadi said,—'Wait a little, thou worst of men, thou wicked-minded Dussasana. I have an act to perform—a high duty that hath not been performed by me yet. Dragged forcibly by this wretch's strong arms, I was deprived of my senses. I salute these reverend seniors in this assembly of the Kurus. That I could not do this before cannot be my fault.'"

Vaisampayana said,—"Dragged with greater force than before, the afflicted and helpless Draupadi, undeserving of such treatment, falling down upon the ground, thus wept in that assembly of the Kurus,—

"'Alas, only once before, on the occasion of the Swayamvara, I was beheld by the assembled kings in the amphitheatre, and never even once beheld afterwards. I am to-day brought before this assembly. She whom even the winds and the sun had seen never before in her palace is to-day before this assembly and exposed to the gaze of the crowd. Alas, she whom the sons of Pandu could not, while in her palace, suffer to be touched even by the wind, is to-day suffered by the Pandavas to be seized and dragged by this wretch. Alas, these Kauravas also suffer their daughter-in-law, so unworthy of such treatment, to be thus afflicted before them. It seemeth that the times are out of joint. What can be more distressing to me, than that though high-born and chaste, I should yet be compelled to enter this public court? Where is that virtue for which these kings were noted? It hath been heard that the kings of ancient days never brought their wedded wives into the public court. Alas, that eternal usage hath disappeared from among the Kauravas. Else, how is it that the chaste wife of the Pandavas, the sister of Prishata's son, the friend of Vasudeva, is brought before this assembly? Ye Kauravas, I am the wedded wife of king Yudhishthira the just, hailing from the same dynasty to which the King belonged. Tell me now if I am a serving-maid or otherwise. I will cheerfully accept your answer. This mean wretch, this destroyer of the fame of the Kurus, is afflicting me hard. Ye Kauravas, I cannot bear it any longer. Ye kings, I desire ye to answer whether ye regard me as won or unwon. I will accept your verdict whatever it be.'

"Hearing these words, Bhishma answered, 'I have already said, O blessed one that the course of morality is subtle. Even the illustrious wise in this world fail to understand it always. What in this world a strong man calls morality is regarded as such by others, however otherwise it may really be; but what a weak man calls morality is scarcely regarded as such even if it be the highest morality. From the importance of the issue involved, from its intricacy and subtlety, I am unable to answer with certitude the question thou hast asked.

However, it is certain that as all the Kurus have become the slaves of covetousness and folly, the destruction of this our race will happen on no distant date. O blessed one, the family into which thou hast been admitted as a daughter-in-law, is such that those who are born in it, however much they might be afflicted by calamities, never deviate from the paths of virtue and morality. O Princess of Panchala, this conduct of thine also, viz, that though sunk in distress, thou still easiest thy eyes on virtue and morality, is assuredly worthy of thee. These persons, Drona and others, of mature years and conversant with morality, sit heads downwards like men that are dead, with bodies from which life hath departed. It seemeth to me, however, that Yudhishthira is an authority on this question. It behoveth him to declare whether thou art won or not won.'"

Section LXIX (69)

Vaisampayana said,—"The kings present in that assembly, from fear of Duryodhana, uttered not a word, good or ill, although they beheld Draupadi crying piteously in affliction like a female osprey, and repeatedly appealing to them. And the son of Dhritarashtra beholding those kings and sons and grand sons of kings all remaining silent, smiled a little, and addressing the daughter of the king of Panchala, said,—'O Yajnaseni, the question thou hast put dependeth on thy husbands—on Bhima of mighty strength, on Arjuna, on Nakula, on Sahadeva. Let them answer thy question. O Panchali, let them for thy sake declare in the midst of these respectable men that Yudhishthira is not their lord, let them thereby make king Yudhishthira the just a liar. Thou shalt then be freed from the condition of slavery. Let the illustrious son of Dharma, always adhering to virtue, who is even like Indra, himself declare whether he is not thy lord. At his words, accept thou the Pandavas or ourselves without delay. Indeed, all the Kauravas present in this assembly are floating in the ocean of thy distress. Endued with magnanimity, they are unable to answer thy question, looking at thy unfortunate husbands.'"

Vaisampayana continued,—"Hearing these words of the Kuru king, all who were present in the assembly loudly applauded them.

And shouting approvingly, they made signs unto one another by motions of their eyes and lips. And amongst some that were there, sounds of distress such as 'O!' and 'Alas!' were heard. And at these words of Duryodhana, so delightful (to his partisans), the Kauravas present in that assembly became exceedingly glad. And the kings, with faces turned sideways, looked upon Yudhishthira conversant with the rules of morality, curious to hear what he would say. And every one present in that assembly became curious to hear what Arjuna, the son of Pandu never defeated in battle, and what Bhimasena, and what the twins also would say. And when that busy hum of many voices became still, Bhimasena, waving his strong and well-formed arms smeared with sandalpaste spake these words,—'If this high-souled king Yudhishthira the just, who is our eldest brother, had not been our lord, we would never have forgiven the Kuru race (for all this). He is the lord of all our religious and ascetic merits, the lord of even our lives. If he regardeth himself as won, we too have all been won. If this were not so, who is there amongst creatures touching the earth with their feet and mortal, that would escape from me with his life after having touched those locks of the princess of Panchala? Behold these mighty, well-formed arms of mine, even like maces of iron. Having once come within them, even he of a hundred sacrifices is incapable of effecting an escape. Bound by the ties of virtue and the reverence that is due to our eldest brother, and repeatedly urged by Arjuna to remain silent, I am not doing anything terrible. If however, I am once commanded by king Yudhishthira the just, I would slay these wretched sons of Dhritarashtra, making slaps do the work of swords, like a lion slaying a number of little animals.'"

Vaisampayana continued,—"Unto Bhima who had spoken these words Bhishma and Drona and Vidura said, 'Forbear, O Bhima. Everything is possible with thee.'"

Section LXX (70)

"Karna said,—'Of all the persons in the assembly, three, *viz.*, Bhishma, Vidura, and the preceptor of the Kurus (Drona) appear to be

1. A word of benediction, similar to 'Amen.'

independent; for they always speak of their master as wicked, always censure him, and never wish for his prosperity. O excellent one, the slave, the son, and the wife are always dependent. They cannot earn wealth, for whatever they earn belongeth to their master. Thou art the wife of a slave incapable of possessing anything on his own account. Repair now to the inner apartments of king Dhritarashtra and serve the king's relatives. We direct that that is now thy proper business. And, O princess, all the sons of Dhritarashtra and not the sons of Pritha are now thy masters. O handsome one, select thou another husband now,—one who will not make thee a slave by gambling. It is well-known that women, especially that are slaves, are not censurable if they proceed with freedom in electing husbands. Therefore let it be done by thee. Nakula hath been won, as also Bhimasena, and Yudhishthira also, and Sahadeva, and Arjuna. And, O Yajnaseni, thou art now a slave. Thy husbands that are slaves cannot continue to be thy lords any longer. Alas, doth not the son of Pritha regards life, prowess and manhood as of no use that he offereth this daughter of Drupada, the king of Panchala, in the presence of all this assembly, as a stake at dice?'"

Vaisampayana continued,—"Hearing these words, the wrathful Bhima breathed hard, a very picture of woe. Obedient to the king and bound by the tie of virtue and duty, burning everything with his eyes inflamed by anger, he said,—'O king, I cannot be angry at these words of this son of a Suta, for we have truly entered the state of servitude. But O king, could our enemies have said so unto me, it thou hadst not played staking this princess?'"

Vaisampayana continued,—"Hearing these words of Bhimasena king Duryodhana addressed Yudhishthira who was silent and deprived of his senses, saying,—'O king, both Bhima and Arjuna, and the twins also, are under thy sway. Answer thou the question (that hath been asked by Draupadi). Say, whether thou regardest Krishna as unwon.' And having spoken thus unto the son of Kunti, Duryodhana. desirous of encouraging the son of Radha and insulting Bhima, quickly uncovered his left thigh that was like unto the stem of a plantain tree or the trunk of an elephant and which was graced with every auspicious sign and endued with the strength of thunder, and showed it to

Draupadi in her very sight. And beholding this, Bhimasena expanding his red eyes, said unto Duryodhana in the midst of all those kings and as if piercing them (with his dart-like words),—'Let not Vrikodara attain to the regions, obtained by his ancestors, if he doth not break that thigh of thine in the great conflict.' And sparkles of fire began to be emitted from every organ of sense of Bhima filled with wrath, like those that come out of every crack and orifice in the body of a blazing tree.

Vidura then, addressing everybody, said,—'Ye kings of Pratipa's race, behold the great danger that ariseth from Bhimasena. Know ye for certain that this great calamity that threateneth to overtake the Bharatas hath been sent by Destiny itself. The sons of Dhritarashtra have, indeed, gambled disregarding every proper consideration. They are even now disputing in this assembly about a lady (of the royal household). The prosperity of our kingdom is at an end. Alas, the Kauravas are even now engaged in sinful consultations. Ye Kauravas, take to your heart this high precept that I declare. If virtue is persecuted, the whole assembly becometh polluted. If Yudhishthira had staked her before he was himself won, he would certainly have been regarded as her master. If, however a person staketh anything at a time when he himself is incapable of holding any wealth, to win it is very like obtaining wealth in a dream. Listening to the words of the king of Gandhara, fall ye not off from this undoubted truth.'

"Duryodhana, hearing Vidura thus speak, said,—'I am willing to abide by the words of Bhima, of Arjuna and of the twins. Let them say that Yudhishthira is not their master. Yajnaseni will then be freed from her state of bondage.'"

"Arjuna at this, said,—"This illustrious son of Kunti, king Yudhishthira the just, was certainly our master before he began to play. But having lost himself, let all the Kauravas judge whose master he could be after that.'"

Vaisampayana continued,—"Just then, a jackal began to cry loudly in the *homa*-chamber of king Dhritarashtra's palace. And, O king, unto the jackal that howled so, the asses began to bray responsively. And terrible birds also, from all sides, began to answer with their cries. And Vidura conversant with everything and the daughter of

Suvala, both understood the meaning of those terrible sounds. And Bhishma and Drona and the learned Gautama loudly cried,—*Swashti! Swashti!*[1] Then Gandhari and the learned Vidura beholding that frightful omen, represented everything, in great affliction, unto the king. And the king (Dhritarashtra) thereupon said,—

'Thou wicked-minded Duryodhana, thou wretch, destruction hath all ready overtaken thee when thou insultest in language such as this the wife of these bulls among the Kurus, especially their wedded wife Draupadi. And having spoken those words, the wise Dhritarashtra endued with knowledge, reflecting with the aid of his wisdom and desirous of saving his relatives and friends from destruction, began to console Krishna, the princess of Panchala, and addressing her, the monarch said,—'Ask of me any boon, O princess of Panchala, that thou desirest, Chaste and devoted to virtue, thou art the first of all my daughters-in-law.'

Draupadi said,—'O bull of the Bharata race, if thou will grant me a boon, I ask the handsome Yudhishthira, obedient to every duty, be freed from slavery. Let not unthinking children call my child Prativindhya endued with great energy of mind as the *son of a slave*. Having been a prince, so superior to all men, and nurtured by kings it is not proper that he should be called the child of a slave.'

Dhritarashtra said unto her,—'O auspicious one, let it be as thou sayest. O excellent one, ask thou another boon, for I will give it. My heart inclineth to give thee a second boon. Thou dost not deserve only one boon.'

"Draupadi said,—'I ask, O king, that Bhimasena and Dhananjaya and the twins also, with their cars and bows, freed from bondage, regain their liberty.'

'Dhritarashtra said,—'O blessed daughter, let it be as thou desirest. Ask thou a third boon, for thou hast not been sufficiently honoured with two boons. Virtuous in thy behaviour, thou art the foremost of all my daughters-in-law.'

Draupadi said,—'O best of kings, O illustrious one, covetousness always bringeth about loss of virtue. I do not deserve a third boon. Therefore I dare not ask any. O king of kings, it hath been said that a Vaisya may ask one boon; a Kshatriya lady, two boons; a Kshatriya male, three, and a Brahmana, a hundred. O king, these my husbands freed from the wretched state of bondage, will be able to achieve prosperity by their own virtuous acts!'"

Section LXXI (71)

"Karna said,—'We have never heard of such an act (as this one of Draupadi), performed by any of the women noted in this world for their beauty. When the sons of both Pandu and Dhritarashtra were excited with wrath, this Draupadi became unto the sons of Pandu as their salvation. Indeed the princess of Panchala, becoming as a boat unto the sons of Pandu who were sinking in a boatless ocean of distress, hath brought them in safety to the shore.'"

Vaisampayana continued,—"Hearing these words of Karna in the midst of the Kurus,—*viz.*, that the sons of Pandu were saved by their wife,—the angry Bhimasena in great affliction said (unto Arjuna),—'O Dhananjaya, it hath been said by Devala three lights reside in every person, *viz.*, offspring, acts and learning, for from these three hath sprung creation. When life becometh extinct and the body becometh impure and is cast off by relatives, these three become of service to every person. But the light that is in us hath been dimmed by this act of insult to our wife. How, O Arjuna, can a son born from this insulted wife of ours prove serviceable to us?'

"Arjuna replied,—'Superior persons, O Bharata, never prate about the harsh words that may or may not be uttered by inferior men. Persons that have earned respect for themselves, even if they are able to retaliate, remember not the acts of hostility done by their enemies, but, on the other hand, treasure up only their good deeds.'

Bhima said,—'Shall I, O king, slay, without loss of time all these foes assembled together, even here, or shall I destroy them, O Bharata, by the roots, outside this palace? Or, what need is there of words or of command? I shall slay all these even now, and rule thou the whole earth, O king, without a rival.' And saying this, Bhima with his younger brothers, like a lion in the midst of a herd of inferior animals, repeatedly cast his angry glances around. But Arjuna, however, of white deeds, with appealing looks began to pacify his elder brother.

And the mighty-armed hero endued with great prowess began to burn with the fire of his wrath. And, O king, this fire began to issue out of Vrikodara's ears and other senses with smoke and sparks and flames. And his face became terrible to behold in consequence of his furrowed brows like those of Yama himself at the time of the universal destruction. Then Yudhishthira forbade the mighty hero, embracing him with his arms and telling him 'Be not so. Stay in silence and peace.' And having pacified the mighty-armed one with eyes red in wrath, the king approached his uncle Dhritarashtra, with hands joined in entreaty."

Section LXXII (72)

"Yudhishthira said,—'O king, thou art our master. Command us as to what we shall do. O Bharata, we desire to remain always in obedience to thee.'

"Dhritarashtra replied.—'O Ajatasatru, blest be thou. Go thou in peace and safety. Commanded by me, go, rule thy own kingdom with thy wealth. And, O child, take to heart this command of an old man, this wholesome advice that I give, and which is even a nutritive regimen. O Yudhishthira, O child, thou knowest the subtle path of morality. Possessed of great wisdom, thou art also humble, and thou waitest also upon the old. Where there is intelligence, there is forbearance. Therefore, O Bharata, follow thou counsels of peace. The axe falleth upon wood, not upon stone. (Thou art open to advice, not Duryodhana). They are the best of men that remember not the acts of hostility of their foes; that behold only the merits, not the faults, of their enemies; and that never enter into hostilities themselves. They that are good remember only the good deeds of their foes and not the hostile acts their foes might have done unto them. The good, besides, do good unto others without expectation of any good, in return. O Yudhishthira, it is only the worst of men that utter harsh words in quarrelling; while they that are indifferent reply to such when spoken by others. But they that are good and wise never think of or recapitulate such harsh words, little caring whether these may or may not have been uttered by their foes. They that are good, having regard to the state of their own feelings, can understand the feelings of others, and therefore remember only the good deeds and not the acts of hostility of their foes. Thou hast acted even as good men of prepossessing countenance do, who transgress not the limits of virtue, wealth, pleasure and salvation. O child, remember not the harsh words of Duryodhana. Look at thy mother Gandhari and myself also, if thou desirest to remember only what is good. O Bharata, look at me, who am thy father unto you and am old and blind, and still alive. It was for seeing our friends and examining also the strength and weakness of my children, that I had, from motives of policy, suffered this match at dice to proceed. O king those amongst the Kurus that have thee for their ruler, and the intelligent Vidura conversant with every branch of learning for their counsellor, have, indeed, nothing to grieve for. In thee is virtue, in Arjuna is patience, in Bhimasena is prowess, and the twins, those foremost of men, is pure reverence for superiors. Blest be thou, O Ajatasatru. Return to Khandavaprastha, and let there be brotherly love between thee and thy cousins. Let thy heart also be ever fixed on virtue.'"

Vaisampayana continued,—"That foremost of the Bharatas—king Yudhishthira the just—then, thus addressed by his uncle, having gone through every ceremony of politeness, set out with his brothers for Khandavaprastha. And accompanied by Draupadi and ascending their cars which were all of the hue of the clouds, with cheerful hearts they all set out for that best of cities called Indraprastha."

Section LXXIII (73)

Janamejaya said,—"How did the sons of Dhritarashtra feel, when they came to know that the Pandavas had, with Dhritarashtra's leave, left Hastinapore with all their wealth and jewels?"

Vaisampayana said,—"O king, learning that the Pandavas had been commanded by the wise Dhritarashtra to return to their capital, Dussasana went without loss of time unto his brother. And, O bull of the Bharata race, having arrived before Duryodhana with his counsellor, the prince, afflicted with grief, began to say,—'Ye mighty warriors, that which we had won after so much trouble, the old man (our father) hath thrown away. Know ye that he hath made over the whole of that wealth to the foes. At these words, Duryodhana and Karna and Sakuni, the son of Suvala, all of whom were guided by vanity, united together, and desirous of counteracting the sons of Pandu, approaching in haste saw privately the wise king Dhritarashtra—the son of Vichitravirya and spake unto him these pleasing and artful words. Duryodhana said,—

'Hast thou not heard, O king, what the learned Vrihaspati the preceptor of the celestials, said in course of counselling Sakra about mortals and politics? Even these, O slayer of foes, were the words of Vrihaspati, 'Those enemies that always do wrong by stratagem or force, should be slain by every means.' If, therefore, with the wealth of the Pandavas, we gratify the kings of the earth and then fight with the sons of Pandu, what reverses can overtake us? When one hath placed on the neck and back of venomous snakes full of wrath for encompassing his destruction, is it possible for him to take them off? Equipped with weapon and seated on their cars, the angry sons of Pandu like wrathful and venomous snakes will assuredly annihilate us, O father. Even now Arjuna proceedeth, encased in mail and furnished with his couple of quivers, frequently taking up the Gandiva and breathing hard and casting angry glances around. It hath (also) been heard by us that Vrikodara, hastily ordering his car to be made ready and riding on it, is proceeding along, frequently whirling his heavy mace. Nakula also is going along, with the sword in his grasp and the semi-circular shield in his hand. And Sahadeva and the king (Yudhishthira) have made signs clearly testifying to their intentions. Having ascended their cars that are full of all kinds of arms, they are whipping their horses (for going to Khandava soon) and assembling their forces. Persecuted thus by us they are incapable of forgiving us those injuries. Who is there among them that will forgive that insult to Draupadi? Blest be thou. We will again gamble with the son of Pandu for sending them to exile. O bull among men, we are competent to bring them thus under our sway. Dressed in skins, either we or they defeated at dice, shall repair to the woods for twelve years. The thirteenth year shall have to be spent in some inhabited country unrecognised; and, if recognised, an exile for another twelve years shall be the consequence. Either we or they shall live so. Let the play begin, casting the dice, let the sons of Pandu once more play. O bull of the Bharata race, O king, even this is our highest duty. This Sakuni knoweth well the whole science of dice. Even if they succeed in observing this vow for thirteen years, we shall be in the meantime firmly rooted in the kingdom and making alliances, assemble a vast invincible host and keep them content, so that we shall, O king, defeat the sons of Pandu if they reappear. Let this plan recommend itself to thee, O slayer of foes.

"Dhritarashtra said,—Bring back the Pandavas then, indeed, even if they have gone a great way. Let them come at once again to cast dice.'"

Vaisampayana continued,—"Then Drona, Somadatta and Valhika, Gautama, Vidura, the son of Drona, and the mighty son of Dhritarashtra by his Vaisya wife, Bhurisravas, and Bhishma, and that mighty warrior Vikarna,—all said, 'Let not the play commence. Let there be peace.' But Dhritarashtra, partial to his sons, disregarding the counsels of all his wise friends and relatives, summoned the sons of Pandu."

Section LXXIV (74)

Vaisampayana said,—'O monarch, it was then that the virtuous Gandhari, afflicted with grief on account of her affection for her sons, addressed king Dhritarashtra and said, 'When Duryodhana was born, Vidura of great intelligence had said, 'It is well to send this disgrace of the race to the other world.' He cried repeatedly and dissonantly like a jackal. It is certain he will prove the destruction of our race. Take this to heart, O king of the Kurus. O Bharata, sink not, for thy own fault, into an ocean of calamity. O lord, accord not thy approbation to the counsels of the wicked ones of immature years. Be not thou the cause of the terrible destruction of this race. Who is there that will break an embankment which hath been completed, or re-kindle a conflagration which hath been extinguished? O bull of the Bharata race, who is there that will provoke the peaceful sons of Pritha? Thou rememberest, O Ajamida, everything, but still I will call thy attention to this. The scriptures can never control the wicked-minded for good or evil. And, O king, a person of immature understanding will never act as one of mature years. Let thy sons follow thee as their leader. Let them not be separated from thee for ever (by losing their lives). Therefore, at my word, O king, abandon this wretch of our race. Thou couldst not, O king, from parental affection, do it before. Know that the time hath come for the destruction of race through him. Err not, O king. Let thy mind, guided by counsels of peace, virtue, and true policy, be what it naturally is. That prosperity which is acquired by the aid of wicked acts, is soon destroyed; while that which is won by mild means taketh root and descendeth from generation to generation.'"

"The king, thus addressed by Gandhari who pointed out to him in such language the path of virtue, replied unto her, saying,—'If the destruction of our race is come, let it take place freely. I am ill able to prevent it. Let it be as they (these my sons) desire. Let the Pandavas return. And let my sons again gamble with the sons of Pandu."

Section LXXV (75)

Vaisampayana said,—'The royal messenger, agreeably to the commands of the intelligent king Dhritarashtra, coming upon Yudhishthira, the son of Pritha who had by that time gone a great way, addressed the monarch and said,—'Even these are the words of thy father-like uncle, O Bharata, spoken unto thee, 'The assembly is ready. O son of Pandu, O king Yudhisthira, come and cast the dice.'

Yudhishthira said,—'Creatures obtain fruits good and ill according to the dispensation of the Ordainer of the creation. Those fruits are inevitable whether I play or not. This is a summons to dice; it is, besides the command of the old king. Although I know that it will prove destructive to me, yet I cannot refuse.'

Vaisampayana continued,—"Although (a living) animal made of gold was an impossibility, yet Rama suffered himself to be tempted by a (golden) deer. Indeed, the minds of men over whom calamities hang, became deranged and out of order. Yudhishthira, therefore, having said these words, retraced his steps along with his brothers. And knowing full well the deception practised by Sakuni, the son of

Pritha came back to sit at dice with him again. These mighty warriors again entered that assembly, afflicting the hearts of all their friends. And compelled by Fate they once more sat down at ease for gambling for the destruction of themselves."

"Sakuni then said,—'The old king hath given ye back all your wealth. That is well. But, O bull of the Bharata race, listen to me, there is a stake of great value. Either defeated by ye at dice, dressed in deer skins we shall enter the great forest and live there for twelve years passing the whole of the thirteenth year in some inhabited region, unrecognised, and if recognised return to an exile of another twelve years; or vanquished by us, dressed in deer skins ye shall, with Krishna, live for twelve years in the woods passing the whole of the thirteenth year unrecognised, in some inhabited region. If recognised, an exile of another twelve years is to be the consequence. On the expiry of the thirteenth year, each is to have his kingdom surrendered by the other. O Yudhishthira, with this resolution, play with us, O Bharata, casting the dice.'

"At these words, they that were in that assembly, raising up their arms said in great anxiety of mind, and from the strength of their feelings these words,—'Alas, fie on the friends of Duryodhana that they do not apprise him of his great danger. Whether he, O bull among the Bharatas, (Dhritarashtra) understandeth or not, of his own sense, it is thy duty to tell him plainly.'"

Vaisampayana continued,—"King Yudhishthira, even hearing these various remarks, from shame and a sense of virtue again sat at dice. And though possessed of great intelligence and fully knowing the consequences, he again began to play, as if knowing that the destruction of the Kurus was at hand.

"And Yudhishthira said,—'How can, O Sakuni, a king like me, always observant of the uses of his own order, refuse, when summoned to dice? Therefore I play with thee.'"

"Sakuni answered,—'We have many kine and horses, and milch cows, and an infinite number of goats and sheep; and elephants and treasures and gold and slaves both male and female. All these were staked by us before but now let this be our one stake, *viz.*, exile into the woods,—being defeated either ye or we will dwell in the woods (for twelve years) and the thirteenth year, unrecognised, in some inhabited place. Ye bulls among men, with this determination, will we play.'"

"O Bharata, this proposal about a stay in the woods was uttered but once. The son of Pritha, however, accepted it and Sakuni took up the dice. And casting them he said unto Yudhishthira,—'Lo, I have won.'"

Section LXXVI (76)

Vaisampayana said,—"Then the vanquished sons of Pritha prepared for their exile into the woods. And they, one after another, in due order, casting off their royal robes, attired themselves in deer-skins. And Dussasana, beholding those chastisers of foes, dressed in deer-skins and deprived of their kingdom and ready to go into exile, exclaimed 'The absolute sovereignty of the illustrious king Duryodhana hath commenced. The sons of Pandu have been vanquished, and plunged into great affliction. Now have we attained the goal either by broad or narrow paths. For today becoming superior to our foes in point of prosperity as also of duration of rule have we become praiseworthy of men. The sons of Pritha have all been plunged by us into everlasting hell. They have been deprived of happiness and kingdom for ever and ever. They who, proud of their wealth, laughed in derision at the son of Dhritarashtra, will now have to go into the woods, defeated and deprived by us of all their wealth. Let them now put off their variegated coats of mail, their resplendent robes of celestial make, and let them all attire themselves in deer-skins according to the stake they had accepted of the son of Suvala. They who always used to boast that they had no equals in all the world, will now know and regard themselves in this their calamity as grains of sesame without the kernel. Although in this dress of theirs the Pandavas seem like unto wise and powerful persons installed in a sacrifice, yet they look like persons not entitled to perform sacrifices, wearing such a guise. The wise Yajnasena of the Somake race, having bestowed his daughter—the princess of Panchala—on the sons of Pandu, acted most unfortunately for the husbands of Yajnaseni—

these sons of Pritha are as eunuchs. And O Yajnaseni, what joy will be thine upon beholding in the woods these thy husbands dressed in skins and thread-bare rags, deprived of their wealth and possessions. Elect thou a husband, whomsoever thou likest, from among all these present here. These Kurus assembled here, are all forbearing and self-controlled, and possessed of great wealth. Elect thou one amongst these as thy lord, so that these great calamity may not drag thee to wretchedness. 'The sons of Pandu now are even like grains of sesame without the kernel, or like show-animals encased in skins, or like grains of rice without the kernel. Why shouldst thou then longer wait upon the fallen sons of Pandu? Vain is the labour used upon pressing the sesame grain devoid of the kernel!'

"Thus did Dussasana, the son of Dhritarashtra, utter in the hearing of the Pandavas, harsh words of the most cruel import. And hearing them, the unforbearing Bhima, in wrath suddenly approaching that prince like a Himalayan lion upon a jackal, loudly and chastisingly rebuked him in these words,—'Wicked-minded villain, ravest thou so in words that are uttered alone by the sinful? Boastest thou thus in the midst of the kings, advanced as thou art by the skill of the king of Gandhara. As thou piercest our hearts hear with these thy arrowy words, so shall I pierce thy heart in battle, recalling all this to thy mind. And they also who from anger or covetousness are walking behind thee as thy protectors,—them also shall I send to the abode of Yama with their descendants and relatives.'"

Vaisampayana continued,— "Unto Bhima dressed in deer-skins and uttering these words of wrath without doing any thing, for he could not deviate from the path of virtue, Dussasana abandoning all sense of shame, dancing around the Kurus, loudly said, 'O cow! O cow!'

Bhima at this once more said,—'Wretch darest thou, O Dussasana, use harsh words as these? Whom doth it behove to boast, thus having won wealth by foul means? I tell thee that if Vrikodara, the son of Pritha, drinketh not thy life-blood, piercing open thy breast in battle, let him not attain to regions of blessedness. I tell thee truly that by slaying the sons of Dhritarashtra in battle, before the very eyes of all the warriors, I shall pacify this wrath of mine soon enough.'"

Vaisampayana continued,—"And as the Pandavas were going away from the assembly, the wicked king Duryodhana from excess of joy mimiced by his own steps the playful leonine trade of Bhima. Then Vrikodara, half turning towards the king said, 'Think not ye fool that by this thou gainest any ascendency over me slay thee shall I soon with all thy followers, and answer thee, recalling all this to thy mind.' And beholding this insult offered to him, the mighty and proud Bhima, suppressing his rising rage and following the steps of Yudhishthira, also spake these words while going out of the Kaurava court, 'I will slay Duryodhana, and Dhananjaya will slay Karna, and Sahadeva will slay Sakuni that gambler with dice. I also repeat in this assembly these proud words which the gods will assuredly make good, if ever we engage in battle with the Kurus, I will slay this wretched Duryodhana in battle with my mace, and prostrating him on the ground I will place my foot on his head. And as regards this (other) wicked person—Dussasana who is audacious in speech, I will drink his blood like a lion.'

"And Arjuna said,—'O Bhima, the resolutions of superior men are not known in words only. On the fourteenth year from this day, they shall see what happeneth.'

"And Bhima again said,—'The earth shall drink the blood of Duryodhana, and Karna, and the wicked Sakuni, and Dussasana that maketh the fourth.'

"And Arjuna said,—'O Bhima, I will, as thou directest, slay in battle this Karna so malicious and jealous and harsh-speeched and vain. For doing what is agreeable to Bhima, Arjuna voweth that he will slay in battle with his arrows this Karna with all his followers. And I will send unto the regions of Yama also all those other kings that will from foolishness fight against me. The mountains of Himavat might be removed from where they are, the maker of the day lose his brightness, the moon his coldness, but this vow of mine will ever be cherished. And all this shall assuredly happen if on the fourteenth year from this, Duryodhana doth not, with proper respect, return us our kingdom.'"

Vaisampayana continued,—"After Arjuna had said this, Sahadeva the handsome son of Madri, endued with great energy, desirous of slaying Sakuni, waving his mighty arms and sighing like snake, exclaimed, with eyes red with anger—'Thou disgrace of the Gandhara kings, those whom thou thinkest as defeated are not really so. Those are even sharp-pointed arrows from whose wounds thou hast run the risk in battle. I shall certainly accomplish all which Bhima hath said adverting to thee with all thy followers. If therefore thou hast anything to do, do it before that day cometh. I shall assuredly slay thee in battle with all thy followers soon enough, if thou, O son of Suvala, stayest in the light pursuant to the Kshatriya usage.'

"Then, O monarch hearing these words of Sahadeva, Nakula the handsomest of men spake these words,—'I shall certainly send unto the abode of Yama all those wicked sons of Dhritarashtra, who desirous of death and impelled by Fate, and moved also by the wish of doing what is agreeable to Duryodhana, have used harsh and insulting speeches towards this daughter of Yajnasena at the gambling match. Soon enough shall I, at the command of Yudhishthira and remembering the wrongs to Draupadi, make the earth destitute of the sons of Dhritarashtra.'

Vaisampayana continued,—"And those tigers among men, all endued with long arms, having thus pledged themselves to virtuous promises approached king Dhritarashtra."

Section LXXVII (77)

Yudhishthira said,—'I bid farewell unto all the Bharatas, unto my old grand-sire (Bhishma), king Somadatta, the great king Vahlika, Drona, Kripa, all the other kings, Aswathaman, Vidura, Dhritarashtra, all the sons of Dhritarashtra, Yayutsu, Sanjaya, and all the courtiers, I bid fare well, all of ye and returning again I shall see you.'"

Vaisampayana continued,—"Overcome with shame none of those that were present there, could tell Yudhishthira anything. Within their hearts, however, they prayed for the welfare of that intelligent prince.

Vidura then said,—'The reverend Pritha is a princess by birth. It behoveth her not to go into the woods. Delicate and old and ever known to happiness the blessed one will live, respected by me, in my abode. Known this, ye sons of Pandu. And let safety be always yours.'

Vaisampayana continued,—"The Pandavas thereupon said,—'O sinless one, let it be as thou sayest. Thou art our uncle, and, therefore like as our father. We also are all obedient to thee. Thou art, O learned one, our most respected superior. We should always obey what thou choosest to command. And, O high-souled one, order thou whatever else there is that remaineth to be done.'

"Vidura replied,—'O Yudhishthira, O bull of the Bharata race, know this to be my opinion, that one that is vanquished by sinful means need not be pained by such defeat. Thou knowest every rule of morality; Dhananjaya is ever victorious in battle; Bhimasena is the slayer of foes; Nakula is the gatherer of wealth; Sahadeva hath administrative talents, Dhaumya is the foremost of all conversant with the *vedas*; and the well-behaved Draupadi is conversant with virtue and economy. Ye are attached to one another and feel delight at one another's sight and enemies can not separate you from one another, and ye are contented. Therefore, who is there that will not envy ye? O Bharata, this patient abstraction from the possession of the world will be of great benefit to thee. No foe, even if he were equal to sakra himself, will be able to stand it. Formerly thou wert instructed on the mountains of Himavat by Meru Savarni; in the town of Varanavata by Krishna Dwaipayana; on the cliff of Bhrigu by Rama; and on the banks of the Dhrishadwati by Sambhu himself. Thou hast also listened to the instruction of the great Rishi Asita on the hills of Anjana; and thou becamest a disciple of Bhrigu on the banks of the Kalmashi. Narada and this thy priest Dhaumya will now become thy instructors. In the matter of the next world, abandon not these excellent lessons thou hast obtained from the *Rishis*. O son of Pandu, thou surpassest in intelligence even Pururavas, the son of Ila; in strength, all other monarchs, and in virtue, even the *Rishis*. Therefore, resolve thou earnestly to win victory, which belongeth to Indra; to control thy wrath, which belongeth to Yama; to give in charity, which belongeth to Kuvera; and to control all passions, which belongeth to Varuna. And, O Bharata, obtain thou the power of gladdening from the moon, the power of sustaining all from water; forbearance from the earth; energy from the entire solar disc; strength from the winds, and affluence from the other elements. Welfare and immunity from ailment be thine; I hope to see thee return. And, O Yudhishthira, act properly and duly in all seasons,—in those of distress—in those of difficulty,—indeed, in respect of everything, O son of Kunti, with our leave go hence. O Bharata, blessing be thine. No one can say that ye have done anything sinful before. We hope to see thee, therefore, return in safety and crowned with success.'"

Vaisampayana continued,—"Thus addressed by Vidura, Yudhishthira the son of Pandu, of prowess incapable of being baffled, saying, 'So be it,' bowing low unto Bhishma and Drona, went away."

Section LXXVIII (78)

Vaisampayana said,—'Then when Draupadi was about to set out she went unto the illustrious Pritha and solicited her leave. And she also asked leave of the other ladies of the household who had all been plunged into grief. And saluting and embracing every one of them as each deserved, she desired to go away. Then there arose within the inner apartments of the Pandavas a loud wail of woe. And Kunti, terribly afflicted upon beholding Draupadi on the eve of her journey, uttered these words in a voice choked with grief,—

'O child, grieve not that this great calamity hath overtaken thee. Thou art well conversant with the duties of the female sex, and thy behaviour and conduct also are as they should be. It behoveth me not, O thou of sweet smiles, to instruct thee as to thy duties towards thy lords. Thou art chaste and accomplished, and thy qualities have adorned the race of thy birth as also the race into which thou hast been admitted by marriage. Fortunate are the Kauravas that they have not been burnt by thy wrath. O child, safely go thou blest by my prayers. Good women never suffer their hearts to the unstung at what is inevitable. Protected by virtue that is superior to everything, soon shalt thou obtain good fortune. While living in the woods, keep thy eye on my child Sahadeva. See that his heart sinketh not under this great calamity.'

"Saying 'So be it!' the princess Draupadi bathed in tears, and clad in one piece of cloth, stained with blood, and with hair dishevelled left her mother-in-law. And as she went away weeping and wailing Pritha herself in grief followed her. She had not gone far when she saw her sons shorn of their ornaments and robes, their bodies clad in deerskins, and their heads down with shame. And she beheld them surrounded by rejoicing foes and pitied by friends. Endued with excess of parental affection, Kunti approached her sons in that state, and embracing them all, and in accents choked by woe, She said these words,—

'Ye are virtuous and good-mannered, and adorned with all excellent qualities and respectful behaviour. Ye are all high-minded, and engaged in the service of your superiors. And ye are also devoted to the gods and the performance of sacrifices. Why, then, hath this calamity overtaken you. Whence is this reverse of fortune? I do not see by whose wickedness this sin hath overtaken you. Alas I have brought you forth. All this must be due to my ill fortune. It is for this that ye have been overtaken by this calamity, though ye all are endued with excellent virtues. In energy and prowess and strength and firmness and might, ye are not wanting. How shall ye now, losing your wealth and possessions, live poor in the pathless woods? If I had known before that ye were destined to live in the woods, I would not have on Pandit's death come from the mountains of Satasringa to Hastinapore. Fortunate was your father, as I now regard, for he truly reaped the fruit of his asceticism, and he was gifted with foresight, as he entertained the wish of ascending heaven, without having to feel any pain on account of his sons. Fortunate also was the virtuous Madri, as I regard her today, who had, it seems, a fore-knowledge of what would happen and who on that account, obtained the high path of emancipation and every blessing therewith. All, Madri looked upon me as her stay, and her mind and her affections were ever fixed on me. Oh, fie on my desire of life, owing to which suffer all this woe. Ye children, ye are all excellent and dear unto me. I have obtained you alter much suffering. I cannot leave you. Even I will go with you. Alas, O Krishna, (Draupadi), why dost thou leave me so? Everything endued with life is sure to perish. Hath *Dhata* (*Brahma*) himself forgotten to ordain my death? Perhaps, it is so, and, therefore, life doth not quit me. O Krishna, O thou who dwellest in Dwaraka, O younger brother of Sankarshana, where art thou? Why dost thou not deliver me and these best of men also from such woe? They say that thou who art without beginning and without end deliverest those that think of thee. Why doth this saying become untrue. These my sons are ever attached to virtue and nobility and good fame and prowess. They deserve not to suffer affliction. Oh, show them mercy. Alas, when there are such elders amongst our race as Bhishma and Drona and Kripa, all conversant with morality and the science of worldly concerns, how could such calamity at all come? O Pandu, O king, where art thou? Why sufferest thou quietly thy good children to be thus sent into exile, defeated at dice? O Sahadeva, desist from going. Thou art my dearest child, dearer, O son of Madri, than my body itself. Forsake me not. It behoveth thee to have some kindness for me. Bound by the ties of virtue, let these thy brothers go. But then, earn thou that virtue which springeth from waiting upon me.'"

Vaisampayana continued,—"The Pandavas then consoled their weeping mother and with hearts plunged in grief set out for the woods. And Vidura himself also much afflicted, consoling the distressed Kunti with reasons, and led her slowly to his house. And the ladies of Dhritarashtra's house, hearing everything as it happened, *viz.*, the exile (of the Pandavas) and the dragging of Krishna into the assembly where the princes had gambled, loudly wept censuring the Kauravas. And the ladies of the royal household also sat silent for a long time, covering their lotus-like faces with their fair hands. And king Dhritarashtra also thinking of the dangers that threatened his sons, became a prey to anxiety and could not enjoy peace of mind. And anxiously meditating on everything, and with mind deprived of its equanimity through grief, he sent a messenger unto Vidura, saying, 'Let Kshatta come to me without a moment's delay.'

"At this summons, Vidura quickly came to Dhritarashtra's palace. And as soon as he came, the monarch asked him with great anxiety how the Pandavas had left Hastinapore."

Section LXXIX (79)

Vaisampayana said,—"As soon as Vidura endued with great foresight came unto him king Dhritarashtra, the son of Amvika, timidly asked his brother,—'How doth Yudhishthira, the son of Dharma, proceed along? And how Arjuna? And how the twin sons of Madri? And how, O Kshatta, doth Dhaumya proceed along? And how the illustrious Draupadi? I desire to hear everything, O Kshatta; describe to me all their acts.'

Vidura replied,—'Yudhishthira, the son of Kunti, hath gone away covering his face with his cloth. And Bhima, O king, hath gone away looking at his own mighty arms. And Jishnu (Arjuna) hath gone away, following the king spreading sand-grains around. And Sahadeva, the son of Madri, hath gone away besmearing his face, and Nakula, the handsomest of men, O king, hath gone away, staining himself with dust and his heart in great affliction. And the large-eyed and beautiful Krishna hath gone away, covering her face with her dishevelled hair following in the wake of the king, weeping and in tears. And O monarch, Dhaumya goeth along the road, with *kusa* grass in hand, and uttering the aweful mantras of *Sama Veda* that relate to *Yama*.'

Dhritarashtra asked,—'Tell me, O Vidura, why is it that the Pandavas are leaving Hastinapore in such varied guise.'

"Vidura replied,—'Though persecuted by thy sons and robbed of his kingdom and wealth the mind of the wise king Yudhishthira the just hath not yet deviated from the path of virtue. King Yudhishthira is always kind, O Bharata, to thy children. Though deprived (of his kingdom and possessions) by foul means, filled with wrath as he is, he doth not open eyes. 'I should not burn the people by looking at them with angry eyes,'—thinking so, the royal son of Pandu goeth covering his face. Listen to me as I tell thee, O bull of the Bharata race, why Bhima goeth so. 'There is none equal to me in strength of arms,' thinking so Bhima goeth repeatedly stretching forth his mighty arms. And, O king, proud of the strength of his arms, Vrikodara goeth, exhibiting them and desiring to do unto his enemies deeds worthy of those arms. And Arjuna the son of Kunti, capable of using both his arms (in wielding the Gandiva) followeth the footsteps of Yudhishthira, scattering sand-grains emblematical of the arrows he would shower in battle. O Bharata, he indicateth that as the sand-grains are scattered by him with ease, so will he rain arrows with perfect ease on the foe (in time of battle). And Sahadeva goeth besmearing his lace, thinking 'None may recognise me in this day of trouble.' And, O exalted one, Nakula goeth staining himself with dust thinking, 'Lest otherwise I steal the hearts of the ladies that may look at me.' And Draupadi goeth, attired in one piece of stained cloth, her hair dishevelled, and weeping, signifying—'The wives of those for whom I have been reduced to such a plight, shall on the fourteenth year hence be deprived of husbands, sons and relatives and dear ones and smeared all over with blood, with hair dishevelled and all in their feminine seasons enter Hastinapore having offered oblations of water (unto the manes of those they will have lost). And O Bharata, the learned Dhaumya with passions under full control, holding the *kusa* grass in his hand and pointing the same towards the south-west, walketh before, singing the mantras of the *Sama Veda* that relate to *Yama*. And, O monarch, that learned Brahamana goeth, also signifying, 'When the Bharatas shall be slain in battle, the priests of the Kurus will thus sing the Soma mantras (for the benefit of the deceased).' And the citizens, afflicted with great grief, are repeatedly crying out, 'Alas, alas, behold our masters are going away! O fie on the Kuru elders that have acted like foolish children in thus banishing heirs of Pandu from covetousness alone. Alas, separated from the son of Pandu we all shall become masterless. What love can we bear to the wicked and avaricious *Kurus*?' Thus O king, have the sons of Kunti, endued with great energy of mind, gone away,—indicating, by manner and signs, the resolutions that are in their hearts. And as those foremost of men had gone away from Hastinapore, flashes of lightning appeared in the sky though without clouds and the earth itself began to tremble. And Rahu came to devour the Sun, although it was not the day of conjunction. And meteors began to fall, keeping the city to their right. And jackals and vultures and ravens and other carnivorous beasts and birds began to shriek and cry aloud from the temples of the gods and the tops of sacred trees and walls and house-tops. And these extraordinary calamitous portents, O king, were seen and heard, indicating the destruction of the Bharatas as the consequence of thy evil counsels.'"

Vaisampayana continued,—"And, O monarch, while king

Dhritarashtra and the wise Vidura were thus talking with each other, there appeared in that assembly of the Kauravas and before the eyes of all, the best of the celestial *Rishis*. And appealing before them all, he uttered these terrible words, 'On the fourteenth year hence, the Kauravas, in consequence of Duryodhana's fault, will all be destroyed by the might of Bhima and Arjuna'. And having said this, that best of celestial Rishis, adorned with surpassing Vedic grace, passing through the skies, disappeared from the scene. Then Duryodhana and Karna and Sakuni, the son of Suvala regarding Drona as their sole refuge, offered the kingdom to him. Drona then, addressing the envious and wrathful Duryodhana and Dussasana and Karna and all the Bharata, said, 'The Brahamanas have said that the Pandavas being of celestial origin are incapable of being slain. The sons of Dhritarashtra, however, having, with all the kings, heartily and with reverence sought my protection, I shall look after them to the best of my power. Destiny is supreme, I cannot abandon them. The sons of Pandu, defeated at dice, are going into exile in pursuance of their promise. They will live in the woods for twelve years. Practising the *Brahmacharyya* mode of life for this period, they will return in anger and to our great grief take the amplest vengeance on their foes. I had formerly deprived Drupada of his kingdom in a friendly dispute. Robbed of his kingdom by me, O Bharata, the king performed a sacrifice for obtaining a son (that should slay me). Aided by the ascetic power of Yaja and Upayaja, Drupada obtained from the (sacrificial) fire a son named Dhrishtadyumna and a daughter, *viz.*, the faultless Krishna, both risen from the sacrificial platform. That Dhrishtadyumna is the brother-in-law of the sons of Pandu by marriage, and dear unto them. It is for him, therefore that I have much fear. Of celestial origin and resplendent as the fire, he was born with bow, arrows, and encased in mail. I am a being that is mortal. Therefore it is for him that I have great fear. That slayer of all foes, the son of Parshatta, hath taken the side of the Pandavas. I shall have to lose my life, if he and I ever encounter each other in battle. What grief can be greater to me in this world than this, ye Kauravas that ' Dhrishtadyumna is the destined slayer of Drona'—this belief is general. That he hath been born for slaying me hath been heard by me and is widely known also in the world. For thy sake, O Duryodhana, that terrible season of destruction is almost come. Do without loss of time, what may be beneficial unto thee. Think not that everything hath been accomplished by sending the Pandavas into exile. This thy happiness will last for but a moment, even as in winter the shadow of the top of the palm tree resteth (for a short time) at its base. Perform various kinds of sacrifices, and enjoy, and give O Bharata, everything thou likest. On the fourteenth year hence, a great calamity will overwhelm thee.'"

Vaisampayana continued,—"Hearing these words of Drona, Dhritarashtra said,—'O Kshatta, the preceptor hath uttered what is true. Go thou and bring back the Pandavas. If they do not come back, let them go treated with respect and affection. Let those my sons go with weapons, and cars, and infantry, and enjoying every other good thing.'"

Section LXXX (80)

Vaisampayana said,—"defeated at dice, after the Pandavas had gone to the woods, Dhritarashtra, O king, was overcome with anxiety. And while he was seated restless with anxiety and sighing in grief, Sanjaya approaching him said, 'O lord of the earth having now obtained the whole earth with all its wealth and sent away the sons of Pandu into exile, why is it, O king, that thou grievest so?'"

Dhritarashtra said,—'What have they not to grieve for who will have to encounter in battle those bulls among warriors—the sons of Pandu—fighting on great cars and aided by allies?'

"Sanjaya said,—"O king, all this great hostility is inevitable on account of thy mistaken action, and this will assuredly bring about the wholesale destruction of the whole world. Forbidden by Bhishma, by Drona, and by Vidura, thy wicked-minded and shameless son Duryodhana sent his *Suta* messenger commanding him to bring into court the beloved and virtuous wife of the Pandavas. The gods first deprive that man of his reason unto whom they send defeat and disgrace. It is for this that such a person seeth things in a strange light. When destruction is at hand, evil appeareth as good unto the understanding polluted by sin, and the man adhereth to it firmly.

That which is improper appeareth as proper, and that which is proper appeareth as improper unto the man about to be overwhelmed by destruction, and evil and impropriety are what he liketh. The time that bringeth on destruction doth not come with upraised club and smash one's head. On the other hand the peculiarity of such a time is that it maketh a man behold evil in good and good in evil. The wretches have brought on themselves this terrible, wholesale, and horrible destruction by dragging the helpless princess of Panchala into the court. Who else than Duryodhana—that false player of dice could bring into the assembly, with insults, the daughter of Drupada, endued with beauty and intelligence, and conversant with every rule of morality and duty, and sprung not from any woman's womb but from the sacred fire? The handsome Krishna, then in her season, attired in one piece of stained cloth when brought into the court cast her eyes upon the Pandavas. She beheld them, however, robbed of their wealth, of their kingdom, of even their attire, of their beauty, of every enjoyment, and plunged into a state of bondage. Bound by the tie of virtue, they were then unable to exert their prowess. And before all the assembled kings Duryodhana and Karna spake cruel and harsh words unto the distressed and enraged Krishna undeserving of such treatment. O monarch, all this appeareth to me as foreboding fearful consequences.'

Dhritarashtra said,—'O Sanjaya, the glances of the distressed daughter of Drupada might consume the whole earth. Can it be possible that even a single son of mine will live? The wives of the Bharatas, uniting with Gandhari upon beholding virtuous Krishna, the wedded wife of the Pandavas, endued with beauty and youth, dragged into the court, set up frightful wail. Even now, along with all my subjects, they weep every day. Enraged at the ill treatment of Draupadi, the Brahmanas in a body did not perform that evening their *Agnihotra* ceremony. The winds blew mightily as they did at the time of the universal dissolution. There was a terrible thunder-storm also. Meteors fell from the sky, and Rahu by swallowing the Sun unseasonably alarmed the people terribly. Our war-chariots were suddenly ablaze, and all their flagstaffs fell down foreboding evil unto the Bharatas. Jackals began to cry frightfully from within the sacred fire-chamber of Duryodhana, and asses from all directions began to bray in response. Then Bhishma and Drona, and Kripa, and Somadatta and the high-souled Vahlika, all left the assembly. It was then that at the advice of Vidura I addressed Krishna and said, 'I will grant thee boons, O Krishna, indeed, whatever thou wouldst ask?' The princess of the Panchala there begged of me the liberation of the Pandavas. Out of my own motion I then set free the Pandavas, commanding them to return (to their capital) on their cars and with their bows and arrows. It was then that Vidura told me, 'Even this will prove the destruction of the Bharata race, *viz.*, this dragging of Krishna into the court. This daughter of the King of Panchala is the faultless Sree herself. Of celestial origin, she is the wedded wife of the Pandavas. The wrathful sons of Pandu will never forgive this insult offered unto her. Nor will the mighty bowmen of the Vrishni race, nor the mighty warriors amongst the Panchalas suffer this in silence. Supported by Vasudeva of unbaffled prowess, Arjuna will assuredly come back, surrounded by the Panchala host. And that mighty warrior amongst them, Bhimasena endued with surpassing strength, will also come back, whirling his mace like Yama himself with his club. These kings will scarcely be able to bear the force of Bhima's mace. Therefore, O king, not hostility but peace for ever with the sons of Pandu is what seemeth to me to be the best. The sons of Pandu are always stronger than the Kurus. Thou knowest, O king, that the illustrious and mighty king Jarasandha was slain in battle by Bhima with his bare arms alone. Therefore, O bull of the Bharata race, it behoveth thee to make peace with the sons of Pandu. Without scruples of any kind, unite the two parties, O king. And it thou actest in this way, thou art sure to obtain good luck, O king.' It was thus, O son of Gavalgani, that Vidura addressed me in words of both virtue and profit. And I did not accept this counsel, moved by affection for my son.'"

The End of Sabha Parva

The Temptation of Karna

From the Udyoga Parva

The Temptation of Karna

Section CXL (140)

"Dhritarashtra said, 'O Sanjaya, in the midst of all the princes and the servants, the slayer of Madhu took Karna upon his car and went out (of our city). What did that slayer of hostile heroes, that one of immeasurable soul, say unto Radha's son? What conciliatory words did Govinda speak unto the Suta's son? Tell me, O Sanjaya, what those words were, mild or fierce, that Krishna, possessed of a voice deep as that of newly-risen clouds during the rainy season said unto Karna?'

"Sanjaya said, 'Listen to me, O Bharata, as I repeat in due order those words, both intimidating and mild, agreeable and consistent with virtue, true and beneficial, and pleasing to the heart, which the slayer of Madhu, of immeasurable soul, said unto Radha's son.'

"Vasudeva said, 'O son of Radha, thou hast worshipped many Brahmanas fully conversant with the *Vedas*. With concentrated attention and mind free from envy thou hast also (on many an occasion) enquired of them after truth. Thou knowest, therefore, O Karna, what the eternal saying of the *Vedas* are. Thou art also well-versed in all the subtle conclusions of the scriptures. It is said by those conversant with the scriptures that the two kinds of sons called *Kanina* and *Sahoda* that are born of a maiden, have him for their father who weddeth the maid. Thou, O Karna, hast been born in this way. Thou art, therefore, morally the son of Pandu. Come, be a king, according to the injunction of the scriptures. On the side of thy father, thou hast the sons of Pritha, on the side of thy mother, thou hast the Vrishnis, (for thy kinsmen). O bull among men, know that thou hast these two for thy own. Proceeding this very day with me hence, O sire, let the Pandavas know thee as a son of Kunti born before Yudhishthira. The brothers, the five Pandavas, the son of Draupadi, and the invincible son of Subhadra, will all embrace thy feet. All the kings and princes, again, that have been assembled for the Pandava-cause, and all the Andhakas and Vrishnis, will also embrace thy feet. Let queens and princesses bring golden and silver and earthen jars (full of water) and delicious herbs and all kinds of seeds and gems, and creepers, for thy installation. During the sixth period, Draupadi also will come to thee (as a wife). Let that best of Brahmanas, Dhaumya, of restrained soul, pour libations of clarified butter on the (sacred) fire, and let those Brahmanas regarding all the four *Vedas* as authoritative (and who are acting as priests unto the Pandavas), perform the ceremony of thy installation. Let the family priest of the Pandavas who is devoted to *Vedic* rites, and those bulls among men—those brothers, the five sons of Pandu,—and the five sons of Draupadi, and the Panchalas, and the Chedis, and myself also, install thee as the lord of the whole earth. Let Dharma's son Yudhishthira, of righteous soul and rigid vows, be thy heir presumptive, ruling the kingdom under thee. Holding the white *chamara* in his hand (for fanning thee), let Yudhishthira, the son of Kunti, ride on the same car behind thee. After thy installation is over, let that other son of Kunti, the mighty Bhimasena, hold the white umbrella over thy head. Indeed, Arjuna then will drive thy car furnished with a hundred tinkling bells, its sides covered with tiger-skins, and with white steeds harnessed to it. Then Nakula and Sahadeva, and the five sons of Draupadi, and the Panchalas with that mighty car-warrior Sikhandin, will all proceed behind thee. I myself, with all the Andhakas and the Vrishnis, will walk behind thee. Indeed, all the Dasarhas and the Dasarnas, will, O king, be numbered with thy relatives. Enjoy the sovereignty of the earth, O thou of mighty arms, with thy brothers the Pandavas, with *yapas* and *homas* and auspicious rites of diverse kinds performed in thy honour. Let the Dravidas, with the Kuntalas, the Andhras, and the Talacharas, and the Shuchupas, and the Venupas, all walk before thee. Let chanters and panegyrists praise thee with innumerable laudatory hymns. Let the Pandavas proclaim,—*Victory to Vasusena.* Surrounded by the Pandavas, like the moon by the stars, rule thou the kingdom, O son of Kunti, and gladden Kunti herself. Let thy friends rejoice, and thy enemies grieve. Let there be, this day, a brotherly union between thee and thy brothers, the sons of Pandu."

Section CXLI (141)

"Karna said, 'Without doubt, O Kesava, thou hast said these words from thy love, affection, and friendship for me, as also in consequence of thy desire of doing me good, O thou of Vrishni's race. I know all that thou hast said unto me. Morally, I am the son of Pandu, as also in consequence of the injunctions of the scriptures, as thou, O Krishna, thinkest. My mother, while a maiden, bore me in her womb, O Janardana, through her connection with *Surya*. And at the command of Surya himself, she abandoned me as soon as I was born. Even thus, O Krishna, I came into the world. Morally, therefore, I am the son of Pandu. Kunti, however, abandoned me without thinking of my welfare. The *Suta*, Adhiratha, as soon as he beheld me, took me to his home, and from her affection for me, Radha's breasts were filled with milk that very day, and she, O Madhava, cleansed my urine and evacuations. How can one like us, conversant with duties and ever engaged in listening to scriptures deprive her of her *Pinda*? So also Adhiratha of the *Suta* class regardeth me as a son, and I too, from affection, always regard him as (my) father. O Madhava, that Adhiratha, O Janardana, from paternal affection caused all the rites of infancy to be performed on my person, according to the rules prescribed in the scriptures. It is that Adhiratha, again, who caused the name Vasusena to be bestowed upon me by the Brahmanas. When also I attained to youth, I married wives according to his selections. Through them have been born my sons and grandsons, O Janardana. My heart also, O Krishna, and all the bonds of affection and love, are fixed on them. From joy or fear. O Govinda. I cannot venture to destroy those bonds even for the sake of the whole earth or heaps of gold. In consequence also of my connection with Duryodhana of Dhritarashtra's race, I have, O Krishna, enjoyed sovereignty for thirteen years, without a thorn on my side. I have performed many sacrifices, always however in connection with persons of the *Suta* tribe. All my family rites and marriage rites have been performed with the *Sutas*. Obtaining me, O Krishna, Duryodhana hath, O thou of Vrishni's race, made this preparations for an armed encounter and provoked hostilities with the sons of Pandu. And it is for this, O *Achyuta*, that in the battle (that will ensue), I, O Krishna, have been chosen as the great antagonist of Arjuna to advance against him in a single combat. For the sake of death, or the ties of blood, or fear, or temptation, I cannot venture, O Janardana, to behave falsely towards the intelligent son of Dhritarashtra. If I do not now engage in a single combat with Arjuna, this will, O Hrishikesa, be inglorious for both myself and Partha. Without doubt, O slayer of Madhu, thou hast told me all this for doing me good. The Pandavas also, obedient as they are to thee, will, without doubt, do all that thou hast said. Thou must, however, conceal this our discourse for the present, O slayer of Madhu. Therein lies our benefit, I think, O delighter of all the Yadavas. If king Yudhishthira, of virtuous soul and well-controlled senses, cometh to know me as the firstborn son of Kunti, he will never accept the kingdom. If, again, O slayer of Madhu, this mighty and swelling empire becometh mine. I shall, O repressor of foes, certainly make it over to Duryodhana only. Let Yudhishthira of virtuous soul become king for ever. He that hath Hrishikesa for his guide, and Dhananjaya and that mighty car-warrior Bhima for his combatants, as also Nakula and Sahadeva, and the sons of Draupadi, is fit, O Madhava, to rule over the whole earth. Dhrishtadyumna, the prince of the Panchalas, that mighty car-warrior Satyaki, Uttamaujas, Yudhamanyu, the prince of Somakas who is devoted to truth, the ruler of the Chedis, Chekitana, the invincible Sikhandin, the Kekaya brothers, all of the hue of *Indragopaka* insects, Bhimasena's uncle Kuntibhoja of high soul and possessed of steeds endued with the colours of the rainbow, the mighty car-warrior Syenajit, Sanka the son of Virata, and thyself, O Janardana, like an ocean,—great is this assemblage, O Krishna, of Kshatriyas (that hath been made by Yudhishthira). This blazing kingdom, celebrated among all the kings of the earth, is already won (by Yudhishthira). O thou of Vrishni's race, a great sacrifice of arms is about to be celebrated by Dhritarashtra's son. Thou, O Janardana, wilt be the *Upadrashtri* of that sacrifice. The office of *Adhyaryu* also, O Krishna, in that sacrifice, will be thine. The ape-bannered Vibhatsu accoutred in mail will be the *Hotri* (his bow), *Gandiva* will be the sacrificial ladle, and the prowess of the warriors will be the clarified butter (that is to be consumed). The weapons called *Aindra, Pasupata, Brahma,* and *Sthunakarna,* applied by Arjuna, will, O Madhava, be the *mantras* (of that sacrifice). Resembling his father, or perhaps, excelling him in prowess, Subhadra's son (Abhimanyu) will be the chief *Vedic* hymn to be chanted. That destroyer of elephant ranks that utterer of fierce roars in battle, that tiger among men, the exceedingly mighty Bhima, will be *Udgatri* and *Prastotri* in this sacrifice. King Yudhishthira of virtuous Soul, ever engaged in *Yapa* and *Homa,* will himself be the Brahma of that sacrifice. The sounds of conchs, tabors, and drums, and the leonine roaring rising high in the welkin, will be the calls upon the invited to eat. The two sons of Madri, Nakula and Sahadeva, of great fame and prowess, will be the slayers of the sacrificial animals; rows of bright cars furnished with standards of variegated hue, will, O Govinda, be stakes (for tying the animals), O Janardana, in this sacrifice. Barbed arrows and *Nalikas,* and long shafts, and arrows with heads like calf's tooth, will play the part of spoons (wherewith to distribute the *Soma* juice) while *Tomaras* will be the vessels of *Soma,* and bows will be *pavitras.* The swords will be *Kapalas,* the heads (of slain warriors) the *Purodasas* and the blood of warriors the clarified butter. O Krishna, in this sacrifice. The lances and bright maces (of the warriors) will be pokers (for stirring the sacrificial fire) and the corner stakes (for keeping the fire-wood from falling down). The disciples of Drona and Kripa, the son of Saradwat, will be the *Sadasyas* (assisting priests). The arrows shot by the wielder of *Gandiva* and by (other) mighty car-warriors, and by Drona and Drona's son, will play the part of ladles for distributing the *Soma.* Satyaki will discharge the duties of the chief assistant of the *Adhyaryu.* Of this sacrifice, Dhritarashtra's son will be installed as the performer, while this vast army will be his wife. O thou of mighty arms, when the nocturnal rites of sacrifice will begin, the mighty Ghatotkacha will play the part of the slayer of (devoted) victims. The mighty Dhrishtadyumna, who sprang into life from the sacrificial fire, having for its mouth the rites celebrated with *mantras,* will, O Krishna, be the *Dakshina* of that sacrifice. For those harsh words, O Krishna, that I said before unto the sons of Pandu for the gratification of Dhritarashtra's son,—for that wicked conduct of mine,—I am consumed with repentance.

When O Krishna, thou wilt behold me slain by Arjuna, then will the *Punachiti* of this sacrifice commence. When the (second) son of Pandu will drink the blood of the loudly roaring Dussasana, then will the *Soma*-drinking of this sacrifice have taken place! When the two princes of Panchala (Dhrishtadyumna and Sikhandin) will overthrow Drona and Bhishma, then, O Janardana, will this sacrifice be suspended for an interval. When mighty Bhimasena will slay Duryodhana, then, O Madhava, will this sacrifice of Dhritarashtra's son be concluded. When the wives of Dhritarashtra's sons and grandsons assembled together, deprived, O Kesava, of their husbands and sons and without protectors, will indulge in lamentations with Gandhari in their midst, on the field of battle haunted by dogs and vultures and other carnivorous birds, then, O Janardana, will the final bath of this sacrifice take place.

'I pray to thee, O bull of the Kshatriya race, let not the Kshatriyas, old in learning and old in years, perish miserably, O Janardana, for thy sake. Oh, let this swelling host of Kshatriyas perish by means of weapons on that most sacred of all spots in the three worlds, *viz.* Kurukshetra, O Kesava. O thou of eyes like lotus-leaves, accomplish on this spot what thou hast in thy mind, so that, O thou of Vrishni's race, the whole Kshatriya order may attain to heaven. As long, O Janardana, as the hills and the rivers will last, so long will the fame of these achievements last. The Brahmanas will recite this great war of the Bharatas. The fame, O thou of Vrishni's race, that they achieve in battles is the wealth that Kshatriyas own. O Kesava, bring Kunti's son (Arjuna) before me for battle, keeping for ever this our discourse a secret, O chastiser of foes."'

Section CXLII (142)

"Sanjaya said, 'Hearing these words of Karna, Kesava, that slayer of hostile heroes, spoke unto him these words smilingly, 'Do not the means of winning an empire recommend themselves to thee. O Karna? Wishest thou not to rule over the whole earth given by me to thee? The victory of the Pandavas, therefore, is very certain. There seems to be no doubt in this. The triumphal banner of Pandu's son, with the fierce ape on it, seems to be already set up. The divine artificer, Bhaumana, hath applied such celestial illusion (in its construction) that it standeth high, displayed like Indra's banner. Various celestial creatures of terrific shape, indicating victory, are seen on that standard. Extending for a *yojana* upwards and all around, that beautiful standard of Arjuna, resembling fire in radiance, is never, O Karna, when set up, obstructed by hills or trees. When thou wilt behold in battle Arjuna, on his car drawn by white steeds and driven by Krishna, applying *Aindra, Agneya* and *Maruta* weapons, and when thou wilt hear the twang of *Gandiva* piercing the welkin like the very thunder, then all signs of the *Krita*, the *Treta*, and the *Dwapara* ages will disappear (but, instead, *Kali* embodied will be present). When thou wilt behold in battle Kunti's son, invincible Yudhishthira, devoted to *Yapa* and *Homa* and resembling the very sun in brilliance, protecting his own mighty army and burning the army of his foes, then all signs of the *Krita*, the *Treta*, and the *Dwapara* ages will disappear. When thou wilt behold in battle the mighty Bhimasena dancing, after having quaffed the blood of Dussasana, like a fierce elephant with rent temples after having killed a mighty antagonist, then all signs of the *Krita*, the *Treta*, and the *Dwapara* ages will disappear. When thou wilt behold in battle Arjuna checking Drona and Santanu's son and Kripa and king Suyodhana, and Jayadratha of Sindhu's race, all rushing fiercely to the encounter, then all signs of the *Krita*, the *Treta* and the *Dwapara* ages will disappear. When thou wilt behold in battle the two mighty sons of Madri,—those heroic car-warriors, capable of breaking into pieces all hostile cars,—agitating, from the very moment when weapons will begin to clash, the army of Dhritarashtra's sons like a couple of infuriated elephants, then all signs of the *Krita*, the *Treta* and the *Dwapara* ages will disappear. Returning hence, O Karna, say unto Drona and Santanu's son and Kripa that the present month is a delightful one, and that food, drink, and fuel are abundant now. All plants and herbs are vigorous now, all trees full of fruits, and flies there are none. The roads are free from mire, and the waters are of agreeable taste. The weather is neither very hot nor very cold and is, therefore, highly pleasant. Seven days after, will be the day of the new moon. Let the battle commence then, for that day, it hath been said, is presided over by Indra. Say also unto all the kings that have come for battling that I will fully accomplish the desire cherished by them. Indeed, all the kings and princes that are obedient to the orders of Duryodhana, obtaining death by weapons, will attain to an excellent state.'"

Section CXLIII (143)

"Sanjaya said, 'Hearing these beneficial and auspicious words of Kesava, Karna worshipped Krishna, the slayer of Madhu, and said these words, 'Knowing (everything), why dost thou yet, O thou of mighty arms, seek to beguile me? The destruction of the whole earth that is at hand for its cause, Sakuni, and myself, and Dussasana, and king Duryodhana, the son of Dhritarashtra. Without doubt, O Krishna, a great and fierce battle is at hand between the Pandavas and the Kurus which will cover the earth with bloody mire. All the kings and princes following the lead of Duryodhana, consumed by the fire of weapons will proceed to the abode of Yama. Diverse frightful visions are seen, O slayer of Madhu, and many terrible portents, and fierce disturbances also. All these omens, making the hairs (of the spectators) stand on their ends, indicate, O thou of Vrishni's race, the defeat of Dhritarashtra's son and the victory of Yudhishthira. That fierce planet of great effulgence, *Sanaischara* (Saturn), is afflicting the constellation called *Rohini,* in order to afflict greatly the creatures of the earth. The planet *Angaraka* (Mars), wheeling, O slayer of Madhu, towards the constellation *Jeshthya,* approacheth towards *Anuradhas,* indicating a great slaughter of friends. Without doubt, O Krishna, a terrible calamity approacheth the Kurus when specially, O thou of Vrishni's race, the planet *Mahapat* afflicteth the constellation *Chitra.* The spot on the lunar disc hath changed its position; and *Rahu* also approacheth towards the sun. Meteors are falling from the sky with loud noise and trembling motion. The elephants are sending forth frightful cries, while the steeds, O Madhava, are shedding tears, without taking any delight in food and drink. They say, O thou of mighty arms, that on the appearance of these portents, a terrible calamity approacheth, productive of a great slaughter. O Kesava, amongst the steeds, elephants and soldiers, in all the divisions of Duryodhana's army, it is seen, O slayer of Madhu, that while small is the food these take, ample is the excreta they evacuate. The wise have said that this is an indication of defect. The elephants and steeds of the Pandavas, O Krishna, all seem to be cheerful, while all the animals wheel along their right. This also is an indication of their success. The same animal, O Kesava, pass by the left side of Duryodhana's army, while incorporeal voices are constantly heard (over their heads). All this is an indication of defeat. All auspicious birds, such as peacocks, swans, cranes, *Chatakas*, *Jivajivas*, and large flights of *Vakas*, follow the Pandavas, while vultures, *Kankas*, hawks, *Rakshasas*, wolves and bees, in flights and herds, follow the Kauravas. The drums in the army of Dhritarashtra's son yield no sounds, while those of the Pandavas yield sounds without being struck. The wells in the midst of Duryodhana's encampment send forth loud roars like those of huge bulls. All this is an indication of defeat. The gods are showering flesh and blood, O Madhava, on Duryodhana's soldiers. Vapoury edifices of great effulgence with high walls, deep trenches, and handsome porches, are suddenly appearing in the skies (over the Kuru encampment). A black circle surrounding the solar disc appears to the view. Both twilights at sunrise and sunset indicate great terrors. The jackals yell hideously. All this is an indication of defeat. Diverse birds, each having but one wing, one eye, and one leg, utter terrible cries. All this, O slayer of Madhu, indicates defeat. Fierce birds with black wings and red legs hover over the Kuru encampment at nightfall. All this is an indication of defeat. The soldiers of Duryodhana betray hatred for Brahmanas first, and then for their preceptors, and then for all their affectionate servants. The eastern horizon of (Duryodhana's encampment) appeareth red; the southern of the hue of weapons; and western, O slayer of Madhu, of an earthy hue. All the quarters around Duryodhana's encampment seem, O Madhava, to be ablaze. In the appearance of all these portents, great is the danger that is indicated.

'I have in a vision, O Achyuta, beheld Yudhishthira ascending with his brothers a palace supported by a thousand columns. All of them appeared with white head-gears and in white robes. And all of them appeared to me to be seated on white seats. In the midst of the same vision, thou, O Janardana, wast beheld by me to be employed in enveloping the blood-dyed earth with weapons. Yudhishthira at the same time, of immeasurable energy, ascending upon a heap of bones, was gladly eating buttered *payasa* of a golden cup. I further beheld Yudhishthira to be employed in swallowing the earth handed over to him by thee. This indicates that he will verily rule the earth I beheld that tiger among men, Vrikodara, of fierce deeds, standing on the summit, mace in hand, and as if devouring this earth. This plainly indicates that he will slay all of us in fierce battle. It is known to me, O lord of the senses, that victory is there where righteousness is. I saw also Dhananjaya, the wielder of *Gandiva*, seated on the back of a white elephant, with thee, O lord of the senses, and blazing forth with great beauty. I have no doubt, O Krishna, that ye will slay in battle all the kings headed by Duryodhana. I saw Nakula and Sahadeva and that mighty car-warrior Satyaki, adorned with white bracelets, white cuirasses, white garlands, and white robes. This tiger among men were seated upon excellent vehicles borne on the shoulders of men. And I saw that umbrellas were held over the heads of all the three. Amongst the soldiers of Dhritarashtra's son, these three, O Janardana, were beheld by me decked with white head-gears. Know, O Kesava, that those three were Aswatthaman, Kripa, and Kritavarman of Satwata's race. All other kings, O Madhava, were seen by me to have blood-red headgears. I saw also, O thou of mighty arms, that those mighty car-warriors Bhishma and Drona, ascending on a vehicle drawn by camels, and by myself, and Dhritarashtra's son, proceeded, O lord, to the quarter, O Janardana, ruled by Agastya. This indicates that we shall soon have to proceed to Yama's abode. I have no doubt that myself and the other kings, indeed, the entire assemblage of Kshatriyas shall have to enter into the *Gandiva* fire.'

Krishna said, 'Indeed, the destruction of the earth is at hand when my words, O Karna, do not become acceptable to thy heart. O sire, when the destruction of all creatures approacheth, wrong assuming the semblance of right leaveth not the heart.'

"Karna said, 'If, O Krishna, we come out of this great battle that will be so destructive of heroic Kshatriyas, with life, then, O thou of mighty arms may we meet here again. Otherwise, O Krishna, we shall certainly meet in heaven. O sinless one, it seemeth to me now that there only it is possible for us to meet.'

"Sanjaya said, 'Having spoken these words, Karna closely pressed Madhava to his bosom. Dismissed by Kesava, he then descended from the car. And riding on his own car decked with gold, Radha's son greatly dejected, came back with us!'"

Section CXLIV (144)

"Vaisampayana said, 'Upon the failure of Krishna's solicitations (for peace), and after he had started for the Pandavas from the Kurus, Kshatri approached Pritha and said these words slowly in grief, 'O mother of living children, thou knowest that my inclination is always for peace, and although I cry myself hoarse, yet Suyodhana doth not accept my words. King Yudhishthira, having the Chedis, the Panchalas, and the Kekayas, Bhima and Arjuna, Krishna, Yuyudhana, and the twins for his allies, stayeth yet at Upaplavya, and from affection for kinsmen, looketh up to righteousness only, like a weak man, though he is possessed of great strength. King Dhritarashtra here, though old in years, doth not effect peace, and intoxicated with pride of children, treadeth a sinful path. In consequence of the wickedness of Jayadratha and Karna and Dussasana and Suvala's son, intestine dissensions will break out. They that behave unrighteously towards him that is righteous, verily that sin of theirs soon produceth its consequences. Who is there that will not be filled with sorrow at the sight of the Kurus persecuting righteousness in this way? When Kesava returneth without being able to bring about peace, the Pandavas will certainly address themselves for battle. Thereupon, the sin of the Kurus will lead to a destruction of heroes. Reflecting on all this, I do not get sleep by day or by night.'

"Hearing these words uttered by Vidura, who always wished her sons the accomplishment of their objects, Kunti began to sigh heavily, afflicted with grief, and began to think within herself, 'Fie to wealth, for the sake of which this great slaughter of kinsmen is about to take place. Indeed, in this war, they that are friends will sustain defeat. What can be a greater grief than this that the Pandavas, the Chedis, the Panchalas, and the Yadavas, assembled together, will fight with the Bharatas? Verily, I behold demerit in war. (On the other hand) if we do not fight, poverty and humiliation would be ours. As regards the person that is poor, even death is beneficial (to him). (On the other hand) the extermination of one's kinsmen is not victory. As I reflect on this, my heart swelleth with sorrow. The grandsire (Bhishma), the son of Santanu, the preceptor (Drona), who is the foremost of warriors, and Karna, having embraced Duryodhana's side, enhance my fears. The preceptor Drona, it seemeth to me, will never fight willingly against his pupils. As regards the Grandsire, why will he not show some affection for the Pandavas? There is only this sinful Karna then, of deluded understanding and ever following the deluded lead of the wicked Duryodhana, that hateth the Pandavas. Obstinately pursuing that which injureth the Pandavas, this Karna is, again, very powerful. It is this which burneth me at present. Proceeding to gratify him. I will today disclose the truth and seek to draw his heart towards the Pandavas. Pleased with me, while I was living in the inner apartments of the palace of my father, Kuntibhoja, the holy Durvasa gave me a boon in the form of an invocation consisting of *mantras*. Long reflecting with a trembling heart on the strength or weakness of those *mantras* and the power also of the Brahmana's words, and in consequence also of my disposition as a woman, and my nature as a girl of unripe years, deliberating repeatedly and while guarded by a confidential nurse and surrounded by my waiting-maids, and thinking also of how not to incur any reproach, how to maintain the honour of my father, and how I myself might have an accession of good fortune without being guilty of any transgression, I, at last, remembered that Brahmana and bowed to him, and having obtained that *mantras* from excess of curiosity and from folly, I summoned, during my maidenhood, the god *Surya*. He, therefore, who was held in my womb during my maidenhood,—why should *he* not obey my words that are certainly acceptable and beneficial to his brothers? And reflecting in this strain, Kunti formed an excellent resolution. And having formed that resolution, she went to the sacred stream called after Bhagiratha. And having reached the banks of *Ganga*, Pritha heard the chanting of the *Vedic* hymns by her son, endued with great kindness and firmly devoted to truth. And as Karna stood with face directed to the east and arms upraised, then helpless Kunti, for the sake of her interest stayed behind him, waiting the completion of prayers. And the lady of Vrishni's race, that wife of Kuru's house, afflicted by the heat of the sun began to look like a faded garland of lotuses. And, at last, she stood in the shade afforded by the upper garments of Karna. And Karna, of regulated vows, said his prayers until his back became heated by the rays of the sun. Then turning behind, he behold Kunti and was filled with surprise. And saluting him in proper form and with joined palms that foremost of virtuous persons, endued with great energy and pride, *viz.*, Vrisha, the son of Vikartana, bowed to her and said (the following words).'"

Section CXLV (145)

"Karna said, 'I am Karna, son of Radha and Adhiratha. For what, O lady, hast thou come here? Tell me what I am to do for thee?'"

"Kunti said, 'Thou art Kunti's son, and not Radha's. Nor is Adhiratha thy father. Thou, O Karna, art not born in the Suta order. Believe what I say. Thou wert brought forth by me while a maiden. I held thee first in my womb. O son, thou wert born in the palace of Kuntiraja. O Karna, that divine Surya who blazeth forth in light and maketh everything visible, O foremost of all wielders of weapons, begat thee upon me. O irresistible one, thou, O son, wert brought forth by me in my father's abode, decked with (natural) ear-rings and accoutred in a (natural) coat of mail, and blazing forth in beauty. That thou, without knowing thy brothers, shouldst, therefore, from ignorance, wait upon Dhritarashtra's son, is not proper. It is improper in thee especially, O son. The gratification of one's father and one's mother, who is the sole displayer of affection (for her child), hath, O son, in the matter of ascertaining the duties of men, been declared to be the highest of all duties. Acquired formerly by Arjuna, the prosperity of Yudhishthira hath, from avarice, been wrested by wicked persons. Snatching it back from Dhritarashtra's sons, do thou enjoy that prosperity. Let the Kurus behold today the union of Karna and Arjuna. Beholding thee and thy brother united together in bonds of brotherly love, let those wicked persons bow down unto ye. Let Karna and Arjuna be named in the same breath as Rama and Janardana. If you two are united together, what cannot be accomplished in the world? O Karna, surrounded by thy brothers, thou wilt, without doubt, blaze forth like Brahma Himself, surrounded by the gods on the platform of a great sacrifice. Endued with every virtue, thou art the first of all my relations. Let not the epithet Suta's son attach to thee. Thou art a Partha, endued with great energy.'"

Section CXLVI (146)

"Vaisampayana said '(After Kunti had said this), Karna heard an affectionate voice issued out of the solar circle. Coming from a great distance, that voice was uttered by Surya himself with paternal affection. (And it said)—The words said by Pritha are true. O Karna, act according to the words of thy mother. O tiger among men, great good will result to thee if thou fully followest those words.'

"Vaisampayana continued, 'Though, thus addressed by his mother, and by also his father Surya himself, Karna's heart did not yet waver, for he was firmly devoted to truth. And he said, 'O Kshatriya lady, I cannot admit what thou hast said, *viz.*, that obedience to thy commands constituteth (in my case) the highest of my duties. O mother, I was abandoned by thee as soon as I was born. This great injury, involving risk to life itself, that thou didst me, hath been destructive of my achievements and fame. If, indeed, I am a Kshatriya, I have, for thee, been deprived of all the rites of a Kshatriya. What enemy would have done me a greater injury? Without showing me mercy, when thou shouldst have shown it, and having kept me divested of all the rites (that are obligatory in consequence of the order of my birth), thou wouldst however, lay thy command on me today! Thou hadst never before sought my good as a mother should. Thou addressest me today, however, desiring to do good to thyself. Who is there that would not be afraid of Dhananjaya having Krishna with him (for the driver of his car)? If, therefore, I go today unto the Parthas, who is there that would not regard me as doing so from fright? Hitherto, nobody knew me to be their brother. If, giving out on the eve of battle that I am their brother, I go to the Pandavas, what would all the Kshatriyas say? Furnished with every object of desire, and worshipped by them with a view to make me happy, how can I render that friendship of Dhritarashtra's sons utterly futile? Having provoked hostilities with others, they always wait on me respectfully, and always bow down to me, as the Vasus bow down to Vasava. They think that aided by my might, they are capable of encountering the foe. How can I then frustrate that cherished hope of theirs? With me as their boat, they desire to cross the impassable ocean of battle. How can I then abandon them that are desirous of crossing that ocean which hath no other ferry? This is the time when all those have been supported by Dhritarashtra's sons should exert themselves for their masters. I shall certainly act for them, reckless of even my life. Those sinful men of unsteady heart, who, well-fed and well-furnished (with every necessary) by their masters, undo the benefit received by them when the time cometh for paying back, are thieves of their master's cakes, have neither this nor the other world for them. I will not speak deceitfully unto thee. For the sake of Dhritarashtra's son, I shall fight against thy sons to the best of my strength and might. I must not, however, abandon kindness and the conduct that becometh the good. Thy words, therefore, however beneficial cannot be obeyed by me now. This thy solicitation to me will not yet be fruitless. Except Arjuna, thy other sons, Yudhishthira, Bhima, and the twins, though capable of being withstood by me in fight and capable also of being slain, shall not yet be slain by me. It is with Arjuna alone, among all the combatants of Yudhishthira, that I will fight. Slaying Arjuna in battle, I shall achieve great merit, or slain by Savyasachin, I shall be covered with glory. O famous lady, the number of thy sons will never be less than five. Five it will always be,—either with me, or with Arjuna, and myself slain.'

"Hearing these words of Karna, Kunti who was trembling with grief, embraced her son who was unmoved in consequence of his fortitude, and said, 'Indeed, O Karna, even if what thou sayest seemeth to be possible, the Kauravas will certainly be exterminated. Destiny is all. Thou hast, however, O grinder of foes, granted to four of thy brothers the pledge of safety. Let that pledge be borne in thy remembrance at the time of shooting of weapons in battle.' And having told all this, Pritha also addressed Karna, saying, 'Blessed be thou, and let health be thine.' And Karna replied unto her, saying, 'Be it so!' And they then left the spot, wending in different directions.'"

Krishna's Peace Proposal

from the Udyoga Parva

Krishna's Peace Proposal

Section LXXXIX (89)

"Vaisampayana said, 'Rising up (from his bed) at day-dawn, Krishna went through his morning rites, and taking leave of the Bharatas, set out for the city (of the Kurus). Ana all the inhabitants of Vrikasthala, bidding farewell unto that mighty one of long arms while he was about to depart, all returned to their homes. And all the Dhartarashtras except Duryodhana, attired in excellent robes, and with Bhishma, Drona, Kripa, and others, went out to meet him. And the citizens by thousands, O king, on cars of diverse kinds, and many on foot, also came out, desirous of beholding Hrishikesa. And meeting on the way Bhishma of spotless deed, and Drona, and Dhritarashtra's sons, he entered the city, surrounded by them all. And in honour of Krishna, the city was beautifully adorned, and the principal streets were decorated with diverse jewels and gems. And, O king, O bull of the Bharata race, on that occasion no one,—man, woman, or child,—remained in doors, so eager were the citizens for beholding Vasudeva. And all the citizens came out and lined the streets and bent their heads down to the ground singing eulogies in his honour, O king, when Hrishikesa entered the city and passed through it. And substantial mansions, filled with high- born ladies, seemed to be on the point of falling down on the ground in consequence of their living weight. And although Vasudeva's steeds were endued with great speed, yet they moved very slowly through that dense mass of human beings. And that lotus-eyed grinder of foes then entered Dhritarashtra's ash-coloured palace which was enriched with numerous buildings. And having passed through the first three chambers of the palace, that chastiser of foes, Kesava, came upon the royal son of Vichitravirya. And upon that son of Dasarha's race approaching his presence, the blind monarch of great fame stood up along with Drona and Bhishma, Kripa and Somadatta, and king Vahlika also,—all stood up for honouring Janardana. And the Vrishni hero, having approached king Dhritarashtra of great fame, worshipped him and Bhishma with proper words and without losing any time. And having offered that worship unto them according to established usage, Madhava the slayer of Madhu, greeted the other kings according to their seniority in years. And Janardana then accosted the illustrious Drona and his son, and Vahlika, and Kripa, and Somadatta. And there in that chamber lay a spacious seat of beautiful workmanship, made of gold and set with jewels. And at Dhritarashtra's request, Achyuta took that seat; and the priests of Dhritarashtra duly offered Janardana a cow, honey and curds and water. And after the rites of hospitality were over, Govinda remained there for a while, surrounded by the Kurus, laughing and jesting with them according to their relationship with him. And that illustrious grinder of foes, honoured and worshipped by Dhritarashtra, came out with the king's permission. And Madhava having duly greeted all the Kurus in their assembly, then went to the delightful abode of Vidura; and Vidura, having approached Janardana of Dasarha's race thus arrived at his abode, worshipped him with every auspicious and desirable offering. And he said, 'What use, O lotus-eyed one, in telling thee of the joy I feel at this advent of thine, for thou art the inner Soul of all embodied creatures.' And after the hospitable reception was over, Vidura, conversant with all the principles of morality, enquired of Govinda, the slayer of Madhu, about the welfare of Pandavas. And that scion of Dasarha's race, that chief of the Vrishnis, unto whom the past and the future were as the present, knowing that Vidura was loved by the Pandavas and friendly towards them, and learned, and firm in morality, and honest, and harbouring no wrath (against the Pandavas), and wise, began to tell him everything in detail about the doings of the sons of Pandu.'"

Section XC (90)

"Vaisampayana said, 'Janardana, the chastiser of foes, after his meeting with Vidura, went then in the afternoon to his paternal aunt, Pritha.

And beholding Krishna whose countenance beamed with the effulgence of the radiant sun arrived at her abode, she encircled his neck with her arms and began to pour forth her lamentations remembering her sons. And at the sight, after a long time, of Govinda of Vrishni's race, the companion of those mighty children of hers, the tears of Pritha flowed fast. And after Krishna, that foremost of warriors, had taken his seat having first received the rites of hospitality, Pritha, with a woe-begone face and voice choked with tears addressed him, saying. They, who, from their earliest years have always waited with reverence on their superiors; they, who, in friendship are attached to one another; they, who, deprived deceitfully of their kingdom had gone to seclusion, however worthy of living in the midst of friends and attendants,—they, who have subjugated both wrath and joy, are devoted to Brahman's, and truthful in speech,—those children of mine, who, abandoning kingdom and enjoyments and leaving my miserable self behind, had gone to the woods, plucking the very roots of my heart,—those illustrious sons of Pandu, O Kesava, who have suffered woe however undeserving of it,—how, alas, did they live in the deep forest abounding with lions and tigers and elephants? Deprived in their infancy of their father, they were all tenderly brought up by me. How, also, did they live in the mighty forest, without seeing both their parents? From their infancy, O Kesava, the Pandavas were aroused from their beds by the music of conchs and drums and flutes. That they who while at home, used to sleep in high palatial chambers on soft blankets and skins of the *Runku* deer and were waked up in the morning by the grunt of elephants, the neighing of steeds, the clatter of car-wheels and the music of conchs and cymbals in accompaniment with the notes of flutes and lyres,—who, adored at early dawn with sacred sounding hymns uttered by Brahmanas, worshipped those amongst them that deserved such worship with robes and jewels and ornaments, and who were blessed with the auspicious benedictions of those illustrious members of the regenerate order, as a return for the homage the latter received,—that they, O Janardana, could sleep in the deep woods resounding with the shrill and dissonant cries of beasts of prey can hardly be believed, undeserving as they were of so much woe. How could they,

O slayer of Madhu, who were roused from their beds by music of cymbals and drums and conchs and flutes, with the honeyed strains of songstresses and the eulogies chanted by bards and professional reciters,—alas, how could they be waked in the deep woods by the yells of wild beasts? He that is endued with modesty, is firm in truth, with senses under control and compassions for all creatures,—he that hath vanquished both lust and malice and always treadeth the path of the righteous, he that ably bore the heavy burthen borne by Amvarisha and Mandhatri Yayati and Nahusha and Bharata and Dilip and Sivi the son of Usinara and other royal sages of old, he that is endued with an excellent character and disposition, he that is conversant with virtue, and whose prowess is incapable of being baffled, he that is fit to become the monarch of the three worlds in consequence of his possession of every accomplishment, he that is the foremost of all the Kurus lawfully and in respect of learning and disposition, who is handsome and mighty-armed and hath no enemy,—Oh, how is that Yudhishthira of virtuous soul, and of complexion like that of pure gold? He that hath the strength of ten thousand elephants and the speed of the wind, he that is mighty and ever wrathful amongst the sons of Pandu, he that always doth good to his brothers and is, therefore, dear to them all, he, O slayer of Madhu, that slew Kichaka with all his relatives, he that is the slayer of the Krodhavasas, of Hidimva, and of Vaka, he that in prowess is equal unto Sakra, and in might unto the Wind-god, he that is terrible, and in wrath is equal unto Madhava himself, he that is the foremost of all smiters,—that wrathful son of Pandu and chastiser of foes, who, restraining his rage, might, impatience, and controlling his soul, is obedient to the commands of his elder brother,—speak to me, O Janardana, tell me how is that smiter of immeasurable valour, that Bhimasena, who in aspect also justifies his name—that Vrikodara possessing arms like maces, that mighty second son of Pandu? O Krishna, that Arjuna of two arms who always regardeth himself as superior to his namesake of old with thousand arms, and who at one stretch shooteth five hundred arrows, that son of Pandu who in the use of weapons is equal unto king Kartavirya, in energy unto Aditya, in restraint of senses unto a great sage, in forgiveness unto the Earth, and in prowess unto Indra himself,—he, by whose prowess, O slayer of Madhu, the Kurus amongst all the kings of the earth have obtained this extensive empire, blazing with effulgence,—he, whose strength of arms is always adored by the Pandavas,— that son of Pandu, who is the foremost of all car-warriors and whose prowess is incapable of being frustrated,—he, from an encounter with whom in battle no foe ever escapeth with life,—he, O Achyuta, who is the conqueror of all, but who is incapable of being conquered by any,—he, who is the refuge of the Pandavas like Vasava of the celestials,—how, O Kesava, is that Dhananjaya now, that brother and friend of thine? He that is compassionate to all creatures, is endued with modesty and acquainted with mighty weapons, is soft and delicate and virtuous,—he that is dear to me,— that mighty bowman Sahadeva, that hero and ornament of assemblies,—he, O Krishna, who is youthful in years, is devoted to the service of his brothers, and is conversant with both virtue and profit, whose brothers, O slayer of Madhu, always applaud the disposition of that high-souled and well-behaved son of mine,—tell me, O thou of the Vrishni race, of that heroic Sahadeva, that foremost of warriors, that son of Madri, who always waiteth submissively on his elder brothers and so reverentially on me. He that is delicate and youthful in years, he that is brave and handsome in person,—that son of Pandu who is dear unto his brothers as also unto all, and who, indeed, is their very life though walking with a separate body,—he that is conversant with various modes of warfare,—he that is endued with great strength and is a mighty bowman,—tell me, O Krishna, whether that dear child of mine, Nakula, who was brought up in luxury, is now well in body and mind? O thou of mighty arms, shall I ever behold again Nakula of mine, that mighty car-warrior, that delicate youth brought up in every luxury and undeserving of woe? Behold, O hero, I am alive today, even I, who could know peace by losing sight of Nakula for the short space of time taken up by a wink of the eye. More than all my sons, O Janardana, is the daughter of Drupada dear to me. High-born and possessed of great beauty, she is endued with every accomplishment. Truthful in speech, she chose the company of her lords, giving up that of her sons, Indeed, leaving her dear children behind, she followeth the sons of Pandu. Waited upon at one time by a large train of servants, and adored by her husbands with every object of enjoyment, the possessor of every auspicious mark and accomplishment, how, O Achyuta, is that Draupadi now? Having five heroic husbands who are all smiters of foes and all mighty bowmen, each equal unto Agni in energy, alas, woe hath yet been the lot of Drupada's daughter. I have not for fourteen long years, O chastiser of foes, beheld the princess of Panchala, that daughter-in-law of mine, who herself hath been a prey to constant anxiety on account of her children, whom she hath not seen for that period. When Drupada's daughter endued with such a disposition, doth not enjoy uninterrupted happiness, it seemeth, O Govinda, that the happiness one enjoyeth is never the fruit of one's acts. When I remember the forcible dragging of Draupadi to the assembly, then neither Vibhatsu nor Yudhishthira, nor Bhima, nor Nakula, nor Sahadeva, becometh an object of affection to me. Never before had a heavier grief been mine than what pierced my heart when that wretch Dussasana, moved by wrath and covetousness, dragged Draupadi, then in her flow, and therefore clad in a single raiment, into the presence of her father-in-law in the assembly and exposed her to the gaze of all the Kurus. It is known that amongst those that were present, king Vahlika, Kripa, Somadatta, were pierced with grief at this sight, but of all present in that assembly, it was Vidura whom I worship. Neither by learning, nor by wealth doth one become worthy of homage. It is by disposition alone that one becomes respectable, O Krishna, endued with great intelligence and profound wisdom, the character of the illustrious Vidura, like unto an ornament (that he wears) adorns the whole world.'

"Vaisampayana continued, 'Filled with delight at the advent of Govinda, and afflicted with sorrow (on account of her sons) Pritha gave expression to all her diverse griefs. And she said, 'Can gambling and the slaughter of deer, which, O chastiser of foes, occupied all wicked kings of old, be a pleasant occupation for the Pandavas? The thought consumeth, O Kesava, that being dragged into the presence of all the Kurus in their assembly by Dhritarashtra's sons, insults worse than death were heaped on Krishna. O chastiser of foes, the banishment of my sons from their capital and their wanderings in the wilderness,—these and various other griefs, O Janardana, have been mine. Nothing could be more painful to me or to my sons themselves, O Madhava, than that they should have had to pass a period of concealment, shut up in a stranger's house. Full fourteen years have passed since the day when Duryodhana first exited my sons. If misery is destructive of fruits of sins, and happiness is dependent on the fruits of religious merit, then it seems that happiness may still be ours after so much misery. I never made any distinction between Dhritarashtra's sons and mine (so far as maternal affection is concerned). By that truth, O Krishna, I shall surely behold thee along with the Pandavas safely come out of the present strife with their foes slain, and the kingdom recovered by them. The Pandavas themselves have observed their vow with such truthfulness sticking to Dharma that they are incapable of being defeated by their enemies. In the matter of my present sorrows, however, I blame neither myself nor Suyodhana, but my father alone. Like a wealthy man giving away a sum of money in gift, my father gave me away to Kuntibhoja. While a child playing with a ball in my hands, thy grandfather, O Kesava, gave me away to his friend, the illustrious Kuntibhoja. Abandoned, O chastiser of foes, by my own father, and my father-in law, and afflicted with insufferable woes, what use, O Madhava, is there in my being alive? On the night of Savyasachin's birth, in the lying-in-room, an invisible voice told me, 'This son of thine will conquer the whole world, and his fame will reach the very heavens. Slaying the Kurus in a great battle and recovering the kingdom, thy son Dhanajaya will, with his brothers, perform three grand sacrifices.' I do not doubt the truth of that announcement. I bow unto Dharma that upholds the creation. If Dharma be not a myth, then, O Krishna, thou wilt surely achieve all that the invisible voice said. Neither the loss of my husband, O Madhava, nor loss of wealth, nor our hostility with the Kurus ever inflicted such rending pains on me as that separation from my children. What peace can my heart know when I do not see before me that wielder of Gandiva, *viz.*, Dhananjaya, that foremost of all bearers of arms? I have not, for fourteen years, O Govinda, seen Yudhishthira, and Dhananjaya, and Vrikodara. Men perform the obsequies of those that are missed for a long time, taking them for dead. Practically, O Janardana, my children are all dead to me and I am dead to them.

'Say unto the virtuous king Yudhishthira, O Madhava, that—Thy virtue, O son, is daily decreasing. Act thou, therefore, in such a way that thy religious merit may not diminish. Fie to them that live, O Janardana, by dependence on others. Even death is better than a livelihood gained by meanness. Thou must also say unto Dhananjaya and the ever-ready Vrikodara that—The time for that event is come in view of which a Kshatriya woman bringeth forth a son. If you allow the time slip without your achieving anything, then, though at present ye are respected by all the world, ye will be only doing that which would be regarded as contemptible. And if contempt touches you, I will abandon you for ever. When the time cometh, even life, which is so dear, should be laid down, O foremost of men, thou must also say unto Madri's sons that are always devoted to Kshatriya customs.—More than life itself, strive ye to win objects of enjoyment, procurable by prowess, since objects won by prowess alone can please the heart of a person desirous of living according to Kshatriya customs. Repairing thither, O mighty-armed one, say unto that foremost of all bearers of arms, Arjuna the heroic son of Pandu,—Tread thou the path that may be pointed out to thee by Draupadi. It is known to thee, O Kesava, that when inflamed with rage, Bhima and Arjuna, each like unto the universal Destroyer himself, can slay the very gods. That was a great insult offered unto them, *viz.*, that their wife Krishna, having been dragged into the assembly was addressed in such humiliating terms by Dussasana and Karna. Duryodhana himself hath insulted Bhima of mighty energy in the very presence of the Kuru chiefs. I am sure he will reap the fruit of that behaviour, for Vrikodara, provoked by a foe, knoweth no peace. Indeed, once provoked, Bhima forgets it not for a long while, even until that grinder of foes exterminates the enemy and his allies. The loss of kingdom did not grieve me; the defeat at dice did not grieve me. That the illustrious and beautiful princess of Panchala was dragged into the assembly while clad in a single raiment and made to hear bitter words grieved me most. What, O Krishna, could be a greater grief to me? Alas, ever devoted to Kshatriya customs and endued with great beauty, the princess, while ill, underwent that cruel treatment, and though possessing powerful protectors was then as helpless as if she had none. O slayer of Madhu, having thee and that foremost of all mighty persons, Rama, and that mighty car-warrior Pradyumna for me and my children's protectors and having, O foremost of men, my sons the invincible Bhima and the unretreating Vijaya both alive, that I had still such grief to bear is certainly strange!'

"Vaisampayana continued, 'Thus addressed by her, Sauri the friend of Partha, then comforted his paternal aunt, Pritha, afflicted with grief on account of her sons. And Vasudeva said, 'What woman is there, O aunt, in the world who is like thee? The daughter of king Surasena, thou art, by marriage, admitted into Ajamida's race. High-born and highly married, thou art like a lotus transplanted from one mighty lake into another. Endued with every prosperity and great good fortune, thou wert adored by thy husband.

The wife of hero, thou hast again given birth to heroic sons. Possessed of every virtue, and endued with great wisdom, it behoveth thee to bear with patience, both happiness and misery. Overcoming sleep and langour, and wrath and joy, and hunger and thirst, and cold and heat, thy children are always in the enjoyment of that happiness, which, as heroes, should by theirs. Endued with great exertion and great might, thy sons, without affecting the comforts derivable from the senses such as satisfy only the low and the mean, always pursue that happiness which as heroes they should. Nor are they satisfied like little men having mean desires. They that are wise enjoy or suffer the same of whatever enjoyable or sufferable, Indeed, ordinary persons, affecting comforts that satisfy the low and the mean, desire an equable state of dullness without excitement of any kind. They, however, that are superior, desire either the acutest of human suffering or the highest of all enjoyments that is given to man. The wise always delight in extremes. They find no pleasure betwixt; they regard the extreme to be happiness, while that which lies between is regarded by them as misery. The Pandavas with Krishna saluteth thee through me. Representing themselves to be well, they have enquired after thy welfare. Thou wilt soon behold them become the lords of the whole world, with their foe slain, and themselves invested with prosperity.'

'Thus consoled by Krishna, Kunti, afflicted with grief on account of her sons, but soon dispelling the darkness caused by her temporary loss of understanding, replied unto Janardana, saying, 'Whatever, O mighty-armed one, thou, O slayer of Madhu, regardest as proper to be done, let that be done without sacrificing righteousness, O chastiser of foes, and without the least guile. I know, O Krishna, what the power of thy truth and of thy lineage is. I know also what judgment and what prowess thou bringest to bear upon the accomplishment of whatever concerns thy friends. In our race, thou art Virtue's self, thou art Truth, and thou art the embodiment of ascetic austerities. Thou art the great *Brahma*, and everything rests on thee. What, therefore, thou hast said must be true.'

"Vaisampayana continued, 'Bidding her farewell and respectfully walking round her, the mighty-armed Govinda then departed for Duryodhana's mansion.'"

Section XCI (91)

"Vaisampayana said, 'With Pritha's leave and having walked round her, the chastiser of foes, Govinda, also called Sauri, went to Duryodhana's palace that was furnished with great wealth, adorned with beautiful seats, and was like unto the abode of Purandara himself. Un-obstructed by the orderlies-in-waiting, that hero of great fame crossed three spacious yards in succession and then entered that mansion looking like a mass of clouds, high as the summit of a hill, and blazing forth in splendour. And he there beheld Dhritarashtra's son of mighty arms seated on his throne in the midst of a thousand kings and surrounded by all the Kurus. And he also beheld there Dussasana and Karna and Sakuni, the son of Suvala, seated on their respective seats by the side of Duryodhana. And on that scion of Dasarha's race entering the court, Dhritarashtra's son of great fame rose up from his seat with his counsellors for honouring the slayer of Madhu. And Kesava then greeted Dhritarashtra's sons and all his counsellors as also all the kings that were present there, according to their respective ages. And Achyuta of Vrishni's race then took his seat on a beautiful seat made of gold and overlaid with carpet embroidered with gold. And the Kuru king then offered unto Janardana a cow, and honey and curds and water, and placed at his service palaces and mansions and the whole kingdom. And then the Kauravas, with all the kings there present, worshipped Govinda on his seat and resembling the sun himself in splendour. The worship being over, king Duryodhana invited him of Vrishni's race—that foremost of victors—to eat at his house, Kesava, however did not accept the invitation. The Kuru king Duryodhana seated in the midst of the Kurus, in a gentle voice but with deception lurking behind his words, eyeing Karna, and addressing Kesava, then said, 'Why, O Janardana, dost thou not accept the diverse kinds of viands and drinks, robes and beds that have all been prepared and kept ready for thee? Thou hast granted aid to both sides; thou art engaged in the good of both parties. Thou art again the foremost of Dhritarashtra's relations and much loved by him. Thou, O Govinda, also knowest fully, and all things in details, both religion and profit. I, therefore, desire to hear, O bearer of the discus and the mace, what the true reason is of this thy refusal.'

"Vaisampayana continued, 'The high-souled Govinda, of eyes like lotus leaves, then raising his mighty (right) arm, and in a voice deep as that of the clouds, replied unto the king in excellent words fraught with reasons,— words that were clear, distinct, correctly pronounced, and without a single letter dropped, saying, 'Envoys, O king, eat and accept worship only after the success of their missions. Therefore, O Bharata, after my mission becomes successful, thou mayest entertain me and my attendants.' Thus answered, Dhritarashtra's son again said unto Janardana, 'It behoveth thee not, O Kesava, to behave towards us in this way, Whether thou becomest successful, or unsuccessful, we are endeavouring to please thee, O slayer of Madhu, because of thy relationship with us. It seems, however, that all our efforts. O thou of Dasarha's race, are fruitless. Nor do we see the reason, O slayer of Madhu, in consequence of which, O foremost of men, thou acceptest not the worship offered by us from love and friendship. With thee, O Govinda, we have no hostility, no war. Therefore, on reflection, it will seem to thee that words such as these scarcely become thee.'

"Vaisampayana continued, 'Thus addressed by the king, Janardana of Dasarha's race, casting his eyes on Dhritarashtra's son and all his counsellors, replied, saying, 'Not from desire, nor from wrath, nor from malice, nor for gain, nor for the sake of argument, nor from temptation, would I abandon virtue. One taketh another's food when one is in distress. At present, however, O king, thou hast not inspired love in me by any act of thine, nor have I myself been plunged into distress. Without any reason, O king, thou hatest, from the moment of their birth, thy dear and gentle brothers,—the Pandavas—endued with every virtue. This unreasonable hatred of thine for the sons of Pritha ill becometh thee. The sons of Pandu are all devoted to virtue. Who, indeed, can do them the least injury? He that hateth them, hateth me; he that loveth them, loveth me. Know that the virtuous Pandavas and my own self have but a common soul. He, who, following the impulses of lust and wrath, and from darkness of soul, hateth and seeketh to injure one that is possessed of every good quality, is regarded as the vilest of men. That wrathful wretch of every good quality, is regarded as the vilest of men. That wrathful wretch of uncontrolled soul, who, from ignorance and avarice hateth his kinsmen endued with every auspicious quality, can never enjoy his prosperity long. He, on the other hand, who, by good offices, winneth over persons endued with good qualities, even if he beareth aversion of them within his heart, enjoyeth prosperity and fame for ever and ever. Defiled by wickedness, all this food, therefore, deserveth not to be eaten by me. The food supplied by Vidura alone, should, I think, be eaten by me.'

'Having said this unto Duryodhana who was ever incapable of bearing anything against his own wishes, Kesava of mighty arms then came out of that blazing palace of Dhritarashtra's son. And the high-souled Vasudeva of mighty arms, coming out of that mansion, directed his steps towards the abode of the illustrious Vidura. And while that mighty-armed one staying within Vidura's abode, thither came unto him Drona, and Kripa, and Bhishma, and Vahlika, and many of the Kauravas. And the Kauravas that came there addressed Madhava, the heroic slayer of Madhu, saying, 'O thou of Vrishni's race, we place at thy disposal our houses with all the wealth within them.'

'The slayer of Madhu, of mighty energy, answered them saying, 'Ye may go away. I am much honoured by these your offers.' And after all the Kurus had gone away, Vidura, with great care entertained that unvanquished hero of Dasarha's race with every object of desire. And Kunti then placed before the illustrious Kesava clean and savoury food in abundance. Therewith the slayer of Madhu first gratified the Brahmanas. Indeed, from that food he first gave a portion, along with much wealth, unto a number of Brahmanas conversant with the *Vedas*, and then with his attendants, like Vasava in the midst of the Marutas, he dined on what remained of the clean and savoury food supplied by Vidura.'"

Section XCII (92)

"Vaisampayana said, 'After Kesava had dined and been refreshed, Vidura said unto him during the night, 'O Kesava, this advent of thine hath not been a well judged one, for, O Janardana, Dhritarashtra's son transgresseth the rules of both profit and religion, is wicked and wrathful, insulteth others, though himself desirous of honours, and disobeyeth the commands of the aged. He is, O Madhava, a transgressor of the scriptures, ignorant, and of wicked soul, already overtaken by fate, untractable, and disposed to do evil to those that seek his good. His soul is possessed by desire and lust. He foolishly regardeth himself as very wise. He is the enemy of all his true friends. Ever-suspicious, without any control over his soul, and ungrateful, he hath abandoned all virtue and is in love with sin. He is foolish, with understanding uncultivated, a slave of his senses, ever obedient to the impulses of lust and avarice, and irresolute in every act that should be done. He is endued with these and many other vices. Although thou wilt point out to him what is for his good, he will yet disregard it all, moved by pride and anger. He hath great faith in Bhishma, and Drona, and Kripa, and Karna, and Drona's son, and Jayadratha, and, therefore, he never setteth his heart on peace, O Janardana. Dhritarashtra's sons, with Karna, firmly believe that the Pandavas are incapable of even looking at Bhishma, Drona, and other heroes, not to speak of fighting against them. The foolish Duryodhana of limited sight, having assembled a huge army regardeth, O slayer of Madhu, that his purposes are already achieved. The foolish son of

Dhritarashtra hath arrived at the conclusion that Karna, single-handed, is competent to vanquish his foes. He will, therefore, never make peace. Thou, O Kesava, desirest to establish peace and brotherly feelings between the two parties. But know that all the sons of Dhritarashtra have come to the conclusion that they would not give unto the Pandavas what, indeed, the latter have a right to. With those that are so resolved thy words will certainly prove vain. Where, O slayer of Madhu, words, good or bad, are of the same effect, no wise man would spend his breath for nothing, like a singer before the deaf. As a Brahmana before a conclave of *Chandalas*, thy words, O Madhava, would command no respect among those ignorant and wicked wretches that have no reverence for all that deserveth reverence. Foolish, as long as he hath strength, he will never obey thy counsels. Whatever words thou mayest speak to him will be perfectly futile. It doth not seem proper to me, O Krishna, that thou shouldst go into the midst of these wicked-minded wretches seated together. It doth not seem proper to me, O Krishna, that going thither thou shouldst utter words against those wicked-souled, foolish, unrighteous wights, strong in number. In consequence of their having never worshipped the aged, in consequence of their having been blinded by prosperity and pride, and owing to the pride of youth and wrath, they will never accept the good advice thou mayest place before them. He hath mustered a strong force, O Madhava, and he hath his suspicions of thyself. He will, therefore, never obey any counsel that thou mayest offer. The sons of Dhritarashtra, O Janardana, are inspired with the firm belief that at present Indra himself, at the head of all the celestials, is incapable of defeating them in battle. Efficacious as thy words always are, they will prove to be of no efficacy with persons impressed with such a conviction and who always follow the impulses of lust and wrath. Staying in the midst of his ranks of elephants and his army consisting of cars and heroic infantry, the foolish and wicked Duryodhana, with all fears dispelled, regardeth the whole earth to have already been subjugated by him. Indeed, Dhritarashtra's son coveteth extensive empire on the earth without any rivals. Peace, therefore, with him is unattainable. That which he hath in his possession he regardeth as unalterably his. Alas, the destruction on the earth seems to be at hand for the sake of Duryodhana, for, impelled by fate, the kings of the earth, with all the Kshatriya warriors, have assembled together, desirous of battling with the Pandavas? All those kings, O Krishna, are in enmity with thee and have all been deprived of their possessions before this by thee. Through fear of thee those heroic monarchs have joined together with Karna and made an alliance with Dhritarashtra's sons. Reckless of their very lives, all those warriors have united with Duryodhana and are filled with delight at the prospect of fighting the Pandavas. O hero of Dasarha's race, it doth not commend itself to me that thou shouldst enter into their midst. How, O grinder of foes, wilt thou repair into the midst of those numerous enemies of thine, of wicked souls, and seated together? O thou of mighty arms, thou art, indeed, incapable of being vanquished by the very gods, and I know, O slayer of foes, thy manliness and intelligence. O Madhava, the love I bear to thee is equal to that I bear to the sons of Pandu. I say, therefore, these words to thee from my affection, regard, and friendship for thee. What need is there in expressing to thee the delight that has been mine at sight of thy persons, for, thou, O thou of eyes like lotus, art the inner Soul of all embodied creatures.'"

Section XCIII (93)

"The holy one said, 'That, indeed, which should be said by a person of great wisdom: that, indeed, which should be said by one possessed of great foresight; that indeed, which should be said by one like thee to a friend like me; that indeed, which is deserving of thee, being consistent with virtue and profit, and truth; that, O Vidura, hath been said by thee, father and mother- like, unto me. That which thou hast told me is certainly true, worthy of approbation and consistent with reason. Listen, however, with attention, O Vidura, to the reason of my coming. Well knowing the wickedness of Dhritarashtra's son and the hostility of the Kshatriyas that have sided with him. I have still, O Vidura, come to the Kurus. Great will be the merit earned by him who will liberate from the meshes of death the whole earth, with her elephants, cars and steeds, overwhelmed with a dreadful calamity. If a man striving to the best of his abilities to perform a virtuous act meets with failure, I have not the least doubt that the merit of that act becomes his, notwithstanding such failure. This also is known to those that are conversant with religion and scripture, that if a person having intended mentally to commit a sinful act does not actually commit it, the demerit of that act can never be his. I will sincerely endeavour, O Vidura; to bring about peace between the Kurus and the Srinjayas who are about to be slaughtered in battle. That terrible calamity (which hangs over them all) hath its origin in the conduct of the Kurus, for it is directly due to the action of Duryodhana and Karna, the other Kshatriyas only following the lead of these two. The learned regard him to be a wretch who doth not by his solicitation seek to save a friend who is about to sink in calamity. Striving to the best of his might, even to the extent of seizing him by the hair, one should seek to dissuade a friend from an improper act. In that case, he that acteth so, instead of incurring blame, reapeth praise. It behoveth Dhritarashtra's son, therefore, O Vidura, with his counsellors, to accept my good and beneficial counsels that are consistent with virtue and profit and competent to dispel the present calamity. I will, therefore, sincerely endeavour to bring about the good of Dhritarashtra's sons and of the Pandavas, as also of all the Kshatriyas on the face of the earth. If while endeavouring to bring about the good (of my friends), Duryodhana judgeth me wrongly, I shall have the satisfaction of my own conscience, and a true friend is one who assumeth the functions of an intercessor when dissensions break out between kinsmen. In order, again, that unrighteous, foolish, and inimical persons may not afterwards say that though competent, still Krishna did not make any attempt to restrain the angry Kurus and the Pandavas from slaughtering one another I have come here. Indeed, it is to serve both parties that I have come hither. Having striven to bring about peace, I will escape the censure of all the kings. If after listening to my auspicious words, fraught with virtue and profit, the foolish Duryodhana accept them not, he will only invite his fate. If without sacrificing the interests of the Pandavas I can bring about peace among the Kurus, my conduct will be regarded as highly meritorious, O high-souled one, and the Kauravas themselves will be liberated from the meshes of death. If the sons of Dhritarashtra reflect coolly on the words I shall utter—words fraught with wisdom, consistent with righteousness, and possessed of grave import,— then that peace which is my object will be brought about and the Kauravas will also worship me (as the agent thereof). If, on the other hand, they seek to injure me, I tell thee that all the kings of the earth; united together, are no match for me, like a herd of deer incapable of standing before an enraged lion.'

"Vaisampayana continued, 'Having said these words, that bull of the Vrishni race and delighter of Yadavas, then laid himself down on his soft bed for sleep.'"

Section XCIV (94)

"Vaisampayana said, 'In such conversation between those two distinguished persons, both of whom were endued with great intelligence, that night, lit with bright stars, passed away. Indeed, the night passed away against the wishes of the illustrious Vidura, who had been listening to the varied conversation of Krishna fraught with virtue, profit, and desire, and made up of delightful words and syllables of agreeable import; and also those of Krishna himself, of immeasurable prowess, listening to discourses equal in style and character. Then, at early dawn a band of choristers and bards gifted with melodious voices, awoke Kesava with sweet sounds of conchs and cymbals. And rising from bed, Janardana of Dasarha's race, that bull amongst all the Sattwatas, went through all the customary acts of the morning. And having cleansed himself by a bath, recited the sacred *Mantras* and poured libations of clarified butter on the sacrificial fire. Madhava decked his person and began to worship the rising sun. And while the unvanquished Krishna of Dasarha's race was still engaged in his morning devotions, Duryodhana and Suvala's son Sakuni came to him and said, 'Dhritarashtra is seated in his court, with all the Kurus headed by Bhishma and with all the kings of the earth. They are all soliciting thy presence, O Govinda, like the celestials in heaven desiring the presence of Sakra himself,—thus addressed, Govinda greeted them both with sweet and courteous enquiries. And when the sun had risen a little higher, Janardana, that chastiser of foes, summoning a number of Brahmanas, made them presents of gold and robes and kine and steeds.

And after he had thus given away much wealth and taken his seat, his driver (Daruka) came and saluted that unvanquished hero of Dasarha's race. And Daruka soon returned with his master's large and blazing car furnished with rows of tinkling bells and harnessed with excellent steeds. And understanding that his handsome car adorned with every ornament and producing a rattle, deep as the rumbling of the mighty masses of clouds, was ready, the high-souled Janardana, that delighter of all the Yadavas, walking round the sacred fire and a band of Brahmanas, and putting on the gem known by the name of *Kaustubha*, and blazing with beauty, surrounded by the Kurus, and well-protected by the Vrishnis, mounted on it. And Vidura, conversant with all the precepts of religion, followed on his own car that scion of Dasarha's race, that foremost of all living creatures, that first of all persons gifted with intelligence. And Duryodhana and Suvala's son Sakuni also, on one car followed Krishna, that chastiser of foes. And Satyaki and Kritavarman and the other mighty car-warriors of the Vrishni race, all rode behind Krishna on cars and steeds and elephants. And, O king, the handsome cars of those heroes, adorned with gold and drawn by excellent steeds and each producing a loud rattle, as they moved forward, shone brilliantly. And Kesava, endued with great intelligence, and beaming with beauty, soon came upon a broad street that had previously been swept and watered, and that was fit to be used by the highest of kings. And when that scion of Dasarha's race set out, cymbals began to play, and conchs began to be blown, and other instruments also to pour forth their music. And great number of youthful heroes, foremost in the world for heroism, and possessed of lion-like prowess, proceeded, surrounding Sauri's car. And many thousands of soldiers, attired in a variegated dresses, bearing swords and lances and axes, marched in advance of Kesava. And there were full five hundred elephants, and cars by thousands, that followed that unvanquished hero of Dasarha's race while he proceeded. And, O chastiser of foes, all the citizens of the capital, of all ages and both sexes, desirous of beholding Janardana came out into the streets. And the terraces and balconies of the houses were so thronged by ladies that the houses were on the point of falling down with the weight. And worshipped by the Kurus, and listening to various sweet speeches, and returning the greetings of all as each deserved, Kesava went along the street, casting his eyes on all. And at last, when Kesava reached the Kuru court, his attendants loudly blew their conchs and trumpets and filled the welkin with that blare. And, thereupon, that whole assembly of kings, of immeasurable prowess, trembled with delight at the expectation of soon setting their eyes on Krishna. And hearing the rattle of his car, that rumbled like the deep roll of rain-charged clouds, the monarchs understood Krishna to be near, and the hair of their bodies stood erect with delight. And having reached the gate of the court, Sauri, that bull among the Satwatas, alighting from his car, that resembled the summit of Kailasa, entered the court which looked like a mass of newly- risen clouds, and blazed forth with beauty, and resembled the very abode of the great Indra. And that illustrious hero entered the court, arm-in-arm with Vidura and Satyaki on either side, and overshadowing with his own the splendour of all the Kurus, like the sun overshadowing the radiance of lesser lights in the firmament. And before Vasudeva sat Karna and Duryodhana, while behind him were seated the Vrishnis with Kritavarman. And Bhishma and Drona, and others with Dhritarashtra were on the point of rising up from their seats for honouring Janardana. Indeed, as soon as he, of Dasarha's race, came, the illustrious blind monarch, Drona and Bhishma, all rose up from their seats. And when that mighty ruler of men, king Dhritarashtra, rose up from his seat, those kings by thousands around him all rose up also. And at Dhritarashtra's command, a seat beautiful all over, and adorned with gold, had been kept there for Krishna, And after taking his seat, Madhava smilingly greeted the king, and Bhishma, and Drona, and all other rulers, each according to his age. And all the kings of the earth, and all the Kurus also, beholding Kesava arrived in that assembly, worshipped him duly: And as that chastiser of foes, that vanquisher of hostile cities, that hero of Dasarha's race, was seated there, he beheld the *Rishis* whom he had seen while proceeding to Hastinapur, staying in the firmament. And beholding those *Rishis* with Narada at their head, he of Dasarha's race, slowly addressed Bhishma the son of Santanu, saying, 'O king, the *Rishis* have come to see this earthly conclave of ours. Invite them with offer of seats and abundant courtesy, for if they are not seated, no one here is capable of taking his seat. Let proper worship, therefore, be speedily offered unto these *Rishis* with souls under proper control. And beholding the *Rishis* then at the gate of the palace, Santanu's son quickly ordered the servants to bring seats for them. And soon enough they brought large and beautiful seats embroidered with gold and set with gems. And after the *Rishis*. O Bharata, had taken their seats and accepted the *Arghyas* offered to them, Krishna took his seat, so also all the kings. And Dussasana gave an excellent seat to Satyaki, while Vivingsati gave another golden one to Kritavarman. And not far from where Krishna sat, that illustrious and wrathful pair, Karna and Duryodhana, sat together on the same seat. And Sakuni, the king of Gandhara, surrounded by the chiefs of his country, sat there, O king, with his son beside him. And the high-souled Vidura sat on a begemmed seat covered with a white deer-skin that almost touched Krishna's seat. And all the kings in the assembly, although they gazed at Janardana of Dasarha's race for a long while, were not, however, gratified with their gaze, like drinkers of the *Amrita*, that are never satiated with quaffing measure after measure. And Janardana attired in yellow robes having the complexion of the Atasi flower, sat in the midst of that assembly like a sapphire mounted on gold. And after Govinda had taken his seat, a perfect silence ensued, for none present there spoke a single word.'"

Section XCV (95)

"Vaisampayana said, 'And after all the kings had been seated and perfect silence had ensued, Krishna possessing fine teeth and having a voice deep as that of the drum, began to speak. And Madhava although he addressed Dhritarashtra, spoke in a voice deep as the roll of clouds in the rainy season, making the whole assembly hear. And he said, 'In order that, O Bharata, peace may be established between the Kurus and the Pandavas without a slaughter of the heroes, I have come hither. Besides this, O king, I have no other beneficial words to utter, O chastiser of foes, everything that should be learnt in this world is already known to thee. This thy race, O king, owing to its learning and behaviour, and owing also to its being adorned with every accomplishment, is most distinguished among all royal dynasties. Joy in the happiness of others, grief at sight of other people's misery, desire to alleviate distress, abstention from injury, sincerity, forgiveness, and truth,—these, O Bharata, prevail amongst the Kurus. Then thy race, therefore, O king, is so noble, it would be a pity if anything improper were done by any one belonging to it, and greater pity still if it were done by thee. O chief of the Kurus, thou art the first of those that should restrain the Kurus if they behave deceitfully towards strangers or those numbering with themselves. Know, O thou of Kuru's race, that those wicked sons of thine, headed by Duryodhana, abandoning both virtue and profit, disregarding morality, and deprived of their senses by avarice, are now acting most unrighteously towards, O bull of men, their foremost of kinsmen. That terrible danger (which threatens all) hath its origin in the conduct of the Kurus. If thou becomest indifferent to it, it will then produce a universal slaughter. If, O Bharata, thou art willing, thou mayest be able to allay that danger even yet, for, O bull of Bharata's race, peace. I think, is not difficult of acquisition. The establishment of peace, O king, depends on thee and myself, O monarch. Set right thy sons, O thou of Kuru's race, and I will set the Pandavas right. Whatever be thy command, O king, it behoveth thy sons with their followers to obey it. If again they live in obedience to thee, that would be the very best they could do. If thou strivest for peace by restraining thy sons, it will be to thy profit, O king, as also to the benefit of the Pandavas. Having reflected carefully, act thou thyself, O king. Let those sons of Bharata (the Pandavas), be, O ruler of men, thy allies. Supported by the Pandavas, O king, seek thou both religion and profit. By every exertion in thy power, thou canst not have, O king, such allies as they who are such. Protected by the illustrious sons of Pandu, Indra himself at the head of the celestials will not be able to vanquish thee. How would it be possible then for mere earthly kings to withstand thy prowess? If with Bhishma, and Drona, and Kripa, and Karna, and Vivingsati, and Aswatthaman, Vikarna, and Somadatta, and Vahlika and the chief of the Sindhus, and the ruler of the Kalingas, and Sudakshina, the king of the Kamvojas, there were Yudhishthira, and Bhimasena and Savyasachin, and the twins, and if Satyaki of mighty energy, and Yuyutsu, that mighty car warrior, are stationed, who is there, O bull of Bharata's race, of such misdirected intelligence that would fight these? If, O slayer of foes, thou hast both the Kurus and the Pandavas at thy back, the sovereignty of the whole world and invincibility before all foes will be thine. All the rulers of the earth, O monarch, that are either equal to thee or superior, will then seek alliance with thee. Protected on all sides by sons, grandsons, fathers, brothers, and friends, thou wilt then be able to live in exceeding happiness. Keeping these before thee and treating them with kindness as in days of yore, thou, O monarch, wilt enjoy the sovereignty of the whole earth. With these as thy supporters and with the sons of Pandu also, thou wilt, O Bharata, be able to conquer all thy foes. Even this is thy best advantage. If, O chastiser of foes, thou art united with thy sons and kinsmen and counsellors, thou wilt' enjoy sovereignty of the whole earth won for thee by them. In battle, O great king, nothing but wholesale destruction is visible. Indeed, in the destruction of both the parties, what merit dost thou see? If the Pandavas are slaughtered in battle, or if thy own mighty sons fall, tell me, O bull of Bharata's race, what happiness wilt thou enjoy? All of them are brave and skilled in weapons. All of them are desirous of battle, the Pandavas as also thy sons. Oh, save them from the terrible danger that threatens them. After the battle thou wilt not behold all the Kurus or all the Pandavas, Car-warriors slain by car-warriors, thou wilt behold the heroes of both parties reduced in numbers and strength. All the rulers of the earth, O best of kings, have been assembled together. Inflamed with wrath, they will certainly exterminate the population of the earth. Save, O king, the world. Let not the population of the earth be exterminated. O son of Kuru's race, if thou regainest thy natural disposition, the earth may continue to be peopled as now. Save, O king, these monarchs, who are all of pure descent, endued with modesty and liberality and piety, and connected with on another in bonds of relationship or alliance, from the terrible danger that threatens them. Abandoning wrath and enmity, O chastiser of foes, let these kings, embracing one another in peace, eating and drinking with one another, dressed in excellent robes and decked with garlands, and doing courtesies to one another, return to their respective homes. Let the affection thou hadst for the Pandavas be revived in thy bosom, and let it, O bull of Bharata's race, lead to the establishment of peace. Deprived of their father while they were infants, they were brought up by thee. Cherish them now as becomes thee, O bull of Bharata's race, as if they were thy own sons. It is thy duty to protect them. And especially it is so when they are distressed. O bull of Bharata's race, let not thy virtue and profit be both lost. Saluting and propitiating thee, the Pandavas have said unto thee, 'At thy command we have, with our followers, suffered great misery. For these twelve years have we lived in the woods, and for the thirteenth year have we lived incognito in an uninhabited part of the world. We broke not our pledge, firmly believing that our father also would abide by his. That we violated not our word is well-known to the Brahman as who were with us. And as we, O bull of the Bharata race, have abided by our promise, also do thou abide by thine. Long have we suffered the greatest misery, but let us now have our share of the kingdom. Fully conversant as thou art with virtue and profit, it behoveth thee to rescue us. Knowing that our obedience is due to thee, we have quietly undergone much misery. Behave thou then unto us like a father or brother. A preceptor should behave as a preceptor towards his disciples, and as disciples we are willing to behave as such towards thee, our preceptor. Act thou, therefore, towards us as a preceptor should. If we go wrong, it is the duty of our father to set us right. Therefore, set us on the way and tread thou also the excellent path of righteousness.' Those sons of thine, O bull of the Bharata race, have also said unto these kings assembled in the court these words, 'If the members of an assembly are conversant with morality, nothing improper should be permitted by them to happen. Where, in the presence of the virtuous members of an assembly, righteousness is sought to be overpowered by unrighteousness, and truth by the untruth, it is those members themselves that are vanquished and slain. When righteousness, pierced by unrighteousness, seeketh the protection of an assembly, if the arrow is not extracted, it is the members themselves that are pierced by that arrow. Indeed, in that case, righteousness slayeth the members of that assembly, like a river eating away the roots of the trees on its bank.' Judge now, O bull of the Bharata race. The Pandavas, with their eyes turned towards righteousness and reflecting on everything, are maintaining a calm attitude, and what they have said is consistent with truth and virtue and justice. O ruler of men, what canst thou say unto them, but that thou art willing to give them back their kingdom? Let these rulers of earth that are sitting here say (what the answer should be)! If it appears to thee that what I have said after reflecting well on virtue to be true, save all these Kshatriyas, O bull of the Bharata race, from the meshes of death. Effect peace, O chief of Bharata's race, and yield not to anger. Giving unto the Pandavas their just share of the paternal kingdom, enjoy thou then, with thy sons, O chastiser of foes, happiness and luxury, thy wishes being all crowned with success. Know that Yudhishthira always treadeth the path that is trod by the righteous. Thou knowest also, O king, what the behaviour of Yudhishthira is towards thee and thy sons. Although thou hadst sought to burn him to death and hadst exiled him from human habitation, yet he came back and once more repose confidence in thee. Again, didst thou with thy sons, banish him to Indraprastha? While there, he brought all the kings of the earth to subjection and yet looked up to thy face, O king, without seeking to disregard thee. Although he behaved in this way, yet Suvala's son, desirous of robbing him of his dominions and wealth and possessions, applied the very efficacious means of dice. Reduced to that condition and even beholding Krishna dragged into the assembly, Yudhishthira of immeasurable soul, did not yet swerve from the duties of a Kshatriya. As regards myself, I desire, O Bharata, thy good as also theirs. For the sake of virtue, of profit, of happiness, make peace, O king, and do not allow the Earth's population to be slaughtered, regarding evil as good and good as evil. Restrain thy sons, O monarch, who have from covetousness proceeded too far. As regards the sons of Pritha, they are equally ready to wait upon thee in dutiful service or to fight. That which, O chastiser of foes, seems to thee to be for thy good, do thou adopt!'

"Vaisampayana continued, 'All the rulers of earth there present highly applauded these words of Kesava within their hearts, but none of them ventured to say anything in the presence of Duryodhana.'

Section XCVI (96)

"Vaisampayana said, 'Hearing these words uttered by the high-souled Kesava, all the persons who sat in that assembly remained silent, their hair standing on their ends. And all the kings thought within themselves that there was no man who could dare reply to that speech. And seeing that all the kings sat silent, Jamadagni's son (addressing Duryodhana) then said these words in that assembly of Kurus, 'Listen confidingly to my words illustrated by an example, and seek thy own good if my speech recommends itself to thee. There was a king of yore named Dambhodbhava, who was the Head of the earth. It hath been heard by us that his sovereignty extended over the whole world. And that mighty car-warrior, rising every morning after the night had passed away, called the Brahmanas and the Kshatriyas unto himself and asked them, saying, 'Be he a Sudra, a Vaisya, a Kshatriya, or a Brahmana, is there any one who is superior or even equal to me in battle?' And uttering these words that king wandered over the earth, intoxicated with pride and thinking of nothing else. And it so happened that certain Brahmanas endued with high souls, conversant with the *Vedas*, and fearing nothing on earth, counselled the monarch, repeatedly boasting of his prowess, to curb his pride. But though forbidden by those Brahmanas to boast in that way, the king continued to ask the Brahmanas as before the same question day after day. And some high-souled Brahmanas then, endued with ascetic merit and acquainted with the proofs furnished by the *Vedas*, were inflamed with anger, and addressing that proud and boastful king intoxicated with prosperity, told him, 'There are two persons who are foremost of all men and who are always victorious in battle. Thou, O king, wilt by no means be equal to them if thou seekest an encounter with any one of them.' And thus addressed by them, the king asked those Brahmanas, saying, 'Where may those two heroes be found? In what race are they born? What feats have they achieved? And who are they? And the Brahmanas answered him, saying, 'It had been heard by us that those two persons are ascetics called Nara and Narayana. They have both taken their births in the race of man. Go and fight with them, O king. It is that illustrious pair, Nara and Narayana, who are now practising the severest of penances in some hidden region of the mountains of Gandhamadana.' Hearing those words of the Brahmanas, that king speedily mustered his large army consisting of six kinds of forces,[1] and unable to bear their reputation, marched to the spot where those unvanquished ascetics were, and arrived at the rugged and frightful mountains of Gandhamadana. He began to search after those *Rishis*, and at last, came upon them concealed within the woods. And beholding those two best of persons emaciated with hunger and thirst, their veins swollen and visible, and themselves much afflicted with cold winds, and the hot rays of the sun, he approached them, and touching their feet, enquired after their welfare. And the two *Rishis* received the king hospitably, with fruits and roots, and a seat and water. And they then enquired after the king's business, saying, '*Let it be done.*' And thus addressed by them, the king said unto them the same words that he was in the habit of saying unto all. And he said, 'The whole earth has been conquered by the might of my arms. All my foes have been slain. Desiring a battle with you both I have come to this mountain. Offer me this hospitality. I have been cherishing this wish from a long time.' Thus addressed, Nara and Narayana said, 'O best of kings, wrath and covetousness have no place in this retreat. How can a battle, therefore, be possible here? There are no weapons here, and nothing of unrighteousness and malice. Seek battle elsewhere. There are many Kshatriyas on earth.'

"Rama continued, 'Although thus addressed, the king still pressed them for giving him battle. The *Rishis*, however, continually soothed him and overlooked his importunity. King Dambhodbhava, still desirous of battle, repeatedly summoned those *Rishis* to fight. Nara, then, O Bharata, taking up a handful of grass-blades, said, 'Desirous of battle as thou art, come, O Kshatriya, and fight! Take up all thy arms, and array thy troops. I will curb thy eagerness for battle

1. Cars, elephants, horses, infantry, vehicles other than cars, and warriors fighting from the backs of camels.

hereafter!' Dambhodbhava then said, 'If, O ascetic, thou thinkest this weapon of thine fit to be used against us, I shall fight with thee though thou mayest use that weapon, for I have come hither desirous of fighting.' Saying this, Dambhodbhava with all his troops, desirous of slaying that ascetic, covered all sides with a shower of arrows. That ascetic, however, by means of those blades of grass, baffled all those terrible shafts of the king that were capable of mangling the bodies of hostile warriors. The invincible Rishi then let off towards the king his own terrible weapon made of grass-blades and which was incapable of being counteracted. And highly wonderful was that which happened, for that ascetic, incapable of missing his aim, pierced and cut off, by those grass-blades alone, the eyes and ears and noses of the hostile warriors, aided also by his power of illusion. And beholding the entire welkin whitened by those grass-blades, the king fell at the feet of the Rishi and said, 'Let me be blessed! Ever inclined to grant protection unto those that sought it, Nara then, O king, said unto that monarch, 'Be obedient to the Brahmanas and be virtuous. Never do so again. O king, O tiger among monarchs, a conqueror of hostile towns, a Kshatriya mindful of the duties of his own or, should never, within even his heart, be as thou art. Filled with pride, never insult anybody on any occasion, be inferior or superior to thee. Even such conduct would befit thee. Acquiring wisdom, abandoning covetousness and pride, controlling thy soul, restraining thy passions, practising forgiveness and humility, and becoming amiable, O king, go, and cherish thy subjects. Without ascertaining the strength and weakness of men, never insult any one under any circumstances. Blessed be thou, and with our leave, go hence, and never again behave in this way. At our command, enquire thou always of the Brahmanas as to what is for thy good! The king then, worshipping the feet of those two illustrious Rishis, returned to his city, and from that time began to practise righteousness. Great indeed, was that feat achieved of old by Nara. Narayana, again, became superior to Nara in consequence of many more qualities. Therefore, O king, besides such weapons as *Kakudika, Suka, Naka, Akshisantarjana, Santana, Nartana, Ghora,* and *Asyamodaka,* are placed on the string of that best of bows called Gandiva, go thou unto Dhananjaya, laying aside thy pride struck with these weapons, men always yield up their lives. Indeed, these weapons have other means corresponding with the eight passions, such as lust, wrath, covetousness, vanity, insolence, pride, malice, and selfishness. Struck with them, men are confounded, and move about frantically deprived of their senses. Under their influence, persons always sleep heavily, cut capers, vomit, pass urine and excreta, weep, and laugh incessantly. Indeed, that Arjuna is irresistible in fight, who hath for his friend Narayana—the Creator and Lord of all the worlds—fully acquainted with the course of everything. Who is there in the three worlds, O Bharata, who would venture to vanquish that hero—the Ape-bannered Jishnu—who hath no equal in battle? Countless are the virtues that reside in Partha. Janardana again, is superior to him. Thou art thyself well-acquainted with Dhananjaya, the son of Kunti. They that were Nara and Narayana in days of yore are now Arjuna and Kesava. Know then, O great king, who those brave and foremost of persons are. If thou believest in this and dost not mistrust me adopt thou a virtuous resolution and make peace with the sons of Pandu. If thou regardest this as thy good, *viz.*, that there should be no disunion in thy family, then make peace, O foremost of Bharata's race, and do not set thy heart upon battle. O thou, that are foremost of Kuru's line, the race to which thou belongest is highly regarded on earth. Let that regard continue to be paid to it. Blessed be thou, think of what conduces to thy own welfare.'"

Section XCVII (97)

"Vaisampayana said, 'Having listened to the words of Jamadagnya, the illustrious Rishi Kanwa also said these words unto Duryodhana in that assembly of the Kurus.'

"Kanwa said, 'Brahman, the Grandsire of the universe, is indestructible and eternal. Those illustrious Rishis, Nara and Narayana, are of the same character. Of all the sons of Aditi, Vishnu alone is eternal. He alone is unconquerable and indestructible, existing forever, the Lord of all, and the possessor of divine attributes. All others, such as the sun and the moon, earth and water, wind, fire and firmament, planets, and stars, are liable to destruction. All these, when the end of the universe cometh, take leave of the three worlds. They are destroyed and created again and again. Others also, such as men and animals and birds, and creatures belonging to other orders of living existence,—indeed, all that move on this world of men,—are endued with short lives. And as regards kings, all of them, having enjoyed great prosperity, reach, at last, the hour of destruction and are reborn in order to enjoy the fruits of good and evil deeds. It behoveth thee then to make peace with Yudhishthira. Let the Pandavas and the Kauravas both rule this earth. O Suyodhana, one should not think in this way, *viz.*, I am strong!—for O bull among men, it is seen that there are persons stronger than those generally regarded strong. O son of Kuru's race, physical strength is scarcely regarded as strength by those that are really strong. As regards the Pandavas, endued as they all are with prowess equal to that of the celestials, they are also regarded as strong. In this connection is cited an old story, as an example, the story, *viz.*, of Matali searching for a bridegroom upon whom to bestow his daughter. The king of the three worlds (Indra) had a charioteer, named Matali, whom he dearly loved. Unto him was born a daughter celebrated over the world for beauty. Endued with the celestial beauty, that daughter of Matali was known by the name of Gunakesi. And, indeed, in both loveliness and symmetry of bodily figure, she far excelled other members of her sex. Knowing that the time for giving her way had come, Matali with his wife became very anxious, thinking, O monarch, of what he was to do next. And he thought within himself, 'Alas, the birth of a daughter in the families of those that are well-behaved and high-born and possess reputation and humility of character, is always attended with evil results. Daughters, when born in respectable families, always endanger the honour of three families, *viz.*, their maternal and paternal families and the family into which they are adopted by marriage. Glancing in my mind's eye the worlds of gods and men, I have searched both, but no eligible bridegroom have I found.'

"Kanwa continued, 'And it so happened that amongst the gods, the *Daityas* and *Gandharvas*, men and numerous *Rishis*, none was regarded by Matali as an eligible husband for his daughter. And having held a consultation then in the night with his wife Sudharma, Matali set his heart upon making a journey to the world of the Nagas. And he thought within himself, 'Amongst both gods and men I have not found a husband fit, in respect of beauty, for my Gunakesi. Surely, one may be found amongst the *Nagas*.' And saying this, he took his wife's leave and sniffing the head of his daughter, Matali entered the nether regions.'"

Section XCVIII (98)

"Kanwa said, 'When Matali was wending his way, he saw the great Rishi Narada proceeding at his pleasure to pay a visit to Varuna (the god of the waters). And beholding Matali, Narada asked him, saying, 'Whither dost thou go? Is it, O charioteer, on any mission of thy own, or is it at Satakratu's command, that this journey of thine is undertaken?' Thus addressed on the way by Narada who was proceeding towards his destination, Matali duly informed Narada, of his mission. And the Rishi, informed of everything, then said unto Matali, 'We shall go together. As regards myself, it is to see the Lord of the waters that I am proceeding, having left the heavens, searching the nether regions, I shall tell you everything. After a good search there, we shall select a bridegroom, O Matali! And penetrating then into nether regions, that illustrious couple, Matali and Narada, beheld that Regent of the world—the Lord of the waters. And there Narada received worship due to a celestial Rishi, and Matali received that equal to what is offered to the great Indra. And both of them skilful in business, informed Varuna of their purpose, and obtaining his leave they began to wander in that region of the *Nagas*. And Narada who knew all the residents of the nether regions then began to describe in detail unto his companion all about the dwellers of the Naga world.'

"And Narada said, 'Thou hast, O charioteer, seen Varuna surrounded by his sons and grandsons. Behold the dominions of the Lord of the waters. It is delightful all round, and full of riches. The son, endued with great wisdom, of Varuna, the Lord of the Ocean, is even much distinguished for his conduct and disposition and for his holiness. Possessed of eyes like lotus leaves, this Pushkara is, indeed, Varuna's much-loved son, endued with great beauty and delightful to behold. He has been chosen by Soma's daughter as her husband. That daughter of Soma, equal in beauty unto a second Sree, is known by the name of Jyotsnakali. Indeed, it is said, that she had once before chosen the eldest and foremost of Aditi's son as her lord. Behold now, O companion of the Lord of the celestials, that abode, made entirely of gold, and full of the wine called *Varuni.* Indeed, having obtained that wine, the gods acquired their god-heads. These blazing weapons also of every kind that thou seest, belonged, O Matali, to the Daityas who have been deprived of their sovereignty. These weapons are incapable of deterioration, and when hurled at the foe always return into the hand that hurleth them. Obtained by the gods as the booty of war, they require considerable mental energy to be used against foes. Here dwelt in days of yore many tribes of Rakshasas and Daityas, possessed of many kinds of celestial weapons, but they were all vanquished by the gods. Behold, there, in Varuna's lake is that fire of blazing flames, and that discus of Vishnu surrounded by the lustrous splendour of mighty caloric. Behold, there lieth that knotty bow that was created for the destruction of the world. It is always protected with great vigilance by the gods, and it is from this bow that the one wielded by Arjuna hath taken its name. Endued with the strength of hundred thousand bows, the power it assumes at the hour of battle is indescribably great. It punishes all punishable wicked kings endued with the nature of Rakshasas. This fierce weapon was first created by Brahman, the utterer of the *Vedas.* The great preceptor Sukra hath said that this weapon is a terrible one in respect of all kings. Endued with great energy, it is held by the sons of the Lord of waters. Behold, there in the umbrella-room is the umbrella of the Lord of the waters. It droppeth refreshing showers like the clouds. The water dropped from this umbrella, though pure as the moon, is yet enveloped by such darkness that it cannot be seen by anybody. There, in these regions, O Matali, innumerable are the wonders to be seen. Your business, however, will suffer if we spend more time here. We will, therefore, leave this region soon.'"

Section XCIX (99)

"Narada continued, 'Here in the very centre of the world of the Nagas is situated the city known by the name of *Patalam*. Celebrated over all the universe, it is worshipped by the Daityas and the Danavas. Creatures inhabiting the earth, if brought hither by force of the water's current, shriek loudly, afflicted with fear. Here the fire known by the name of the *Asura-fire*[1] and which is fed by water, continually blazeth forth. Held fast by the fiat of the celestials, it moveth not, regarding itself as bound and confined. It was here that the gods, having first vanquished and slain their foes, quaffed the Amrita and deposited the residue. It is from this place that the waning and waxing of the moon are seen. It is here that son of Aditi, the Horse-headed (Vishnu), on the recurrence of every auspicious occasion, riseth, filling at such times the universe, otherwise called *Suvarna*,[2] with the sound of Vedic hymns and *Mantras*. And because all watery forms such as the Moon and others shower their water on the region, therefore hath this excellent region been called *Patala*.[3] It is from here that the celestial elephant Airavata, for the benefit of the universe, taketh up cool water in order to impart it to the clouds, and it is that water which Indra poureth down as rain. Here dwell diverse kinds of aquatic animals, of various shapes such as the *Timi* and others, which subsist on the rays of the moon. O charioteer, here are many kinds of creatures that die during the day, being pierced by the rays of the sun, but all of whom revive in the night, the reason being that the moon, rising here every day, laying those deceased creatures with Amrita by means of rays, that constitute his arms, resuscitate them by that touch. Deprived of their prosperity by Vasava, it is here that many sinful Danavas live confined, defeated by him and afflicted by Time. It was here that the

1. Called also the Badava fire.
2. The allusion is to the incarnation of Vishnu as the Horse-necked, Nilakantha explains *suvarnakhyam Jagat* to be *Veda prancha i.e.*, the whole Vedas with all their contents. According to him, the sense of the passage is that Vishnu in that form swells with his own voice the Vedic notes chanted by the Brahmanas.
3. *Patauti Jalam sravantiti patalam.* Thus Nilakantha.

Lord of creatures—that great Master of all created things—Mahadeva—had practised the severest of ascetic austerities for the benefit of all creatures. Here dwell many regenerate and great Rishis observant of vows called '*Go*' and emaciated with the recitation and study of the Vedas, and who, having suspended the vital air called *Prana*, have attained to heaven by force of their austerities. A man is said to adopt the vow called *Go*, when he sleepeth wherever he listeth, and when he subsisteth on anything that others place before him, and is clad with robes that others may supply. Here in the race of the celebrated elephant Supratika were born those best of elephants known by the names of Airavata, Vamana, Kumuda and Anjana, the first being the king of his tribe. Look, O Matali, if there be any bridegroom here, that is distinguished by the possession of superior merits, for then I will go to him for respectfully soliciting him to accept thy daughter. Behold, here lieth an egg in these waters, blazing with beauty. From the commencement of the creation it is here. It moveth not, nor doth it burst. I have never heard any body speaking of its birth or nature. Nobody knoweth who its father or mother is. It is said, O Matali, that when the end of the world cometh, mighty fire burst forth from within it, and spreading consumeth the three worlds with all their mobile and immobile objects.' Hearing those words of Narada, Matali answered him, saying, 'No one here seems to me to be eligible. Let us go hence, therefore, without delay!'"

Section C (100)

"Narada continued, 'Here is that spacious and celebrated city of cities, called Hiranyapura, belonging to the *Daityas* and *Danavas*, possessing a hundred diverse kinds of illusion. Here in these regions called Patala, it hath been built with great care by the divine artificer, and planned by the Danava Maya. Endued with great energy and heroism, many Danavas, having obtained boons (from Brahman) in days of old, lived here, exhibiting a thousand different kinds of illusion. They were incapable of being vanquished by Sakra or any other celestial, that is, by either Yama, or Varuna, or the Lord of treasures (Kuvera). Here dwell, O Matali, those Asuras called *Kalakhanjas* who sprang from Vishnu, and those Rakshasas also called Yatudhanas who sprang from the feet of Brahman. All of them are endued with frightful teeth, terrible impetus, the speed and prowess of the wind, and great energy depending on powers of illusion. Besides these, another class of Danavas called *Nivatakavachas*, who are invincible in battle, have their abode here. Thou knowest bow Sakra is unable to vanquish them. Many times, O Matali, thou, with thy son Gomukha, and the chief of the celestials and lord of Sachi, along with his son, had to retreat before them. Behold their homes, O Matali, that are all made of silver and gold, and well-adorned with decorations done according to the rules of art. All those mansions are decked with *lapis lazuli* and corals, and made effulgent with the lustre of the *Arkasphatika*, and the radiance of gem called *Vajrasara*. And many of those palatial residences seem, as if, they have been made of the shine of these gems called *Padmaragas*, or of bright marble, or of excellent wood. And they are also possessed of the radiance of the sun, or blazing fire. And all the edifices, adorned with gems and jewels, are very high and stand close to another. Of spacious proportions and great architectural beauty, it is impossible to say of what material these mansions are built or to describe their style of beauty. Indeed, they are exceedingly beautiful in consequence of their decorations. Behold these retreats of the Daityas for recreation and sport, these beds of theirs for sleep, these costly utensils of theirs set with precious stones, and these seats also for their use. Behold these hills of theirs, looking like clouds, those fountains of water, these trees also that move of their own will and that yield all fruits and flowers that one may ask. See, O Matali, if any bridegroom may be had here, acceptable to thee. If no one can be found, we shall, if thou likest, go hence to some other part of the world.' Thus addressed, Matali answered Narada, saying, 'O celestial Rishi, it behoveth me not to do anything that may be disagreeable to dwellers of heaven. The gods and the Danavas, though brothers, are ever at hostility with each other. How can I, therefore, make an alliance with those that are our enemies? Let us repair, therefore, to some other place. It behoveth me not to search among the Danavas. As regards thyself, I know thy heart is ever set on fomenting quarrels.'"

Section CI (101)

"Narada said, 'This region belongeth to the birds, all of whom possess excellent feathers. They all subsist on snakes. They never feel any fatigue in putting forth their prowess, or in making journeys, or in bearing burthens. This race, O charioteer, hath multiplied from the six sons of Garuda. They are Sumukha, Sunaman, Sunetra, Suvarchas, Suanch and that prince of birds called Suvala. Born of Kasyapa's line and enhancing the glory of Vinata's race, many winged creatures, the foremost of their species, have by begetting children founded and increased a thousand dynasties of birds, all endued with nobility of blood. All these creatures are endued with great prosperity, have the auspicious whirl called Sreevatsa, possess great wealth, and are inspired with great might. By their acts they may be said to belong to the Kshatriya order, but they are all without any compassion, subsisting as they do on snakes. They never attain to spiritual enlightenment in consequence of their preying on their kinsmen. I will now enumerate the chiefs by their names, listen to me, O Matali. This race is much regarded in consequence of the favour that is shown to it by Vishnu. They all worship Vishnu, and Vishnu is their protector. Vishnu always dwelleth in their hearts, and Vishnu is their great refuge. These then are their names— Suvarnachuda, Nagasin Daruna, Chandatundaka, Anala, Vaisalaksha, Kundalin, Pankajit, Vajraviskambha, Vainateya, Vamana, Vatavega, Disachakshu, Nimisha, Animisha, Trirava, Saptarava, Valmiki, Dipaka, Daityadwipa, Saridwipa, Sarasa, Padmaketana, Sumukha, Chitraketu, Chitravara, Anagha, Meshahrit, Kumuda, Daksha, Sarpanta, Somabhojana, Gurubhara, Kapota, Suryanetra, Chirantaka, Vishnudharman, Kumara, Parivarha, Hari, Suswara, Madhuparka, Hemavarna, Malaya, Matariswan, Nisakara and Divakara. These sons of Garuda that I name dwell in only a single province of this region. I have mentioned those only that have won distinction by might, fame and achievements. If thou likest none here, come, we will go hence, O Matali. I will take thee to another region where thou mayest find an eligible husband for thy daughter.'"

Section CII (102)

"Narada said, 'The region where we now are is called Rasatala and is the seventh stratum below the Earth. Here dwelleth Surabhi, the mother of all kine, she, who was born of the Amrita. She always yieldeth milk which is the essence of all the best things of the earth, and which, excellent as it is, and of one taste, springeth from the essence of the six different kinds of tastes (that are talked of). The faultless Surabhi herself sprang in days of old from the mouth of the Grandsire, gratified with drinking the Amrita and vomiting the best things. A single jet only of her milk, falling on the earth, created what is known as the sacred and the excellent "Milky Ocean." The verge of that ocean all round is always covered with white foam resembling a belt of flowers. Those best of ascetics that are known by the name of the Foam-drinkers dwell around this ocean, subsisting on that foam only. They are called Foam-drinkers because they live, O Matali, on nothing else save that foam. Engaged in the practice of the severest of austerities, the very gods are known to fear them. From her are born four other kine, O Matali, supporting the four quarters and therefore, they are called the supporters of the quarters (Dikpali). Born of Surabhi herself, she who supporteth the eastern quarter is called Surupa. She, who supporteth the southern quarter is called Hansika. That illustrious cow, O Matali, of universal form, who supporteth the western quarter ruled by Varuna is known by the name of Subhadra. The northern quarter comprising the region of virtue, and called after Kuvera the Lord of treasures, is supported by the cow named Sarva-kamadugha. The gods, uniting with the Asuras, and making the Mandara mountain their pole, churned the waters of the ocean and obtained the wine called Varuni, and (the Goddess of Prosperity and Grace called) Lakshmi, and Amrita, and that prince of steeds called Uchchhaisrava, and that best of gems called Kaustubha. Those waters, O Matali, that yielded these precious things had all been mixed with the milk of these four cows. As regards Surabhi, the milk she yielded becometh Swaha unto those that live on Swaha, Swadha unto those that live on Swadha, and Amrita unto those that live on Amrita. The couplet that was sung by the dwellers of Rasatala in day of old, is still heard to be recited in the world by the persons of learning. That couplet is this,—Neither in the region of the Nagas, nor in Swarga, nor in Vimana, nor in Tripishtapa is residence so happy as in Rasatala!'"

Section CIII (103)

"Narada said, 'This foremost of cities that thou beholdest and which resembles the Amaravati of the chief of the celestials himself, is known by the name of Bhogavati. It is ruled over by Vasuki, the king of the Nagas. That Shesha dwelleth here, who, in consequence of his ascetic austerities of the foremost order, is able to support this earth with all her vastness. His body is like that of a white mountain. He is decked in celestial ornaments. He hath a thousand heads. His tongues are blazing like flames of fire, and he is endued with great strength. There dwell in happiness innumerable Nagas—sons of Surasa—possessed of diverse forms, and decked on ornaments of diverse kinds, bearing the signs of gems, Swastika, circles and drinking vessels. All of them endued with great strength are by nature fierce. Some have a thousand heads, some five hundred, and some three. And some have two heads, and some five, and some have seven faces. And all of them are possessed of huge bodies that resemble the mountains stretching over the earth. Millions and tens of millions are they, in fact, uncountable, even as regards those of' them that belong to a single race. Listen, however, to me as I name a few of the more famous ones amongst them. They are Vasuki, Takshaka, Karkotaka, Dhanjaya, Kaliya, Nahusha, Aswatara, Vakyakunda, Mani, Apurana, Khaga, Vamana, Elapatra, Kukura, Kukuna, Aryaka, Nandaka, Kalasa, Potaka, Kalilasaka, Pinjaraka, Airavata, Sumanmukha, Dadhimukha, Sankha, Nanda, Upanandaka, Apta, Kotaraka, Sikhi, Nishthuraka, Tittiri, Hastibhadra, Kumuda, Maylapindaka, the two Padmas, Pundarika, Pushpa, Mudgaraparnaka, Karavira, Pitharaka, Samvritta, Vritta, Pindara, Vilwapatra, Mushikada, Sirishaka, Dilipa, Sankha-sirsha, Jyotishka, Aparajita, Kauravya, Dhritarashtra, Kuhara, Krisaka, Virajas, Dharana, Savahu, Mukhara, Jaya, Vidhira, Andha, Visundi, Virasa, and Sarasa. These and many others there are amongst the sons of Kasyapa. See O

Matali, if there is anybody here whom thou canst elect.'

"Kanwa continued, 'Matali, meanwhile, had been looking attentively at a person that stood by. And after Narada had ceased speaking, the celestial charioteer with gratified mind asked the *Rishi*, saying, 'Of what race is he the delighter—that comely youth of great radiance—who standeth before Aryaka of Kauravya's line? Who is his father, and who is his mother? Of what Naga's race is he? Indeed, of what line doth he stand as a high flag-staff? In consequence of his intelligence, his patience, his beauty, and his youth, my heart, O celestial Rishi, hath been attracted towards him. That youth will make the best of husbands for my Gunakesi.'

"Kanwa continued, 'Beholding Matali's gratification at seeing the Naga called Sumukha, Narada informed him of the nobility of his parentage and of his feats. And he said, 'Born in the race of Airavata this prince of Nagas is named Sumukha. He is the favourite grandson of Aryaka, and the daughter's son of Vamana. The father of this youth was, O Matali, the Naga called Chikura. Not long before was he slain by Vinata's Son.' Hearing this Matali became highly pleased, and addressing Narada, the charioteer said, 'This best of Nagas is, O sire, very acceptable to me for a son-in-law. Make an endeavour to secure him, for I am highly pleased at the thought of bestowing on this Naga, O muni, my dear daughter.'"

Section CIV (104)

"Narada then said, 'This one is the charioteer of the name of Matali. He is besides a dear friend of Sakra. Pure in conduct, he hath an excellent disposition and possesses numerous virtues. Endued with strength of mind, he hath great energy and great might. He is the friend, counsellor, and charioteer of Sakra. It has been seen in every battle that small is the difference that exists between him and Vasava as regards prowess and strength. In all the battles between the gods and *Asuras*, it is this Matali that driveth, by his mind alone, that ever-victorious and best of cars belonging to Indra, which is drawn by thousand steeds. Vanquished by his management of the steeds, the enemies of the gods are subjugated by Vasava by the use of his hands.

Defeated before-hand by Matali, the Asuras are subsequently slain by Indra. Matali hath an excellent daughter, who in beauty is unrivalled in the world. Truthful and possessed of every accomplishment, she is known by the name of Gunakesi. He was searching the three worlds for an eligible bridegroom. O thou that art possessed of the splendour of a celestial, thy grandson, Sumukha, hath become acceptable to him as a husband for his daughter. If O best of serpents, his proposal be acceptable to thee, quickly make up thy mind, O Aryaka, to take his daughter in gift for thy grandson. As Lakshmi in Vishnu's house, or Swaha in that of Agni so let the slender-waisted Gunakesi be a wife in thy race. Let Gunakesi, therefore be accepted by thee for thy grandson, like Sachi for Vasava who deserveth her. Although this youth hath lost his father, yet we choose him for his virtues, and for the respectability of Airavata and thy own. Indeed, it is in consequence of Sumukha's merits, his disposition, purity, self-restraint and other qualifications that Matali hath become himself desirous of giving away his daughter unto him. It behoveth thee, therefore, to honour Matali.'

"Kanwa continued, 'Thus addressed by Narada, Aryaka beholding his grandson elected as a bridegroom and remembering the death of his son was filled with delight and sorrow at the same time. And he then addressed Narada and said, 'How, O celestial Rishi, can I desire Gunakesi for a daughter-in-law'? It cannot be, O great *Rishi*, that thy words are not highly honoured by me, for who is there that would not desire an alliance with the friend of Indra? I hesitate, however, O great Muni, in consequence of the instability of the very cause that would not make that alliance lasting. O thou of great effulgence, the author of this youth, *viz.*, my son, hath been devoured by Garuda. We are afflicted with sorrow on that account. But worse still, O lord, Vinata's son, at the time of leaving these regions, said, 'After a month I will devour this Sumukha also. Surely, it will happen as he hath said, for we know with whom we have to deal. At these words, therefore, of Suparna we have become cheerless!'

"Kanwa continued, 'Matali then said unto Aryaka, 'I have formed a plan. This thy grandson is elected by me as my son-in-law, Let this *Naga* then, proceeding with me and Narada, come to the Lord of heaven the chief of the celestials, O best of *Nagas*. I shall then endeavour to place obstacles in the way of Suparna, and as a last resource, we will ascertain the period of life that hath been vouchsafed to Sumukha. Blessed be thou, O *Naga*, let Sumukha, therefore, come with me to the presence of the Lord of the celestials.' Saying this, they took Sumukha with them, and all the four, endued with great splendour, coming to heaven beheld Sakra the chief of the gods seated in all his glory. And it so happened that the illustrious Vishnu of four arms was also present there. Narada then represented the whole story about Matali and his choice.'

"Kanwa continued, 'Hearing all that Narada said, Vishnu directed Purandara, the Lord of the universe, saying, 'Let *Amrita* be given to this youth, and let him be made immortal like gods themselves. Let Matali, and Narada, and Sumukha, O Vasava, all attain their cherished wish through thy grace.' Purandara, however, reflecting on the prowess of Vinata's son, said unto Vishnu, 'Let *Amrita* be given unto him by thee.' Thus addressed, Vishnu said, 'Thou art the Lord of all mobile and immobile creatures. Who is there, O lord, that would refuse a gift that may be made by thee?' At these words Sakra gave unto that *Naga* length of days. The slayer of Vala and Vritra did not make him a drinker of *Amrita*. Sumukha, having obtained that boon, became *Sumukha*[1] (in reality) for his face was suffused with marks of joy. And having married Matali's daughter, he cheerfully returned home. And Narada and Aryaka also filled with delight at the success of their object, went away, after having worshipped the glorious chief of the celestials.'"

Section CV (105)

"Kanwa said, 'Meanwhile, O Bharata, the mighty Garuda heard what had happened, *viz.*, the bestowal by Sakra of length of days on the *Naga* Sumukha. And inflamed with great anger, that ranger of the firmament, Suparna, smiting the three worlds by the hurricane caused by the flappings of his wings, quickly came to Vasava. And Garuda said, 'O illustrious one, disregarding me why hast thou interfered

1. Literally, one that hath a beautiful or excellent face.

with my sustenance. Having granted me a boon of thy own will, why dost thou now withdraw it? The Supreme Lord of all creatures hath, from the beginning, ordained what my food is to be. Why dost thou then stand in the way of that divine decree? I had selected this great *Naga* and had fixed time, for O god, I had intended to offer the meat of his body, as sustenance to my numerous progeny. When he, therefore, hath obtained a boon from thee and hath become indestructible by me, how can I henceforth dare kill another of his species? Dost thou sport thus, O Vasava, as thou listest? I, however, shall have to die, as also the members of my family, and the servants whom I have engaged in my house. That will, I think, gratify thee, O Vasava! Indeed, O slayer of Vala and Vritra, I deserve all this, nay more, since being the lord of the three worlds in might. I yet consented to become the servant of another. O monarch of the three worlds, Vishnu, however, is not the only cause of my inferiority, for though, O Vasava, I am quite thy equal, yet the sovereignty of the three worlds resteth on thee, O chief of the celestials. Like thee, I also have a daughter of Daksha for my mother and Kasyapa for my father. Like thee, I also can, without any fatigue, bear the weight of the three worlds. I have strength that is immeasurable and incapable of being resisted by any creature. In the war with the Daityas I also achieved grand feats. Srutasri and Srutasena and Vivaswat, and Rochanamukha, and Prasrura, and Kalakaksha amongst the sons of Diti were slain by me. Perching yet on the flag-staff of thy younger brother's car I carefully protect it in battle, and sometimes also I bear that brother of thine on my back. It is, perhaps, for this that thou disregardest me. Who else in the universe is there that is capable of bearing such heavy burthens? Who is there that is stronger than myself? Superior though I am, I yet bear on my back this younger brother of thine with all his friends. When, however, disregarding me thou hast interfered with my foods, thou hast, O Vasava, inflicted disgrace on me, like this younger brother of thine that had hitherto been disgracing me by making me bear him on my back. As regards thyself, O Vishnu, amongst all those endued with prowess and strength that have been born of Aditi's womb, thou art superior in strength. Yet thee I bear without any fatigue, with only one of my feathers. Think coolly then, O brother, who amongst us is stronger?'

"Kanwa continued, 'Hearing the proud words of that bird foreshadowing danger the bearer of the discus, provoking Tarkshya still more, said unto him, 'Though so very weak, why dost thou, O Garuda, yet regard thyself strong, O oviparous creature, it ill behoveth thee to vaunt thus in our presence. The three worlds united together cannot bear the weight of my body. I myself bear my own weight and thine also. Come now, bear thou the weight of this one right arm of mine. If thou canst bear even this, thy boast would be regarded as reasonable. Saying this, the holy one placed his arms on Garuda's shoulders. Thereupon the latter fell down, afflicted with its weight, confounded, and deprived of his senses. And Garuda, felt that the weight of that one arm of Vishnu was as great as that of the entire Earth with her mountains. Endued with might infinitely greater, Vishnu, however, did not afflict him much. Indeed, Achyuta did not take his life. That ranger of the sky, afflicted then by that immense weight, gasped for breath, and began to cast off his feathers. With every limb weakened, and utterly confounded, Garuda was almost deprived of his senses. The winged offspring of Vinata then, thus confounded and almost deprived of his senses, and rendered utterly helpless, bowing unto Vishnu with bent bead, feebly addressed him, saying, 'O illustrious Lord, the essence of that strength which sustains the universe dwelleth in this body of thine. What wonder, therefore, that I should be crushed down to the earth by a single arm of thine, stretched out at thy pleasure. It behoveth thee, O divine Lord, to forgive this winged creature that perches on thy flag-staff—this fool intoxicated with pride of strength, but now rendered utterly helpless. Thy great strength, O divine Lord, was never known to me before. It was for this that I regarded my own might to be unequalled.' Thus addressed, the illustrious Vishnu became gratified, and addressing Garuda with affection, said, 'Let not thy behaviour be such again.' And saying this, Upendra threw Sumukha with the toe of his foot upon Garuda's breast. And from that time, O king, Garuda hath ever lived in friendship with that snake. It was thus, O king, that mighty and illustrious Garuda, the son of Vinata, afflicted by the might of Vishnu, was cured of his pride.'

"Kanwa continued, 'In the same way, O son of Gandhari, thou livest, O son, as long as thou approachest not the heroic sons of Pandu in battle. Who is there whom Bhima, that foremost of smiters, that mighty son of Vayu and Dhananjaya, the son of Indra, cannot slay in battle? Vishnu himself, and Vayu and Dharma, and the Aswins,—these gods are thy enemies. Let alone an encounter with them, thou art not competent even to look at them on the field. Therefore, O prince, do not set thy heart upon war; let peace be made through the agency of Vasudeva. It behoveth thee to save thy race thus. This great ascetic Narada witnessed with his own eyes the incident (I have related to thee) which shows the greatness of Vishnu, and know that this Krishna is that bearer of the discus and the mace!'

"Vaisampayana continued, 'Hearing these words of the *Rishi*, Duryodhana contracted his eye-brows and began to breathe heavily. And casting his eyes then on Radha's son, he burst out into a loud laughter. And setting at naught those words of the *Rishi*, that wicked wretch began to slap his thigh that resembled the trunk of an elephant. And addressing the *Rishi*, he said, 'I am, O great *Rishi*, precisely what the Creator hath made me. What is to be, must be. What also hath been ordained in my case must happen, I cannot act otherwise. What can these senseless declamations, therefore, avail?'"

Section CVI (106)

"Janamejaya said, 'Interminably wedded to evil, blinded by avarice, addicted to wicked courses, resolved upon bringing destruction on his head, inspiring grief in the hearts of kinsmen, enhancing the woes of friends, afflicting all his well-wishers, augmenting the joys of foes, and treading the wrong path, why did not his friends seek to restrain him, and why also did not that great friend (of Kuru's race), the holy one; with tranquil soul, or the Grandsire tell him anything from affection?'

"Vaisampayana said, 'Yes, the holy one did speak. Bhishma also spoke what was beneficial. And Narada too said much. Listen to all that these said.'

"Vaisampayana continued, 'Narada said, 'Persons that listen to the counsels of friends are rare. Friends again are rare that offer beneficial counsels, for a friend (in need of counsel) is never there where a friend (offering counsel) is. O son of Kuru's race, I think, the word of friends ought to be listened to. Obstinacy ought to be avoided; for it is fraught with great evil. In this connection is cited an old story regarding Galava's having met with disgrace through obstinacy. In ancient times, in order to test Viswamitra, who was then engaged in ascetic austerities Dharma personally came to him, having assumed the form of the *Rishi*, Vasishtha. Thus assuming, O Bharata, the form of the one of the seven *Rishis*, and feigning himself hungry and desirous of eating, he came, O king, to the hermitage of Kausika. Thereupon, Viswamitra struck with awe, began to cook *Charu* (which was a preparation of rice and milk). And in consequence of the care he took in preparing that excellent food, he could not properly wait upon his guest. And it was not till after the guest had dined on the food offered by the other hermits that Viswamitra succeeded in approaching him with the *Charu* he had cooked and which was still steaming. 'I have already dined; wait here,'— were the words that the holy one said. And having said that the holy one went away. And thereupon, the illustrious Viswamitra, O king, waited there. And bearing that food on his head and holding it with his arms, that ascetic of rigid vow stood in his hermitage, still as a post, subsisting on air. And as he stood there, an ascetic of the name of Galava, from motives of respect and reverence and from affection and desire of doing what was agreeable, began to wait upon him. And after a hundred years had passed away, Dharma, again assuming the form of Vasishtha, came to Kausika from desire of eating. And beholding the great *Rishi* Viswamitra, who was endued with high wisdom, standing there with that food on his head, himself subsisting all the while on air, Dharma accepted that food which was still warm and fresh. And having eaten that food, the god said,— *Gratified am I, O regenerate Rishi.* And saying this, he went away. And at those words of Dharma, Viswamitra divested of *Kshatriyahood* because endued with the status of a *Brahmana* and was filled with delight.[1] And pleased as he was with the services and

1. The story of Viswamitra's promotion to the status of a Brahmana is

devotion of his discipline, the ascetic Galava, Viswamitra, addressed him and said, 'With my leave, O Galava, go whithersoever thou mayest wish.' Thus commanded by his preceptor, Galava, highly pleased, said in a sweet voice unto Viswamitra of great effulgence, 'What final gift shall I make thee in consequence of thy services as preceptor? O giver of honours, it is in consequence of the (final) present that a sacrifice becometh successful. The giver of such gifts obtains emancipation. Indeed, these gifts constitute the fruit (that one enjoys in heaven). They are regarded as peace and tranquillity personified. What, therefore, shall I procure for my preceptor? Oh, let that be said.' The illustrious Viswamitra knew that he had really been conquered by Galava by means of the latter's services, and the *Rishi*, therefore, sought to dismiss him by repeatedly saying, 'Go, Go.' But thou repeatedly commanded by Viswamitra to go away, Galava still addressed him saying, 'What shall I give?' And seeing this obstinacy on the part of ascetic Galava, Viswamitra felt a slight rise of anger and

---

highly characteristic. Engaged in a dispute with the Brahmana Rishi Vasishtha, Viswamitra who was a Kshatriya king (the son of Kusika) found, by bitter experience, that Kshatriya energy and might backed by the whole science of arms, availed nothing against a Brahmana's might, for Vasishtha by his ascetic powers created myriads and myriads of fierce troops who inflicted a signal defeat on the great Kshatriya king. Baffled thus, Viswamitra retired to the breast of Himavat and paid court to Siva. The great God appeared and Viswamitra begged him for the mastery of the whole science of weapons. The god granted his prayer. Viswamitra then came back and sought an encounter with Vasishtha, but the latter by the aid only of his Brahmanical (bamboo) stick baffled the fiercest weapons of Viswamitra, of even celestial efficacy. Humiliated and disgraced, Viswamitra set his heart on becoming a Brahmana. He gave up his kingdom and retiring into the woods with his queen began to practise to severest austerities. After the expiration of ten thousand years, the Creator Brahma appeared before him and addressed him as a royal Rishi. Dispirited at this, he devoted himself to still severer austerities. At last, at Dharma's command (as here referred to) the great Kshatriya king became a Brahmana. This, in the Hindu scriptures, is the sole instance of a person belonging to a lower order becoming a Brahmana by ascetic austerities.

at last said, 'Give me eight hundred steeds, every one of which should be as white as the rays of the moon, and every one of which should have one ear black. Go now, O Galava, and tarry not.'"

Section CVII (107)

"Narada said, 'Thus addressed by Viswamitra of great intelligence Galava was filled with such anxiety that he could not sit or lie down, or take his food. A prey to anxiety and regret, lamenting bitterly, and burning with remorse, Galava grew pale, and was reduced to a skeleton. And smitten with sorrow, O Suyodhana, he indulged in these lamentations, 'Where shall I find affluent friends? Where shall I find money? Have I any savings? Where shall I find eight hundred steeds of lunar whiteness? What pleasure can I have in eating? What happiness can be mine in objects of enjoyment? The very love of life is extinct in me. What need have I of life? Repairing to the other shore of the great ocean, or to the furthest verge of the earth, I will relinquish my life. Of what use can life be to me? What happiness, without severe exertion, can be his who is poor, unsuccessful, deprived of all the good things of life, and burthened with debt? Death is preferable to life as regards him who having enjoyed the wealth of friends through their friendship for himself, is unable to return their favour. The religious acts of that man lose their efficacy who having promised to do an act fails to perform it and is thus stained with falsehood. One that is stained by falsehood cannot have beauty, or children, or power, or influence. How, therefore, can such a one attain to a blissful state? What ungrateful man hath ever earned fame? Where, indeed, is his place, and where his happiness? An ungrateful person can never win esteem and affection. Salvation also can never be his. He that is destitute of wealth is a wretch that can scarcely be said to live. Such a wretch cannot support his kinsmen and friends. Unable to make any return for the benefits he receiveth, he certainly meeteth with destruction. Even I am that wretch, ungrateful, destitute of resources, and stained with falsehood, for having obtained my objects from my preceptor, I am unable to do his bidding. Having first endeavoured to the utmost, I will lay down my life. Before this, I never craved for any thing from the very gods. The deities regard me for this in sacrificial place. I will go and seek the protection of Vishnu, the divine Lord of the three worlds, of Krishna the great refuge of all who are blessed with protection. Bowing down unto him, I desire to see that highest of all ascetics, the Eternal Krishna from whom flow all those possessions and enjoyments that are owned by both gods and *Asuras*.' And while Galava was thus lamenting, his friend Garuda, the son of Vinata, appeared in his sight. And Garuda, from desire of doing him good, cheerfully addressed him, saying, 'Thou art a dear friend, of mine. It is the duty of a friend, when himself in prosperity, to look to the accomplishment of the wishes of his friends. The prosperity that I have, O Brahmana, is constituted by Vasava's younger brother Vishnu. Before this, I spoke to him on thy behalf and he hath been pleased to grant my wishes. Come now, we will go together. I will bear thee comfortably to the other shore of the ocean, or to the furthest extremity of the earth. Come, O Galava, do not tarry.'"

Section CVIII (108)

"Garuda said, 'O Galava, commanded I have been by God, who is the cause of all knowledge. I ask thee, towards which quarter shall I first take thee to see what lie there? The eastern, the southern, the western, or the northern, towards which, O best of regenerate persons, shall I go, O Galava? That quarter towards which Surya the illuminator of the universe first riseth; where, at eve, the *Sadhyas* engage in their ascetic austerities; where that Intelligence, which pervades the whole universe first springeth; where the two eyes of Dharma, as well as he himself, are stationed; where the clarified butter first poured in sacrifice subsequently flowed all around; that quarter, O best of all regenerate persons, is the gate of Day and Time. There the daughters of Daksha, in primeval times, gave birth to their children. There the sons of Kasyapa first multiplied. That quarter is the source of all the prosperity of the gods, for it was there that Sakra was first anointed as the king of the celestials. It was there, O regenerate Rishi, that both Indra and the gods underwent their ascetic penances. It is for this, O Brahmana, that this quarter is called *Purva* (the first). And because in the earliest of times this quarter was overspread by the *Suras*, it is for this that it is called Purva.

The gods, desirous of prosperity, performed all their religious ceremonies here. It was here that the divine Creator of the universe first sang the *Vedas*. It was here that the *Gayatri* was first preached by Surya unto the reciters of that sacred hymn. It was here, O best of Brahmanas, that the *Yajurvedas* were delivered by Surya (unto Yajnavalkya). It was here that the *Soma* juice, sanctified by boons, was first drunk in sacrifices by Suras. It was here that the *Homa*-fires, (gratified by mantras), first drank articles of cognate origin.[1] It was here that Varuna first repaired to the nether regions, and attained to all his prosperity. It was here, O bull among the twice-born, that the birth, growth, and death of the ancient Vasishtha took place. Here first grew the hundred different branches of *Om*![2] It was here that the smoke- eating *Munis* are the smoke of sacrificial fires. It was in that region that myriads of boars and other animals were killed by Sakra and offered as sacrificial portions unto the gods. It is here that the thousand-rayed sun, arising, consumeth, out of ire, all those that are wicked and ungrateful among men and the Asuras. This is the gate of the three worlds. This is the path of heaven and felicity. This quarter is called Purva (east). We will go hither, if it pleaseth thee. I shall always do what is agreeable to him who is my friend. Tell me, O Galava, if any other quarter pleaseth thee, for we will then go there. Listen now to what I say of another quarter.'"

Section CIX (109)

"Garuda continued, 'In days of yore, Vivaswat, having performed a sacrifice, gave this quarter away as a present (*Dakshina*) unto his preceptor, And it is for this that this region is known by the name of

1. These articles of cognate origin are clarified butter, milk, and other things used as libations in sacrifices.
2. i.e., the subdivisions of the *Pranava*, the mysterious *Mantra*, which is the beginning of everything, were first promulgated here. Nilakantha supposes this to refer to the origin of the *Vedas*, the *Upanishads*, and the various branches of the Srutis and the Smritis.

Dakshina (south). It is here that the Pitris of the three worlds have their habitation. And, O Brahmana, it is said that a class of celestials subsisting upon smoke alone also live there. Those celestials also that go by the name of *Viswedevas* always dwell in this region along with the *Pitris*. Worshipped in sacrifices in all the worlds, they are equal sharers with the *Pitris*. This quarter is called the second door of Yama. It is here that the periods allotted to men are calculated in *Trutis and Lavas*.[1] In this region always dwell the celestial Rishis, the *Pitriloka Rishis*, and the royal Rishis, in great happiness. Here are religion and truth. It is here that the acts (of persons) exhibit their fruits. This region, O best of the twice-born, is the goal of the acts of the dead. It is this region, O best of regenerate persons, whither all must repair. And as creatures are all overwhelmed by darkness, they cannot, therefore, come hither in bliss. Here, O bull among regenerate persons, are many thousands of Malevolent Rakshasas in order to be seen by the sinful. Here, O Brahmana, in the bowers on the breast of *Mandara* and in the abodes of regenerate Rishis, the Gandharvas chant psalms, stealing away both the heart and the intellect. It was here that *Raivata* (a Daitya), hearing the *Sama* hymns sung in a sweet voice, retired to the woods, leaving his wife and friends and kingdom. In this region, O Brahmana, Manu and Yavakrita's son together set a limit which *Surya* can never overstep. It was here that the illustrious descendant of Pulastya, Ravana, the king of the Rakshasas, undergoing ascetic austerities, solicited (the boon of) immortality from the gods. It was here that (the Asura) Vritra, in consequence of his wicked conduct, incurred the enmity of Sakra. It is in this region that lives of diverse forms all come and are then dissociated into their five (constituent) elements. It is in this region, O Galava, that men of wicked deeds rot (in tortures). It is here that the river *Vaitarani* flows, filled with the bodies of persons condemned to hell. Arrived here, persons attain to the extremes of happiness and misery. Reaching this region, the sun droppeth sweet waters and thence proceeding again to the direction named after (Vasishtha), once more droppeth dew. It was here that I once obtained (for food), a prodigious elephant

1. Small divisions of time.

battling with an enormous tortoise. It was here that the great sage *Chakradhanu* took his birth from Surya. That divine sage afterwards came to be known by the name of Kapila, and it was by him that the (sixty thousand) sons of Sagara were afflicted. It was here that a class of Brahmanas named Sivas, fully mastering the Vedas, became crowned with (ascetic) success. Having studied all the Vedas they at last attained eternal salvation. In this region is the city called Bhogavati that is ruled by Vasuki, by the Naga Takshaka and also by Airavata. They that have to journey hither (after death) encounter here a thick gloom. And so thick is that gloom that it cannot be penetrated by either the Sun himself or by Agni. Worthy of worship as thou art, even thou shalt have to pass this road. Tell me now if thou wishest to sojourn towards this direction. Else, I listen to an account of the western direction.'"

Section CX (110)

"Garuda said, 'This quarter is the favourite one of king Varuna, the ruler of the ocean. Indeed, the lord of the waters had his origin here, and it is hither that sovereignty lieth. And since it is here that towards the day's end (paschat) the sun dismisseth his rays that this quarter, O best of the twice-born ones, is called the west (paschima). For ruling over all aquatic creatures and for the protection of the water themselves, illustrious and divine Kasyapa installed Varuna here (as the king of this region). Quaffing all the six juices of Varuna, the moon, the dispeller of darkness, becometh young again in the beginning of the fortnight. It was in the quarter, O Brahmana, that the Daityas were routed and bound fast by the wind-god. And afflicted by a mighty tempest, and breathing hard (as they fled), they at last laid themselves down in this region to sleep (the sleep that knows no waking). Hither is that mountain called Asta which is the cause of the evening twilight, and which (daily) receiveth the sun lovingly turning towards it. It is from this quarter that both Night and Sleep, issuing out at the close of day, spread themselves, as if, for robbing all living creatures of half their allotted periods of life. It was here that Sakra, beholding (his stepmother) the goddess Diti lying asleep in a state of pregnancy, cut off the foetus (into forty-nine parts), whence sprang the (forty-nine) Maruts. It is towards this direction that the roots of Himavat stretch towards the eternal Mandara (sunk in the ocean). By journeying for even a thousand years one cannot attain to the end of those roots. It is in this region that Surabhi (the mother of cows), repairing to the shores of the extensive lake, adorned with golden lotuses, poureth forth her milk. Here in the midst of the ocean is seen the headless trunk of the illustrious Swarbhanu (Rahu) who is always bent upon devouring both sun and the moon. Here is heard the loud chanting of the Vedas by Suvarnasiras, who is invincible and of immeasurable energy, and whose hair is eternally green. It is in this region that the daughter of Muni Harimedhas remained transfixed in the welkin in consequence of Surya's injunction couched in the words—Stop, Stop. Here, O Galava, wind, and fire, and earth, and water, are all free, both day and night, from their painful sensations. It is from this region that the sun's course begins to deviate from the straight path, and it is in this direction that all the luminous bodies (the constellations) enter the solar sphere. And having moved for twenty-eight nights with the sun, they come out of the sun's course to move in accompaniment with the moon. It is in this region that the rivers which always feed the ocean have their sources. Here, in the abode of Varuna, are the waters of the three worlds. In this region is situate the abode of Anarta, the prince of snakes. And here is the unrivalled abode also of Vishnu, who is without beginning and without end. In this region is also situate the abode of the great Rishi Kasyapa, the son of Maricha. The western quarter is thus narrated to thee in course of telling thee of the different points. Tell me now, O Galava, towards which side, O best of regenerate persons, shall we go?'"

Section CXI (111)

"Garuda said, 'O Brahmanas, since this quarter saveth from sin, and since one attaineth to salvation here, it is for this saying (Uttarana) power that it is called the north (uttara). And, O Galava, because the abode of all the treasures of the north stretches in a line towards the east and the west, therefore is the north sometimes called the central region (madhyama).

And, O bull among the twice-born, in this region that is superior to all, none can live that is unamiable, or of unbridled passions, or unrighteous. Hither, in the asylum, known by the name of Vadari, eternally dwell Krishna who is Narayana's self, and Jishnu that most exalted, of all male beings, and Brahman (the Creator). Hither, on the breast of Himavat always dwelleth Maheswara endued with the effulgence of the fire that blazeth up at the end of the Yuga. As Purusha, he sporteth here with Prakriti (the universal mother). Except by Nara and Narayana, he is incapable of being seen by the diverse classes of Munis, the gods with Vasava at their head, the Gandharvas, the Yakshas, and the Siddhas. Though invested with Maya, him the eternal Vishnu alone, of a thousand heads and thousand legs, can behold. It was in this region that Chandramas (the moon) was installed into the sovereignty of the entire regenerate order. It was in this region, O thou foremost of all acquainted with Brahma, that Mahadeva first receiving her on his head, afterwards let (the sacred stream) Ganga fall from the heavens to the world of men. It was here that the Goddess (Uma) underwent her ascetic austerities from her desire of obtaining Maheswara (as her Lord). It was in this region that Kama, the wrath (of Siva), Himavat, and Uma, all together shone brilliantly. It was here, on the breast of Kailasa, O Galava, that Kuvera, was installed on the sovereignty of the Rakshasas, the Yakshas, and the Gandharvas. It is in this region that (Kuvera's gardens called) Chitraratha lie, and it is here that the asylum of (the Munis called the) Vaikhanasas is situate. It is here, O bull among the twice-born, that the celestial stream called Mandakini, and the mountain Mandara are to be seen. It is here that the gardens called Saugandhi-kanaka are always guarded by the Rakshasas. Here are many plains covered with grassy verdure, as also the plantain forest, and those celestial trees called the Sautanakas. It is in this, region, O Galava, that the Siddhas, with souls ever under control and always sporting at will, have their fit abodes, abounding with every object of enjoyment. It is here that the seven Rishis with Arundhati may be seen. It is here that the constellation Swati is to be seen, and it is here that it first rises to the view. It is in this region that the Grandsire Brahman dwelleth in the vicinity of Yajna (sacrifice embodied). It is in this quarter that the sun, the moon, and the other luminaries are seen to revolve regularly.

It is in this region, O foremost of Brahmanas, that those illustrious and truth-speaking Munis called by the name of Dharma, guard the source of the Ganges. The origin and physical features and ascetic penances of these Munis are not known to all. The thousand dishes they use for serving the food offered in hospitality and the edibles also they create at will, are all a mystery, The man, O Galava, that passeth beyond the point guarded by these Munis, is certain, O foremost of Brahmanas, to meet with destruction. None else, O bull among Brahmanas, save the divine Narayana, and the eternal Nara called also Jishnu, succeeded in passing beyond the point so guarded. It is in this region that the mountains of Kailasa lie, the abode of Ailavila (Kuvera). It is here that the ten Apsaras known by the name of Vidyutprabha had their origin. In covering, O Brahmana, the three worlds with three steps in the sacrifice of Vali (the Asura king), Vishnu had covered this whole northern region; and, accordingly, there is a spot here called Vishnupada. And it is so called after the footprint of Vishnu caused on that occasion. Here, in this quarter, at a place called Usiravija, by the side of the golden lake, king Marutta performed, O foremost of Brahmanas, a sacrifice. It is here that the brilliant and shining gold mines of Himavat exhibit themselves to the illustrious and regenerate Rishi Jimuta. And Jimuta gave away the whole of that wealth to the Brahmanas. And having given it away, that great Rishi solicited them to call it after his own name. And hence that wealth is known by the name of the Jaimuta gold. Here, in this region, O bull among Bharatas, the regents of the worlds, O Galava, every morning and evening, proclaim, 'What business of what person shall we do?' It is for these, O foremost of Brahmanas, and other incidents, that the northern region is superior to all quarters. And because this region is superior (uttara) to all, therefore, it is called the north (uttara). The four regions have thus, O sire, been, one after another described to thee in details. Towards which quarter then dost thou desire to go? I am ready, O foremost of Brahmanas, to show thee all the quarters of the earth!'"

Section CXII (112)

"Galava said, 'O Garuda, O slayer of foremost snakes, O thou of beautiful feathers, O son of Vinata, carry me, O Tarkhya, to the east where the two eyes of Dharma are first opened. O, take me to the east which thou hast first described, and whither, thou hast said, the gods are always present. Thou hast said that thither both truth and virtue reside. I desire to meet all the gods. Therefore, O younger brother of Aruna, take me thither, so that I may behold the gods.'

"Narada continued, 'Thus addressed, the son of Vinata replied unto that Brahmana saying, 'Mount thou on my back.' And thereupon, the Muni Galava rode on the back of Garuda. And Galava said, 'Thy beauty, O devourer of snakes, as thou proceedest, seemeth to be like that of the sun himself in the morning, that maker of the day endued with a thousand rays. And, O ranger of the skies, thy speed is so great that the very trees, broken by the storm caused by the flapping of thy wings, seem to pursue thee in the course. Thou seemest, O tenant of the welkin, to drag by the storm caused by the wings, the very Earth with all the waters of her oceans, and with all her mountains, woods and forests. Indeed, the tempest caused by the motion of thy wings seems to continually raise into mid air the waters of the sea, with all their fishes and snakes and crocodiles. I see fishes possessed of similar faces, and *Timis and Timingilas* and snakes endued with human faces, all crushed by the tempest raised by thy wings. My ears are deafened by the roar of the deep. So stunned am I that I can neither hear nor see anything. Indeed, I have forgotten my own purpose. Slacken thy speed, O ranger of the sky, remembering the risk to a Brahmana's life. O sire, neither the sun, nor the cardinal points, nor the welkin itself, is any longer perceptible to me. I see only a thick gloom around me. The body is no longer visible to me. I see only thy two eyes, O oviparous being, resembling two radiant gems. I cannot see either thy body or my own. At every step, I behold sparks of fire emitted from thy frame. Stop without delay these sparks of fire and extinguish the dazzling radiance of thy eyes. O son of Vinata, slacken this exceeding speed of thy course. O devourer of snakes, I have no business to go with thee. Desist, O blessed one, I am unable to bear this speed of thine. I have promised to give my preceptor eight hundred white steeds of lunar effulgence, each having one ear black in hue. I see no way, O oviparous being, of fulfilling my pledge. There is but one way that I can see, and that is to lay down my own life. I have no wealth of my own, nor any wealthy friend, nor can wealth, however immense, procure the accomplishment of my object.'

"Narada continued, 'Unto Galava uttering these and many other words of entreaty and sorrow, the son of Vinata, without slackening his speed, laughingly replied, saying, 'Thou hast little wisdom, O regenerate Rishi, since thou wishest to put an end to thy own life. Death can never be brought about by one's effort. Indeed, Death is God himself. Why didst thou not, before this, inform me of thy purpose? There are excellent means by which all this may be accomplished. Here is this mountain called Rishabha on the seaside. Resting here for some time and refreshing ourselves with food, I will, O Galava, return.'"

Section CXIII (113)

"Narada said, 'Alighting then on the peak of the Rishabha, the Brahmana and the Bird beheld a Brahmana lady of the name of Sandili, engaged there on ascetic penances. And Galava and Garuda both saluted her by bending their heads, and worshipped her. And thereupon, the lady enquired after their welfare and gave them seats. And having taken their seats, both of them took the cooked food the lady offered them, after having first dedicated it to the gods with *Mantras*. And having taken that food, they laid themselves down on the ground and fell into a profound sleep. And Garuda, from desire of leaving that place, upon awakening, found that his wings, had fallen off. Indeed, he had become like a ball of flesh, with only his head and legs. And beholding him come to that plight, Galava sorrowfully enquired, saying, 'What is this condition that has overtaken thee as the consequence of thy sojourn here? Alas, how long shall we have to reside here? Hadst thou harboured any evil and sinful thought in thy mind? It cannot, I am sure, be any trivial sin of which thou hast been guilty.' Thus addressed, Garuda replied unto the Brahmana, saying, 'Indeed, O regenerate one, I entertained the thought of carrying away this lady crowned with ascetic success from this spot to where the Creator himself, the divine Mahadeva, the eternal Vishnu, and both Virtue and Sacrifice personified, live together, for as I thought this lady should live there. I shall now, from desire of doing myself good, prostrate myself before this holy lady, and pray unto her, saying,—with a heart full of pity, I had, indeed, entertained such a thought. Whether I acted rightly or wrongly, even this was the wish, evidently against thy own, that was cherished by me from my respect for thee. It behoveth thee, therefore, to grant me forgiveness, from the nobility of thy heart.' That lady became gratified with that prince of birds and that bull of Brahmanas. And addressing Garuda, she said, 'Fear not, O thou of beautiful feathers. Resume thy wings, and cast off thy fears. I was contempted by thee, but know that I do not pardon contempt. That sinful being who entertains contempt for me, would speedily fall away from all blissful regions. Without a single inauspicious indication about me, and perfectly blameless as I am, I have, in consequence of the purity of my conduct, attained to high ascetic success. Purity of conduct beareth virtue as its fruit. Purity of conduct beareth wealth as its fruit. It is purity of conduct that bringeth on prosperity. And it is purity of conduct that driveth away all inauspicious indications. Go thou, O blessed prince of birds, whithersoever thou wishest, from this place. Never entertain contempt for me, and take care that thou dost not contempt women that may even be truly blamable. Thou shalt again be, as before, invested with both strength and energy.' At these words of that lady Garuda had his wings again, and they became even stronger than before. And then with Sandili's leave, Garuda with Galava on his back took his departure. But they failed to find the kind of steeds they were in search of. And it so happened that Viswamitra met Galava on the way. And thereupon, that foremost of speakers addressed Galava in the presence of Vinata's son and said, 'O regenerate one, the time is already come when thou shouldst give me the wealth thou hadst promised me of thy own accord. I do not know what thou mayst. I have waited so long. I will wait for some time more. Seek thou the way by which thou mayst succeed (in the matter of thy promise).' Hearing these words, Garuda addressed cheerless Galava who was overwhelmed with sorrow, saying, 'What Viswamitra said unto thee before hath now been repeated in my presence. Come, therefore, O Galava, best of Brahmanas, we will deliberate on the matter. Without giving thy preceptor the whole of the wealth (promised by thee), thou canst not even sit down.' "

Section CXIV (114)

"Narada said, 'Garuda then, that foremost of winged beings, addressed the cheerless Galava and said, 'Because it is created by Agni, in the bowels of the earth and augmented by Vayu, and because also the earth itself is said to be **Hiranmaya**, therefore, is wealth called *Hiranya.* And because wealth supports the world and sustains life, therefore, is it called *Dhana.* It is for serving these ends that *Dhana* (wealth) exists from the beginning in the three worlds. On that Friday, when either of the two constellations—the *Purvabhadra* or the *Uttarabhadra*—is ascendant, Agni, creating wealth by a flat of his will, bestoweth it on mankind for the increase of Kuvera's stock. The wealth that is embowelled in the Earth is guarded by the deities called the *Ajaikapats* and the *Ahivradnas,* and also by Kuvera. Exceedingly difficult of attainment, that wealth, therefore, O bull among Brahmanas, is rarely attained. Without wealth there is no chance of thy acquisition of the promised steeds. Beg thou, therefore, of some king born in the race of some royal sage, who may, without oppressing his subjects, crown our suit with success. There is a king born in the lunar race, that is my friend. We shall go to him, for he, amongst all on Earth, hath great wealth. That royal sage is known by the name of Yayati, and he is the son of Nahusha. His prowess is incapable of being baffled. Solicited by thee in person, and urged by me, he will give what we seek, for he hath immense wealth, equal unto what belongeth to Kuvera, the lord of treasures. Even thus, by accepting a gift, O learned one, pay off thy debt to thy preceptor.' Talking thus, and thinking upon what was best to be done, Garuda and Galava together went to king Yayati, who was then in his capital called Pratisthana. The king received them hospitably and gave them excellent *Arghya* and water to wash their feet. And the king then asked them the cause of their advent. And thereupon Garuda answered, saying, 'O son of Nahusha, this ocean of asceticism, called Galava, is my friend. He had been, O monarch, a disciple of Viswamitra for many thousand years. This holy Brahmana, when commanded by Viswamitra to go away whithersoever he chose, addressed his preceptor at that time, saying,—*I desire to give something as preceptor's fee.* Knowing this one's resources to be poor, Viswamitra did not ask for anything. But when he was repeatedly addressed by this Brahmana on the subject of the tutorial fee, the preceptor, under a slight accession of wrath, said, 'Give me eight hundred white steeds of good pedigree and of lunar radiance, and each having one ear black in hue. If, O Galava, thou desirest to give anything to thy preceptor, let this then be given!' It was thus that Viswamitra endued with wealth of asceticism said unto him in anger. And this bull among Brahmanas is on that account smarting with great grief. Unable to fulfil that command (of his preceptor), he hath now come to take thy shelter. O tiger among men, accepting this as alms from thee, and filled once more with cheerfulness, he will, after paying his preceptor's debt, devote himself again to serve ascetic penances. A royal *Rishi* as thou art, and, therefore, endued with wealth of asceticism of thy own, this Brahmana, by giving thee a portion of his wealth of asceticism, will make thee richer in wealth of that kind. As many hairs, O lord of men, as there are on a horse's body, so many regions of bliss, O ruler of Earth, are attained by him that giveth away a horse in gift. This one is as fit to accept a gift as thou art to make a gift. Let therefore, thy gift in this instance be like milk deposited in a conch-shell.'"

Section CXV (115)

"Narada said, 'Thus addressed by Suparna in excellent words fraught with truth, that performer of thousand sacrifices, that foremost of givers, that liberal ruler of all the Kasis, the lord Yayati, revolving those words in his mind and reflecting on them coolly, and seeing before him his dear friend, Tarkshya, and that bull among Brahmanas, Galava, and regarding the alms sought as an indication, highly praiseworthy, of (Galava's) ascetic merit, and in view particularly of the fact that those two came to him having passed over all the kings of the Solar race, said, 'Blessed is my life today, and the race also in which I am born, hath, indeed, been blessed today. This very province also of mine hath equally been blessed by thee, O sinless Tarkshya. There is one thing, however, O friend, that I desire to say unto thee, and that is, I am not so rich now as thou thinkest, for my wealth hath suffered a great diminution. I cannot, however, O ranger of the skies, make thy advent here a fruitless one. Nor can I venture to frustrate the hopes entertained by this regenerate *Rishi.* I shall, therefore, give him that which will accomplish his purpose. If one having come for alms, returneth disappointed, he may consume the (host's) race. O son of Vinata, it is said that there is no act more sinful than that of saying, 'I have nothing'—and thus destroying the hope of one that cometh, saying, 'Give.' The disappointed man whose hopes have been killed and his object not accomplished, can destroy the sons and grandsons of the person that faileth to do him good.

Therefore, O Galava, take thou this daughter of mine, this perpetrator of four families. In beauty, she resembleth a daughter of the celestials. She is capable of prompting every virtue. Indeed, owing to her beauty, she is always solicited (at my hands) by gods and men, and *Asuras.* Let alone twice four hundred steeds each with a black ear, the kings of the earth will give away their whole kingdoms as her dower. Take thou, therefore, this daughter of mine, named Madhavi. My sole desire is that I may have a daughter's son by her. Accepting that daughter in gift, Galava then, with Garuda, went away, saying, 'We will again see thee'. And they took that maiden with them. And Galava's oviparous friend addressed him, saying, 'The means have at last been obtained whereby the steeds may be obtained.' And saying this, Garuda went away to his own abode, having obtained Galava's permission. And after the prince of birds had gone, Galava, with that maiden in his company, began to think of going to some one among the kings who would be able to give (fit) dower for the maiden. And he first thought of that best of kings, Haryyaswa of Ikshaku's race, who ruled at Ayodhya, was endued with great energy, possessed of a large army consisting of four kinds of forces, had a well-filled treasury and abundance of corn, and who was dearly loved by his subjects, and who loved the Brahmanas well. Desirous of offspring, he was living in quiet and peace, and engaged in excellent austerities. And the Brahmana Galava, repairing unto Haryyaswa, said, 'This maiden, O king of kings, will increase the family of her husband by bringing forth offspring. Accept her from me, O Haryyaswa, as thy wife, by giving me a dower. I will tell thee what dower thou shalt have to give. Hearing it, settle what thou shalt do.'"

Section CXVI (116)

"Narada said, 'That best of monarchs, king Haryyaswa, after reflecting for a long while and breathing a long and hot sigh about the birth of a son, at last said, 'Those six limbs[1] that ought to be high are high in this maiden. Those seven, again, that ought to be slender are slender in her. Those three, again, which ought to be deep are deep in her. And lastly, those five that ought to be red are red in her. It seems that she is worth being looked at by even the gods and the *Asuras*, and is accomplished in all the arts and sciences. Possessed of all auspicious signs, she will certainly bring forth many children. She is even capable of bringing forth a son who may become an emperor. Having regard to my wealth, tell me, O foremost of Brahmanas, what should be her dower.' Galava said, 'Give me eight hundred steeds, born in a good country, of lunar whiteness, and each with one ear black in hue. This auspicious and large-eyed maiden will then become the mother of

1. The limbs that should be 'prominent' or 'elevated' in order to constitute an indication of beauty or auspiciousness are variously mentioned. The general opinion seems to be that these six only, *viz.*, the back of each palm, the two *dorsa*, and the two bosoms should be elevated. Another opinion would seem to indicate that the two bosoms, the two hips, and the two eyes should be so. The seven that should be delicate or slender are unanimously mentioned as the skin, the hair, the teeth, the fingers of the hands, the fingers of the feet, the waist, and the neck. The three that should be deep are the navel, the voice, and the understanding. The five that should be red are the two palms, the two outer corners of the eyes, the tongue, the nether and the upper-lips, and the palate. These five also, are variously given.

thy sons, like the fire-stick becoming the genetrix of fire.'"

"Narada continued, 'Hearing these words, that royal sage, king Haryyaswa, filled with sorrow, but blinded by lust, addressed Galava, that foremost of *Rishis*, saying, 'I have only two hundred steeds about me of the kind wanted by thee, although of other kinds all worthy of sacrifice, I have many thousand moving about (in my dominions), O Galava, I desire to beget only one son upon this damsel. Kindly grant this request of mine.' Hearing these words of the king, that damsel said unto Galava, 'A reciter of *Brahma* granted me a boon that I would after each delivery, be a maiden again. Give me away, therefore, to this king, accepting his excellent steeds. In this way, full eight hundred steeds may be obtained by thee from four kings in succession, and I also may have four sons. Collect thou the wealth intended for thy preceptor, in this way. Even this is what I think. It depends, however, oil thee, O Brahmana, as to how thou shouldst act.' Thus addressed by that maiden, the *Muni* Galava said these words unto king Haryyaswa, 'O Haryyaswa, O best of men, accept this damsel for a fourth part of the dower that I have settled, and beget only one son upon her.' Taking then that maiden and worshipping Galava, the king in due time and place had by her a son of the kind wished for. And the son so born came to be called by the name of Vasumanas. Richer than all the wealthy kings of the earth, and resembling one of the Vasus themselves he became a king and giver of great wealth.

'After some time, intelligent Galava came back and approaching the delighted Haryyaswa, said unto him, 'Thou hast, O king obtained a son. Indeed, this child is like the sun himself in splendour. The time hath come, O foremost of men, for me to go to some other king for alms.' Hearing these words, Haryyaswa who was even truthful in speech and steady in acts of manliness, and remembering that the balance of six hundred steeds could not be made up by him, gave Madhavi back to Galava. And Madhavi also, abandoning that blazing, kingly prosperity, and once more becoming a maiden, followed the footsteps of Galava. And Galava too, saying, 'Let the steeds remain with thee' then went, accompanied by the maiden, to king Divodasa.'"

Section CXVII (117)

"Narada said, 'Galava then, addressing Madhavi, said, 'The ruler of the Kasis is an illustrious king known by the name of Divodasa. He is the son of Bhimasena, is endued with great prowess, and is a mighty sovereign. O blessed maiden, we are now going to him. Follow me slowly and grieve not. That ruler of men is virtuous and devoted to truth and hath his passions under control.'

"Narada Continued, 'When the *muni* came before that king he was received with due hospitality by the latter. Galava, then, began to urge the monarch for begetting a child. Thus addressed, Divodasa said, 'I heard of all this before. Thou needest not speak much, O Brahmana. I may tell thee, O best of Brahmanas, that as soon as I heard of this matter, my heart was set upon it. This also is a mark of great honour to me that passing over all other kings thou hast come to me. Without doubt, thy object will be gained. In the matter of the steeds, O Galava, my wealth is like that of king Haryyaswa. I shall, therefore, beget only one royal son upon this maiden.' Hearing these words, that best of Brahmanas gave that damsel unto the king; and, the king, thereupon, duly wedded her. And the royal sage then sported with her, as Surya with Prabhavati, Agni with Swaha, Vasava with Sachi, Chandra with Rohini, Yama with Urmila, Varuna with Gauri, Kuvera with Riddhi, Narayana with Lakshmi, Sagara with Jahnavi, Rudra with Rudrani, the Grandsire with Saraswati, Vasishtha's son Saktri with Adrisyanti, Vasishtha with Arundhati (called also Akshamala), Chyavana with Sukanya, Pulastya with Sandhya, Agastya with the princess of Vidarbha Lopamudra, Satyavan with Savitri, Bhrigu with Puloma, Kasyapa with Aditi, Richika's son Jamadagni with Renuka, Kusika's son Viswamitra with Himavati, Vrihaspati with Tara, Sukra with Sataprava, Bhumipati with Bhumi, Pururavas with Urvasi, Richika with Satyavati, Manu with Saraswati, Dushyanta with Sakuntala, the eternal Dharma with Dhriti, Nala with Damayanti, Narada, with Satyavati, Jaratkaru with Jaratkaru, Pulastya with Pratichya, Urnayus with Menaka, Tumvuru with Rambha, Vasuki with Satasirsha, Dhananjaya with Kamari, Rama with the princess of Videha Sita, or Janardana with Rukmini. And unto king Divodasa, that sporting with and taking delight in her, Madhavi bore a son named Pratardana. And after she had borne him a son, the holy Galava came to Divodasa at the appointed time, and said unto him, 'Let the maiden come with me, and let the steeds also thou art to give me remain with thee, for I desire to go elsewhere, O ruler of Earth, for dower.' Thus addressed, the virtuous king Divodasa, who was devoted to truth, thereupon, gave back the maiden to Galava at the appointed time.'"

Section XCVIII (118)

"Narada said, 'The illustrious Madhavi, faithful to her promise, abandoning that prosperity and once more becoming a maiden, followed the footsteps of the Brahmana Galava. And Galava, whose heart was set upon the accomplishment of his own business, reflecting upon what he should do next then went to the city of the Bhojas for waiting upon king Usinara. And arrived before that king of unbaffled prowess, Galava addressed him, saying, 'This maiden will bear thee two royal sons. And, O king, begetting upon her two sons equal unto the Sun and the Moon, thou mayst attain all thy objects both here and hereafter. As her dower, however, O thou that art conversant with every duty, thou shalt have to give me four hundred steeds of lunar splendour, each having ear black of hue. This effort of mine for obtaining the steeds is only on account of my preceptor, otherwise I myself have nothing to do with them. If thou art able to accept (my terms), do as I bid thee without any hesitation. O royal sage, thou art now childless. Beget, O king, a couple of children. With offspring so begot as a raft, save they *Pitris* and thyself also. O royal sage, he that hath fruit in the shape of offspring to enjoy, never falleth from heaven. Nor hath such a person to go to that frightful hell whither the childless are doomed to go.' Hearing these and other words of Galava, king Usinara replied unto him, saying, 'I have heard what thou, O Galava, hast said. My heart also is inclined to do thy bidding. The Supreme Ordainer, however, is all-powerful. I have only two hundred steeds of the kind indicated by thee, O best of Brahmanas. Of other kinds, I have many thousands moving about in my dominions. I will, O Galava, beget only one son upon her, by treading the path that hath been told by others such as Haryyaswa and Divodasa. I will act after their manner in the matter of the dower. O best of Brahmanas, my wealth exists for only my subjects residing in the city and the country, and not for my own comforts and enjoyment. That king, O virtuous one, who giveth away for his own pleasure the wealth that belongeth to others, can never earn virtue or fame. Let this maiden, endued with the radiance of a celestial girl, be presented to me. I will accept her for begetting only one child.' Hearing these and many other words that Usinara spoke, that best of Brahmanas, Galava, then applauded the monarch and gave him the maiden. And making Usinara accept that damsel, Galava went into the woods. And like a righteous man enjoying the prosperity (won by his deeds), Usinara began to sport with and enjoy that damsel in valleys and dales of mountains by fountains and falls of rivers, in mansions, delightful chambers, variegated gardens, forests and woods, agreeable places, and terraces of houses. And, in due time, was born unto him a son of the splendour of the morning sun, who afterwards became an excellent king, celebrated by the name Sivi. And after the birth of that son, the Brahmana Galava came to Usinara, and taking back from him the maiden went, O king, to see the son of Vinata.'"

Section CXIX (119)

"Narada said, 'Seeing Galava, Vinata's son smilingly addressed him, saying, 'By good luck it is, O Brahmana, that I behold thee successful.' Galava, however, hearing the words spoken by Garuda informed him that a fourth part of the task was still unfinished.' Garuda then, that foremost of all speakers, said unto Galava, 'Do not make any endeavour (to obtain the remaining two hundred), for it will not succeed. In days of yore, Richika sought at Kanyakuyja Gadhi's daughter, Satyavati, for making her his wife.' Thereupon Gadhi, O Galava, addressing the *Rishi*, said, 'O holy one, let a thousand steeds of lunar brightness, each with one ear black of hue, be presented to me.' Thus requested, Richika said, 'So be it'. And then wending his way to the great mart of steeds (*Aswatirtha*) in Varuna's abode, the Rishi obtained what he sought and gave them unto the king. Performing a sacrifice then of the name of *Pundarika*, that monarch gave away those steeds (as *Dakshina*) unto the Brahmanas. The three kings to whom thou hadst applied had purchased those horses from the Brahmanas, each to the number of two hundred. The remaining four hundred, O best of Brahmanas, while being transported over the river, were taken by the *Vitasta*.[1] Therefore, O Galava, thou canst never have that which is not to be had. Do thou then, O virtuous one, present unto Viswamitra this maiden as an equivalent for two hundred steeds, along with the six hundred thou hast already obtained. Thou wilt then, O best of Brahmanas, be freed from thy grief and crowned with success. Galava then, saying, 'So be it,' and taking with him both the maiden and the steeds, went with Garuda in his company unto Viswamitra. And arrived in his presence, Galava said, 'Here are six hundred steeds of the kind demanded by thee. And this maiden is offered as an equivalent for the remaining two hundred. Let all these be accepted by thee. Upon this maiden have been begotten three virtuous sons by three royal sages. Let a fourth, foremost of all, be begotten upon her by thee. And thus let the number of steeds, eight hundred, be regarded by thee as full, and let me also, being freed from thy debt, go and practise ascetic penances as I list.' Viswamitra then, beholding Galava in the company of the bird, and that highly beautiful maiden, said, 'Why, O Galava, didst thou not give me this maiden before? Four sons then, sanctifiers of my race, would all have been mine alone. I accept this maiden of thine for begetting upon her one son. As regards the steeds, let them graze in my asylum.' Saying this, Viswamitra of great effulgence began to pass his time happily with her. And Madhavi bore him a son of the name of Ashtaka. And as soon as that son was born, the great Muni Viswamitra addressed him to both virtue and profit, and gave him those six hundred steeds. Ashtaka then went to a city, bright as the city of Soma. And Kusika's son Viswamitra also having made over the damsel to his disciple, himself went into the

1. The latter half of this Sloka is variously read. The correct reading, I apprehend, is Niyamanani Santare Hritanyasan Vitastaya, *i.e.*, 'while transported across, were taken (down) by the (river) Vitasta'—the latter being one of the five rivers of the Punjab.

Woods. And Galava also, with his friend Suparna, having in this way succeeded in giving his preceptor the fee he had demanded, with a cheerful heart addressed that maiden and said, 'Thou hast borne a son who is exceedingly charitable, and another who is exceedingly brave, and a third who is devoted to truth and righteousness, and yet another who is a performer of great sacrifices. O beautiful maiden, thou hast, by these sons, saved not only thy father, but four kings and myself, also. Go now, O thou of slender waist.' Saying this, Galava dismissed Garuda that devourer of snakes, and returning the maiden unto her father himself went into the woods.'"

Section CXX (120)

"Narada said, 'King Yayati then, desirous again of disposing of his daughter in *Swayamvara*, went to a hermitage on the confluence of the Ganga and the Yamuna, taking Madhavi with him on a chariot, her person decked with garlands of flowers. And both Puru and Yadu followed their sister to that sacred asylum. And in that spot was assembled a vast concourse of *Nagas* and *Yakshas* and human beings, of *Gandharvas* and animals and birds, and of dwellers of mountains and trees and forests, and of many inhabitants of that particular province. And the woods all around that asylum were filled with numerous Rishis resembling Brahman himself. And while the selection had commenced of husband, that maiden of the fairest complexion, passing over all the bridegrooms there assembled, selected the forest as her lord. Descending from her chariot and saluting all her friends, the daughter of Yayati went into the forest which is always sacred, and devoted herself to ascetic austerities. Reducing her body by means of fasts of various kinds and religious rites and rigid vows, she adopted the deer's mode of life And subsisting upon soft and green grass-blades, resembling the sprouts of *lapis lazuli* and which were both bitter and sweet to the taste, and drinking the sweet, pure, cool, crystal, and very superior water of sacred mountain-streams, and wandering with the deer in forests destitute of lions and tigers, in deserts free from forest-conflagration, and in thick woods, that maiden, leading the life of a wild doe, earned great religious merit by the practice of *Brahmacharya* austerities.

'(Meanwhile) king Yayati, following the practice of kings before him, submitted to the influence of Time, after having lived for many thousands of years. The progeny of two of his sons—those foremost of men—Puru and Yadu, multiplied greatly, and in consequence thereof, Nahusha's son won great respect both in this and the other world. O monarch, dwelling in heaven, king Yayati, resembling a great Rishi, became an object of much regard, and enjoyed the highest fruits of those regions. And after many thousands of years had passed away in great happiness, on one occasion while seated among the illustrious royal sages and great Rishis, king Yayati, from folly, ignorance, and pride, mentally disregarded all the gods and Rishis, and all human beings. Thereat the divine Sakra—the slayer of Vala—at once read his heart. And those royal sages also addressed him saying, 'Fie, fie.' And beholding the son of Nahusha, the questions were asked, 'Who is this person? What king's son is he? Why is he in heaven? By what acts hath he won success? Where did he earn ascetic merit? For what hath he been known here? Who knoweth him? The dwellers of heaven, thus speaking of that monarch, asked one another these questions about Yayati, that ruler of men. And hundreds of heaven's charioteers, and hundreds of those that kept heaven's gates, and of those what were in charge of heaven's seats, thus questioned, all answered, 'We do not know him.' And the minds of all were temporarily clouded, so that none recognised the king and thereupon the monarch was soon divested of his splendour.'"

Section CXXI (121)

"Narada said, 'Removed from his place and pushed away from his seat with heart trembling in fear, and consumed by burning remorse, with his garlands dimmed in lustre and his knowledge clouded, shorn of his crown and bracelets, with head swimming and every limb relaxed divested of ornaments and robes, incapable of being recognised, sometimes not seeing the other residents of heaven, filled with despair, and his understanding a perfect blank, king Yayati fell headlong towards the earth. And before the king fell down, he thought within himself,

'What inauspicious and sinful thought was entertained by me in consequence of which I am hurled from my place?' And all the kings there, as also the Siddhas and the Apsaras, laughed at seeing Yayati losing his hold, and on the point of falling down. And soon, O king, at the command of the king of the gods, there came a person whose business it was to hurl down those whose merits were exhausted. And coming there, he said unto Yayati, 'Extremely intoxicated with pride, there is none whom thou hast not disregarded. In consequence of this thy pride, heaven is no longer for thee. Thou deservest not a residence here, O son of a king. Thou art not recognised here, go and fall down.' Even thus the celestial messenger spoke unto him, Nahusha's son then said, repeating the words three times, 'If fall I must, let me fall amongst the righteous.' And saying this, that foremost of persons that had won high regions by their acts, began to think of the particular region whereon he should fall. Beholding meanwhile four mighty kings, *viz.*, Pratardana, Vasumanas, Sivi, the son of Usinara, and Ashtaka, assembled together in the woods of Naimisha, the king fell amongst them. And those monarchs were then engaged in gratifying the lord of the celestials by performance of the sacrifice known by the name of Vajapeya. And the smoke arising from their sacrificial altar reached the very gates of heaven. And the smoke that rose thus, looked like a river connecting both the earth and the heaven. And it resembled the sacred stream Ganga while descending from heaven to earth. And smelling that smoke and guiding his course by it. Yayati, the lord of the universe, descended on the earth. And the king thus fell amongst those four lions among rulers, who were all endued with great beauty, who were foremost of all the performers of sacrifices, who were, indeed, his own relatives, and who resembled the four regents of the four quarters, and looked like four mighty sacrificial fires. And thus, in consequence of the exhaustion of his merits, the royal sage Yayati fell amongst them. And beholding him blazing with beauty, those kings asked him, saying, "Who art thou? Of what race, country, or city art thou? Art thou a Yaksha, or a god, a Gandharva, or a Rakshasa? Thou does not seem to be a human being. What object hast thou in view?" Thus questioned, Yayati answered, 'I am the royal sage Yayati. Fallen am I from heaven in consequence of the expiration of my virtue. Having desired to fall amongst the righteous, I have fallen amongst you.' The kings then said, 'O foremost of persons, may that wish of thine, be realized. Accept thou our virtues and the fruits of all our sacrifices.' Yayati replied saying, 'I am not a Brahmana competent to accept a gift. On the other hand, I am a Kshatriya. Nor is my heart inclined towards lessening the virtues of others.'

"Narada continued, 'About this time, Madhavi, in course of her purposeless wanderings, came there. Beholding her, those monarchs saluted her and said, 'What object hast thou in coming here? What command of thine shall we obey? Thou deservest to command us, for all of us are thy sons, O thou that art endued with wealth of asceticism!' Hearing these words of theirs, Madhavi was filled with delight and approaching then her father, she reverentially saluted Yayati. And touching the heads of all her sons, that lady engaged in ascetic austerities said to her father, 'Being my sons these all are thy daughter's sons, O king of kings. They are not strangers to thee. These will save thee. The practice is not new, its origin extends to antiquity. I am thy daughter Madhavi, O king, living in the woods after the manner of the deer. I also have earned virtue. Take thou a moiety. And because, O king, all men have a right to enjoy a portion of the merits earned by their offspring, it is for this that they desire to have daughter's sons. Even this was the case with thyself, O king (when thou madest me over to Galava).' At these words of their mother, those monarchs saluted her, and bowing down unto also their maternal grandsire, repeated those very words in a loud, incomparable, and sweet voice, and making, as it were, the whole earth resounded therewith, in order to rescue that maternal grandsire of theirs who had fallen down from heaven. And at that time Galava also came there, and addressing Yayati, said, 'Accepting an eighth part of my ascetic austerities, ascend thou to heaven again.'"

Section CXXII (122)

"Narada said, 'As soon as that bull among men, king Yayati was recognised by those virtuous persons, he rose again to heaven, without having had to touch the surface of the earth. And he regained his celestial form and had all his anxieties entirely dispelled. And he rose again, decked with celestial garlands and robes, adorned with celestial ornaments, sprinkled with celestial scents, and furnished with heavenly attributes, and without having been compelled to touch the earth with his feet. Meanwhile, Vasumanas who was celebrated in the world for his liberality, first addressing the king, uttered these words in a loud voice, 'The merit that I have won on earth by my unblamable conduct towards men of all orders, I give unto thee. Be it all thine, O king. The merit that one winneth by liberality and forgiveness, the merit that is mine in consequence of the sacrifices I have performed, let all that also be thine.' After this, Pratardana, that bull among Kshatriyas, said, 'Ever devoted to virtue as also to war, the fame that hath here been mine as a Kshatriya, in consequence of the appellation of hero (by which I am known),—be that merit thine. After this, Sivi, the intelligent son of Usinara, said these sweet words, 'Unto children and women in jest, danger, or calamity, in distress, or at dice, I have never spoken a falsehood. By that truth which I never sacrificed ascend thou to heaven. I can, O king, give up all objects of desire and enjoyment, my kingdom, yea, life itself, but truth I cannot give up. By that truth, ascend thou to heaven; that truth for which Dharma, that truth for which agni, that truth for which he of a hundred sacrifices, have each been gratified with me, by that truth ascend thou to heaven.' And lastly, the royal sage Ashtaka, the offspring of Kusika's son and Madhavi, addressing Nahusha's son Yayati who had performed many hundreds of sacrifices, said, 'I have, O lord, performed hundreds of Pundarika, Gosava and Vajapeya sacrifices. Take thou the merit of these. Wealth, gems, robes, I have spared nothing for the performance of sacrifices. By that truth ascend thou to heaven.' And that king thereupon leaving the earth, began to ascend towards heaven, higher and higher, as those daughter's sons of his, one after another, said those words unto him. And it was thus that those kings by their good acts, speedily saved Yayati, who had been hurled from heaven. It was thus that those daughter's sons born in four royal lines, those multipliers of their races, by means of their virtues, sacrifices, and gifts, caused their wise maternal grandfather to ascend again to heaven. And those monarchs jointly said, 'Endued with the attributes of royalty and possessed of every virtue, we are, O king, thy daughter's sons! (By virtue of our good deeds) ascend thou to heaven.'"

Section CXXIII (123)

"Narada said, 'Sent back to heaven by those righteous kings, distinguished by the liberality of their sacrificial presents, Yayati possessed of daughter's sons, dismissed them and reached the celestial regions. Attaining to the eternal region obtained through the merit of his daughter's sons, and adorned by his own deeds, Yayati, bathed in shower of fragrant flowers and hugged by perfumed and delicious breezes, blazed forth with great beauty. And cheerfully, received back into heaven with sounds of cymbals, he was entertained with songs and dances by various tribes of Gandharvas and Asuras. And diverse celestial and royal Rishis and Charanas began to pay their adorations to him. And deities worshipped him with an excellent Arghya and delighted him with other honours. And after he had thus regained heaven and tranquillity of heart, and had once more become freed from anxiety, the Grandsire, gratifying him by his words said, 'Thou hadst earned the full measure I of virtue by thy earthly deeds, and this region (that thou hadst won) is eternal, as thy deeds are in heaven. Thou hadst, however, O royal sage, destroyed thy acquisition by thy vanity alone, and thereby covered the hearts of all the denizens of heaven with darkness in consequence of which none of them could recognise thee. And since thou couldst not be recognised, thou wert hurled hence! Saved once more by the love and affection of thy daughter's sons, thou hast once more arrived here, and regained this unchangeable, eternal, sacred, excellent, stable, and indestructible region won before by thy own deeds.' Thus addressed, Yayati said, 'O holy one, I have a doubt, which, it behoveth thee, to dispel. O Grandsire of all the worlds, it behoveth me not to ask any one else. Great was my merit, augmented by a (virtuous) rule over my subjects for many thousands of years and won by innumerable sacrifices and gifts. How could merit (so great) be exhausted so soon in consequence of which I was hurled hence? Thou knowest, O holy one, that the regions created for me were all eternal. Why were all those regions of mine destroyed, O thou of great effulgence? The Grandsire answered, saying, 'Thy merit, augmented by a (virtuous) rule over thy subjects for many thousands of years and won by innumerable sacrifices and gifts, was exhausted by only one fault, in consequence of which thou wert hurled (from this region). That fault, O king of kings, was thy vanity for which thou hadst become an object of contempt with all the residents of heaven. O royal sage, this region can never be rendered eternal by vanity, or pride of strength, or malice, or deceitfulness, or deception. Never disregard those that are inferior, or superior, or in the middle station. There is not a greater sinner than he who is consumed by the fire of vanity. Those men that will converse upon this fall and re-ascension of thine, will, without doubt, be protected even if overtaken by calamity.'

"Narada continued, 'O monarch, even such was the distress into which Yayati fell in consequence of vanity, and such was the distress into which Galava fell owing to his obstinacy. They that desire their own good should listen to friends that wish them well. Obstinacy should never be entertained, for obstinacy is always the root of ruin. For this reason, O son of Gandhari, forsake vanity and wrath. O hero, make peace with the sons of Pandu. Avoid anger, O king, that which is given away, that which is done, the austerities that are practised, the libations that are poured on fire, nor one of these is ever destroyed or suffereth any diminution. None else, again, enjoyeth the fruits of these save he that is their agent. He that succeedeth in understanding this truly superior and excellent history, that is approved by persons of great learning as well as by those that are freed from anger and lust, and that is enforced by various references to scriptures and reason, obtaineth a knowledge of virtue and profit and desire, and enjoyeth the sovereignty of the whole world!'"

Section CXXIV (124)

"Dhritarashtra said, 'O holy one, it is even so as thou, O Narada, sayest. My wish also is precisely such, but, O holy one, I have no power (to carry them out)!'

"Vaisampayana continued, 'The Kuru king, having said these words unto Narada, then addressed Krishna and said, 'Thou hast, O Kesava, told me that which leadeth to heaven, what is beneficial to the world, consistent with virtue, and fraught with reason. I am not, however, O sire, independent. Duryodhana never doth what is agreeable to me. Do thou, therefore, O mighty-armed Krishna, O best of persons, strive to persuade that foolish and wicked son of mine, who disobeyeth my commands. O mighty-armed one, he never listeneth to the beneficial words, O Hrishikesa, of Gandhari, or of wise Vidura, or of other friends headed by Bhishma, all of whom seek his good. Do thou, therefore, thyself counsel that crooked, senseless, and wicked-souled prince, of evil disposition and sinful heart. By doing this, O Janardana, thou shalt have done that noble act which a friend should ever do.' Thus addressed, he of Vrishni's race, conversant with the truths of virtue and profit, approached nearer to the ever-wrathful Duryodhana and said unto him these sweet words, 'O Duryodhana, O best of the Kurus, listen to these words of mine, uttered especially for thy good, as also, O Bharata, for that of thy followers. Thou art born in a race that is distinguished for its great wisdom. It behoveth thee to act righteously as I indicate. Possessed of learning and endued with excellent behaviour, thou art adorned with every excellent quality. They that are born in ignoble families, or are wicked-souled, cruel, and shameless, they only, O sire, act in the way that seemeth acceptable to thee. In this world, the inclinations of those only that are righteous seem to be consistent with the dictates of virtue and profit. The inclinations, however, of those that are unrighteous seem to be perverse. O bull of Bharata's race, the disposition that thou art repeatedly manifesting is of that perverse kind. Persistence in such behaviour is sinful, frightful, highly wicked, and capable of leading to death itself. It is besides, causeless, while, again, thou canst not, O Bharata, adhere to it long. If by avoiding this which is productive only of woe, thou wilt achieve thy own good, if, O chastiser of foes, thou wilt escape from the sinful and disreputable deeds of thy brothers, followers, and counsellors, then, O tiger among men, make peace, O bull among the Bharatas, with the sons of Pandu who are all endued with great wisdom and great bravery with great exertion and great learning an all of whom have their souls under complete control. Such conduct will be agreeable to and conducive to the happiness of Dhritarashtra who is endued with great wisdom, of grandsire (Bhishma), Drona, the high-souled Kripa, Somadatta, wise Vahlika, Aswatthaman, Vikarna, Sanjaya, Vivingsati, and of many of thy kinsmen, O chastiser of foes, and many of thy friends also. The whole world, O sire, will derive benefit from that peace. Thou art endued with modesty, born in a noble race, hast learning and kindness of heart. Be obedient, O sire, to the commands of thy father, and also of thy mother, O bull of Bharata's race. They that are good sons always regard that to be beneficial which their fathers command. Indeed, when overtaken by calamity, every one recollects the injunctions of his father. Peace with the Pandavas, O sire, recommend itself to thy father. Let it, therefore, O chief of the Kurus recommend itself to thee also with thy counsellors. That mortal who having listened to the counsels of friends doth not act according to them, is consumed at the end by the consequences of his disregard, like him who swalloweth the fruit called *Kimpaka*. He that from folly doth not accept beneficial counsels, unnerved by procrastination and unable to attain his object, is obliged to repent at last. He, on the other hand, who having listened to beneficial counsels accepteth them at once, abandoning his opinion, always winneth happiness in the world. He that rejects the words of well-meaning friends, regarding those words as opposed to his interest, but accepts words that are really so opposed, is soon subjugated by his foes. Disregarding the opinions of the righteous he that abideth by the opinions of the wicked, soon maketh his friends weep for him in consequence of his being plunged into distress. Forsaking superior counsellors he that seeketh the advice of inferior ones, soon falleth into great distress and succeedeth not in saving himself. That companion of the sinful, who behaveth falsely and never listeneth to good friends, who honoureth strangers but hateth those that are his own, is soon, O Bharata, cast off by the Earth. O bull of Bharata's race, having quarrelled with those (the sons of Pandu), thou seekest protection from others *viz.*, those that are sinful, incapable, and foolish. What other man is there on earth besides thee, who, disregarding kinsmen, that are all mighty charioteers, and each of whom resembleth

Sakra himself, would seek protection and aid from strangers? Thou hast persecuted the sons of Kunti, from their very birth. They have not been angry with thee, for the sons of Pandu are indeed virtuous. Although thou hast behaved deceitfully towards the Pandavas from their very birth, yet, O mighty-armed one, those distinguished persons have acted generously towards thee. It behoveth thee, therefore, O bull of Bharata's race, to act towards those principal kinsmen of thine with equal generosity. Do not yield thyself to the influence of wrath. O bull of Bharata's race, the exertions of the wise are always associated with virtue, profit, and desire. If, indeed, all these three cannot be attained, men follow at least virtue and profit. If, again, these three are pursued separately, it is seen that they that have their hearts under control, choose virtue; they that are neither good nor bad but occupy a middle station, choose profit, which is always the subject of dispute; while they that are fools choose the gratification of desire. The fool that from temptation giveth up virtue and pursueth profit and desire by unrighteous means, is soon destroyed by his senses. He that speaketh profit and desire, should yet practise virtue at the outset, for neither profit nor desire is (really) dissociated from virtue. O king, it hath been said that virtue alone is the cause of the three, for he that seeketh the three, may, by the aid of virtue alone, grow like fire when brought into contact with a heap of dry grass. O bull of Bharata's race, thou seeketh, O sire, by unrighteous means this extensive empire, flourishing with prosperity and well-known to all the monarchs of the earth. O king, he that behaveth falsely towards those that live and conduct themselves righteously, certainly cutteth down his own self, like a forest with an axe. One must not seek to confound his understanding whose overthrow one doth not like, for, if one's understanding is confounded, one can never devote his attention to what is beneficial. One that hath his soul under control never, O Bharata, disregardeth anybody in the three worlds,—no, not even the commonest creature, far less those bulls among men, the sons of Pandu. He that surrendereth himself to the influence of anger loseth his sense of right and wrong. Rank growth must always be cut off. Behold, O Bharata, this is the proof. At present, O sire, union with the sons of Pandu is better for thee than thy union with the wicked. If thou makest peace with them, thou mayst obtain the fruition of all thy wishes. O best of kings, while enjoying the kingdom that has been founded by the Pandavas, thou seekest protection from others, disregarding the Pandavas themselves. Reposing the cares of thy state on Dussasana, Durvisaha, Karna, and Suvala's son, thou desirest the continuance of thy prosperity, O Bharata. These, however, are far inferior to the Pandavas in knowledge, in virtue, in capacity for acquiring wealth, and in prowess. Indeed, O Bharata, (let alone the four I have mentioned) all these kings together, with thee at their head, are incapable of even looking at the face of Bhima, when angry, on the field of battle. O sire, this force consisting of all the kings of the earth is, indeed, at thy elbow. There are also Bhishma, and Drona, and this Karna, and Kripa, and Bhurisrava, and Somadatta, and Aswatthaman, and Jayadratha. All these together are incapable of fighting against Dhananjaya. Indeed, Arjuna is incapable of being vanquished in battle even by all the gods, *Asuras*, men, and Gandharvas. Do not set thy heart for battle. Seest thou the man in any of the royal races of the earth, who having encountered Arjuna in battle can return home safe and sound? O bull of Bharata's race, what advantage is there in a universal slaughter? Show me a single man who will defeat that Arjuna, by defeating whom alone victory may be thine? Who will encounter that son of Pandu in battle, who had vanquished all the celestials with the Gandharvas, Yakshas and Pannagas at Khandavaprastha? Then also the marvellous account that is heard of what happened at Virata's city, touching that encounter between one and many, is sufficient proof of this, Hopest thou to vanquish in battle Arjuna who when excited with rage is invincible, irresistible, ever-victorious, and undeteriorating Arjuna, that hero, who gratified the God of gods, Siva himself in fight? With myself again as his second when that son of Pritha will rush to the field of battle against an enemy, who is there that is competent to challenge him then? Can Purandara himself do so? He that would vanquish Arjuna in battle would support the Earth on his arms, consume in rage the whole population of the Earth, and hurl the very gods from heaven. Look at thy sons, thy brothers, kinsmen, and other relatives. Let not these chiefs of Bharata's race all perish on thy account. Let not the race of

Kauravas be exterminated or reduced. O king, let not people say that thou art the exterminator of thy race and the destroyer of its achievements. Those mighty car-warriors, the Pandavas (if peace be made) will install thee as the *Yuvaraja*, and thy father Dhritarashtra, that lord of men, as the sovereign of this extensive empire. Do not, O sire, disregard the prosperity that is awaiting thee and is sure to come. Giving to the sons of Pritha half the kingdom, win thou great prosperity. Making peace with the Pandavas and acting according to the counsels of thy friends, and rejoicing with them, thou art sure to obtain what is for thy good for ever and ever.'"

Section CXXV (125)

"Vaisampayana said, 'Hearing, O bull of Bharata's race, these words of Kesava, Bhishma, the son of Santanu, then said unto vindictive Duryodhana, 'Krishna hath spoken to thee, desirous of bringing about peace between kinsmen. O sire, follow those counsels, and do not yield to the infiuence of wrath. If thou dost not act, O sire, according to the words of the high-souled Kesava, neither prosperity, nor happiness nor what is for thy good, wilt thou ever have. The mighty-armed Kesava, O sire, hath said unto thee what is consistent with virtue and profit. Accept thou that object, and do not, O king, exterminate the population of the earth. This resplendent prosperity of the Bharatas amongst all the kings of the earth, thou wilt, during the very life of Dhritarashtra, destroy through thy wickedness, and thou wilt also, through this arrogant disposition of thine, deprive thyself with all thy counsellors, sons, brothers, and kinsmen, of life, if, O thou foremost of Bharata's race, thou transgressest the words of Kesava, thy father, and of wise Vidura,—words that are consistent with truth and fraught with benefit to thyself. Be not the exterminator of thy race, be not a wicked man, let not thy heart be sinful, do not tread the path of unrighteousness. Do not sink thy father and mother into an ocean of grief.' After Bhishma had concluded, Drona also said these words unto Duryodhana, who, filled with wrath, was then breathing heavily, 'O sire, the words that Kesava hath spoken unto thee are fraught with virtue and profit, Santanu's son Bhishma also hath said the same. Accept those words, O monarch. Both of them are wise, endued with great intelligence, with souls under control, desirous of doing what is for thy good, and possessed of great learning. They have said what is beneficial. Accept their words, O king, O thou possessed of great wisdom, act according to what both Krishna and Bhishma have said. O chastiser of foes, do not, from delusion of understanding, disregard Madhava. They that are always encouraging thee, are unable to give thee victory. During the time of battle they will throw the burthen of hostility on other's necks. Do not slaughter the Earth's population. Do not slay thy sons and brothers. Know that host is invincible in the midst of which are Vasudeva and Arjuna. If, O Bharata, thou dost not accept the truthful words of thy friends, Krishna and Bhishma, then, O sire, thou wilt surely have to repent. Arjuna is even greater than what Jamadagni's son hath described him to be. As regards Krishna, the son of Devaki, he is incapable of being resisted by even the gods. O bull of Bharata's race, what use is there in telling thee what is really conducive to thy happiness and good? Everything hath now been said unto thee. Do what thou wishest. I do not wish to say anything more unto thee, O foremost of Bharata's race.'

"Vaisampayana continued, 'After Drona had ceased, Vidura also, otherwise called Kshattri, casting his eyes on Duryodhana, said unto that vindictive son of Dhritarashtra, 'O Duryodhana, O bull of Bharata's race, I do not grieve for thee. I grieve, however, for this old couple, *viz.*, Gandhari and thy father. Having thee, of wicked soul for their protector (of whom they will shortly be deprived), they will have to wander with anybody to look after them, and deprived also of friends and counsellors, like a pair of birds shorn of their wings. Having begotten such a wicked son who is the exterminator of his race, alas, these two will have to wander over the earth in sorrow, subsisting on alms.' After this, king Dhritarashtra, addressing Duryodhana, seated in the midst of his brothers and surrounded by all the kings, said, 'Listen, O Duryodhana, to what the high-souled Sauri hath said. Accept those words which are eternal, highly beneficial and conducive to what is for thy highest good. With the aid of this Krishna of faultless deeds, we amongst all the kings, are sure to have all our cherished objects. Firmly united by Kesava, be reconciled, O sire, with

Yudhishthira. Seek thou this great good of the Bharatas like unto an august ceremony of propitiation. Through Vasudeva's agency, bind thyself closely with the Pandavas. I think, the time for that is come. Do not let the opportunity pass away. If, however, thou disregardest Kesava, who from a desire of achieving what is for good, is soliciting thee to make peace, then victory will never be thine.'"

Section CXXVI (126)

"Vaisampayana said, 'Hearing these words of Dhritarashtra, both Bhishma and Drona who sympathised with the old king, again addressed disobedient Duryodhana and said, 'As yet the two Krishnas are not accoutred in mail, as yet Gandiva resteth inactive, as yet Dhaumya doth not consume the enemy's strength by pouring libations on the war-fire, as yet that mighty bowman Yudhishthira, having modesty for his ornament, doth not cast angry glances on thy troops, so let hostility cease. As yet that mighty bowman, Bhimasena, the son of Pritha, is not seen stationed in the midst of his division, so let hostility cease. As yet Bhimasena, doth not, mace in *band*, stalk on the field of battle, grinding (hostile) divisions, so let peace be made with the Pandavas. As yet Bhima doth not, with his hero-slaying mace, make the heads of warriors fighting from the backs of elephants roll on the field of battle, like the palmyra-fruits in the season of their ripening, so let hostility cease. As yet Nakula, and Sahadeva, Dhrishtadyumna of Prishata's race, and Virata, and Sikhandin, and Sisupal's son, accoutred in mail and all well-versed in arms, do not penetrate thy ranks, like huge crocodiles penetrating the deep, and pour their arrowy showers, so let hostility cease. As yet fierce-winged shafts do not fall upon the delicate bodies of the assembled kings, so let hostility cease. As yet fierce weapons made of iron and steel, shot unerringly by mighty bowmen well-skilled in arms, endued with lightness of hand and capable of hitting howsoever long distance, do not penetrate the breasts of warriors, smeared with sandal and other fragrant unguents, and adorned with golden garlands and gems, so let hostility cease. Let that elephant among kings, Yudhishthira the Just, receive thee with an embrace while thou salutest him bending thy head. O bull of Bharata's race, let that king, distinguished for the liberality of his sacrificial presents, place on thy shoulder that right arm of his, the palm of which beareth the marks of the banner and the hook. Let him, with hands begemmed and red, adorned with fingers, pat thy back while thou art seated. Let the mighty-armed Vrikodara, with shoulder broad as those of the *sala* tree, embrace thee, O bull of Bharata's race, and gently converse with thee for peace. And, O king, saluted with reverence by those three, *viz.*, Arjuna and the Twins, smell thou their heads and converse with them affectionately. And beholding the united with thy heroic brothers—the sons of Pandu—let all these monarchs shed tears of joy. Let the tidings of this cordial union be proclaimed in the cities of all the kings. Let the Earth be ruled by thee with feelings of brotherly affection (in thy bosom), and let thy heart be freed from the fever (of jealousy and wrath).'"

Section CXXVII (127)

"Vaisampayana said, 'Hearing in that assembly of the Kurus these words that were disagreeable to him, Duryodhana replied unto the mighty-armed Kesava of great fame, saying. 'It behoveth thee, O Kesava, to speak after reflecting on all circumstances. Indeed, uttering such harsh words, thou, without any reason, findest fault with me alone, addressed regardfully as thou always art by the sons of Pritha, O slayer of Madhu. But dost thou censure me, having surveyed the strength and weakness (of both sides)? Indeed, thyself and Kshattri, the King, the Preceptor, and the Grandsire, all reproach me alone and not any other monarch. I, however, do not find the least fault in myself. Yet all of you, including the (old) king himself, hate me. O repressor of foes, I do not, even after reflection, behold any grave fault in me, or even O Kesava, any fault however minute. In the game at dice, O slayer of Madhu, that was joyfully accepted by them, the Pandavas were vanquished and their kingdom was won by Sakuni. What blame can be mine as regards that? On the other hand, O slayer of Madhu, the wealth that was won from the Pandavas then, was ordered by me, to be returned unto them. It cannot, again, O foremost of victors, be any fault of ours that the invincible Pandavas, were defeated once again at dice and had to go to the woods. Imputing what fault to us, do they regard us as their enemies? And, O Krishna, though (really) weak, why do the Pandavas yet so cheerfully seek a quarrel with us, as if they were strong? What have we done to them? For what injury (done to them) do the sons of Pandu, along with the Srinjayas, seek to slaughter the sons of Dhritarashtra? We shall not in consequence of any fierce deed, or (alarming) word (of theirs), bow down to them in fear, deprived of our senses. We cannot bow down to Indra himself, let alone the sons of Pandu. I do not, O Krishna, see the man, observant of Kshatriya virtues, who can, O slayer of foes, venture to conquer us in battle. Let alone the Pandavas, O slayer of Madhu, the very gods are not competent to vanquish Bhishma, Kripa, Drona and Karna, in battle. If, O Madhava, we are, in the observance of the practices of our order, cut off with weapons in battle, when our end comes, even that will lead us to heaven. Even this, O Janardana, is our highest duty as Kshatriyas, *viz.*, that we should lay ourselves down on the field of battle on a bed of arrows. If, without bowing to our enemies, ours be the bed of arrows in battle, that, O Madhava, will never grieve us. Who is there, born in a noble race and conforming to Kshatriya practices, that would from fear bow to an enemy, desirous only of saving his life? Those Kshatriyas that desire their own good, accept regardfully this saying of Matanga, *viz.*, that (as regards a Kshatriya), one should always keep himself erect, and never bow down, for exertion alone is manliness; one should rather break at the knots than bend. A person like me should only bow down to the Brahmanas for the sake of piety, without regarding anybody else. (As regards persons other than Brahmanas), one should, as long as one lives, act according to Matanga's saying. Even this is the duty of Kshatriyas; even this is ever my opinion. That share in the kingdom which was formerly given them by my father shall never again, O Kesava, be obtainable by them as long as I live. As long, O Janardana, as king Dhritarashtra liveth, both ourselves and they, sheathing our weapons, O Madhava, should live in dependence on him. Given away formerly from ignorance or fear, when I was a child and dependent on others, the kingdom, O Janardana, incapable of being given away again, shall not, O delighter of Vrishni's race, be obtainable by the Pandavas. At present, O Kesava of mighty arms, as long as I live, even that much of our land which may be covered by the point of a sharp needle shall not, O Madhava, be given by us unto the Pandavas.'"

Section CXXVIII (128)

"Vaisampayana said, 'Reflecting (for a moment), with eyes red in anger, he, of Dasarha's race, addressing Duryodhana in that assembly of the Kurus, then said these words, 'Wishest thou for a bed of heroes? Verily, thou shalt have it, with thy consellors. Wait (for a short while), a great slaughter will ensue. Thou thinkest, O thou of little understanding, that thou hast committed no offence against the Pandavas? Let the (assembled) monarchs judge. Grieved at the prosperity of the high-souled Pandavas, thou conspirest, O Bharata, with Suvala's son about the gambling match. O sire, how could those virtuous, honest, and superior kinsmen of thine (otherwise) engage in such a wicked act with the deceitful Sakuni? O thou that art endued with great wisdom, gambling robs even the good of their understanding, and as regards the wicked, disunion and dire consequence spring from it. It was thou who hadst devised with thy wicked counsellors, that terrible source of calamity in the form of the gambling match, without consulting with persons of righteous behaviour. Who else is there, capable of insulting a brother's wife in the way thou didst or of dragging her into the assembly and addressing her in language thou hadst used towards Draupadi? Of noble parentage, and endued with excellent behaviour, and dearer to them than their very lives, the queen-consort of Pandu's sons was treated even thus by thee. All the Kauravas know what words were addressed in their assembly by Dussasana unto those chastisers of foes,—the sons of Kunti,—when they were about to set out for the woods. Who is there capable of behaving so wretchedly towards his own honest kinsmen, that are ever engaged in the practice of virtue, that are untainted by avarice, and that are always correct in their behaviour? Language such as becomes only those that are heartless and despicable, was frequently repeated by Karna and Dussasana and also by thee. Thou hadst taken great pains to burn to death, at Varanavata, the sons of Pandu with their mother, while they were children, although that effort of thine was not crowned with success. After this, the Pandavas with their mother were obliged to live for a long while, concealed in the town of Ekachakra in the abode of a Brahmana. With poison, with snakes and cords, thou hadst, by every means, sought the destruction of the Pandavas, although none of thy designs was successful. With such feelings when thou hadst always acted towards them so deceitfully, how canst thou say that thou hast not offended against the high-souled Pandavas? Thou art not, O sinful man, willing to give them their paternal share in the kingdom, although they are begging it of thee. Thou shalt have to give it them, this, when divested of prosperity, thou shalt be laid low. Having, like a heartless fellow, done innumerable wrongs to the Pandavas and behaved so deceitfully towards them, thou seekest now to appear in a different garb. Though repeatedly solicited by thy parents, by Bhishma, Drona, and Vidura, to make peace, thou dost not yet, O king, make peace. Great is the advantage in peace, O king, both to thyself and Yudhishthira. Peace, however, does not recommend itself to thee. To what else can it be due, but to thy loss of understanding? Transgressing the words of thy friends, thou canst never attain to what is for thy benefit. Sinful and disreputable is that act, which thou, O king, art about to do.'

"Vaisampayana continued, 'While he, of Dasarha's race, was saying this, Dussasana addressed vindictive Duryodhana and said unto him these words in the midst of the Kurus, 'If, O king, thou dost not willingly make peace with the Pandavas, verily the Kauravas will bind thee (hand and foot) and make over thee to the son of Kunti. Bhishma, and Drona, and thy (own) father, O bull amongst men, will make over us three, *viz.*, Vikartana's son, thyself, and myself, to the Pandavas!'

"Vaisampayana continued, 'Hearing these words of his brother, Dhritarashtra's son, wicked, shameless, disobedient, disrespectful, and vain Suyodhana, breathing heavily like a great snake rose up from his seat in anger, and disregarding Vidura, and Dhritarashtra and the great king Vahlika, and Kripa, and Somadatta, and Bhishma, and Drona, and Janardana, in fact, all of them, went out of the court. And beholding that bull among men leave the court, his brother and all his counsellors, and all the kings, followed him. And seeing

Duryodhana rise and leave the court in anger with his brothers, Santanu's son, Bhishma said, 'The enemies of that person, who, abandoning both virtue and profit, followeth the impulses of wrath, rejoice on beholding him plunged into distress at no distant date. This wicked son of Dhritarashtra, this one unacquainted with the true means (of accomplishing his objects), this fool that is wrongly vain of his sovereignty, obeyeth only the dictates of wrath and avarice. I see also, O Janardana, that the hour of all those Kshatriyas is arrived, for all those kings, from delusion, have with their counsellors followed Duryodhana.' Hearing these words of Bhishma, the lotus-eyed hero of Dasarha's race, possessed of great powers, addressing all those (that were still there) headed by Bhishma and Drona, said, 'Even this is great transgression, of which all the elders of the Kuru race are becoming guilty, for they do not forcibly seize and bind this wicked king in the enjoyment of sovereignty. Ye chastiser of foes, I think the time hath come for doing this. If this is done, it may still be productive of good. Listen to me, ye sinless ones. The words I will speak will soon lead to beneficial results, if, indeed, ye Bharatas, ye accept what I say in consequence of its recommending itself to you. The wicked son, of ill-regulated soul, of the old Bhoja king, having usurped his father's sovereignty during the latter's life-time, subjected himself to death. Indeed, Kansa, the son of Ugrasena, abandoned by his relatives, was slain by me in a great encounter, from desire of benefiting my kinsmen.

Ourselves with our kinsmen then, having paid due honours to Ugrasena, the son of Ahuka, installed that extender of Bhoja's kingdom on the throne. And all the Yadavas and Andhakas and the Vrishnis, abandoning a single person, *viz.*, Kansa for the sake of their whole race, have prospered and obtained happiness. O king, when the gods and *Asuras* were arrayed for battle and weapons were upraised for striking, the lord of all creatures, Parameshthin said thus (something which applies to the case at hand). Indeed, O Bharata, when the population of the worlds was divided into two parties and was about to be slaughtered, the divine and holy cause of the universe, *viz.*, the Creator, said, 'The Asuras and the Daityas with the Danavas will be vanquished, and the Adityas, the Vasus, the Rudras and other dwellers of heaven will be victorious. Indeed, the gods, and Asuras, and human beings, and

Gandharvas, and Snakes, and Rakshasas, will in rage slaughter one another in this battle.' Thinking so, the Lord of all creatures, Parameshthin, commanded Dharma, saying, 'Binding fast, the Daityas and the Danavas, make them over to Varuna.' Thus addressed, Dharma, at the command of Parameshthin, binding the Daityas and the Danavas, made them over to Varuna. And Varuna, the Lord of the waters, having bound those Danavas, with Dharma's noose, as also with his own, keepeth them within the depths of the ocean, always guarding them carefully. Binding in the same way Duryodhana and Karna and Sakuni, the son of Suvala, and Dussasana, make them over to the Pandavas. For the sake of a family, an individual may be sacrificed. For a village, a family may be sacrificed. For the sake of a province, a village may be sacrificed. And lastly, for the sake of one's self, the whole earth may be sacrificed. O monarch, binding Duryodhana fast, make peace with the Pandavas. O bull among Kshatriyas, let not the whole Kshatriya race be slaughtered on thy account.'"

Section CXXIX (129)

"Vaisampayana said, 'Hearing these words of Krishna, king Dhritarashtra lost no time in addressing Vidura, who was conversant with all dictates of virtue. And the king said, 'Go, O child, unto Gandhari, possessed of great wisdom and foresight and bring her hither. With her I will solicit this wicked-hearted (son of mine). If she can pacify this wicked wretch, of evil heart, we may yet be able to act according to the words of our friend Krishna. It may be that speaking words in recommendation of peace, she may yet succeed in pointing out the right path to this fool, affiicted by avarice and having wicked allies. If she can dispel this great and dreadful calamity (about to be) occasioned by Duryodhana, it will then conduce to the attainment and preservation of happiness and peace for ever and ever.' Hearing these words of the king, Vidura, at Dhritarashtra's command, brought (thither) Gandhari, possessed of great foresight. And Dhritarashtra then addressed Gandhari and said, 'Behold, O Gandhari, this thy son of wicked soul, transgressing all my commands, is about to sacrifice both sovereignty and life in consequence of his lust for sovereignty.

Of wicked soul and little understanding, he hath, like one of uncultivated mind, left the court, with his sinful counsellors, disregarding his superiors and setting at naught the words of his well-wishers.'

"Vaisampayana said, 'Hearing these words of her husband, that princess of great fame, Gandhari, desirous of what was highly beneficial, said these words, 'Bring hither, without loss of time, that kingdom-coveting, sick son of mine. He that is of uncultivated heart and sacrificeth both virtue and profit, doth not deserve to govern a kingdom. For all that, however, Duryodhana, who is destitute of humility hath, by every means, obtained a kingdom. Indeed, O Dhritarashtra, thou so fond of thy son, art very much to be blamed for this, for knowing well his sinfulness, thou followest yet his counsel. That son of thine, completely possessed by lust and wrath is now the slave of delusion, and is, therefore, incapable, O king, of being now forcibly turned back by thee. Thou art now reaping the fruit, O Dhritarashtra, of having made over the kingdom to an ignorant fool of wicked soul, possessed by avarice and having wicked counsellors. Why is the king indifferent (today) to that disunion, which is about to take place between persons related so closely? Indeed, beholding thee disunited with those that are thy own, thy enemies will laugh at thee. Who is there that would use force for getting over that calamity, O king, which can be overcome by conciliation and gift?'

"Vaisampayana continued, 'Kshattri then, and at Dhritarashtra's command, and of his mother's also, once more caused vindictive Duryodhana to enter the court. Expectant of his mother's words, the prince re-entered the court, with eyes red as copper from wrath, and breathing heavily as a snake. And beholding her son, who was treading in a wrong path, enter the court, Gandhari rebuked him severely and said these words for bringing about peace.'

"Gandhari said, 'O Duryodhana, attend, O dear son, to these words of mine that are beneficial to thee as also to all thy followers,—words that thou art competent to obey and that will conduce to thy happiness. O Duryodhana, obey thou the words of thy well-wishers, those words, *viz.*, which that best of the Bharatas—thy father—and Bhishma, and Drona, and Kripa, and Kshattri, have spoken. If thou makest peace, thou wouldst by that render homage to Bhishma, to thy father, to me, and to all thy well-wishers with Drona at their head. O thou of great wisdom, nobody, O best of the Bharatas, succeedeth by his own desire alone in acquiring and keeping or enjoying a kingdom. One that hath not his senses under control, cannot enjoy sovereignty for any length of time. He that hath his soul under control and is endued with great intelligence, can rule a kingdom. Lust and wrath wean away a man from his possessions and enjoyments. Conquering these foes first, a king bringeth the earth under his subjection. Sovereignty over men is a great thing. Those that are of wicked souls may easily desire to win a kingdom, but they are not competent to retain a kingdom (when won). He that desireth to obtain extensive empire must bind his senses to both profit and virtue, for if the senses are restrained, intelligence increaseth, like fire that increaseth when fed with fuel. If not controlled, these can even slay their possessor, like unbroken and furious horses, capable of killing an unskilful driver. One that seeketh to conquer his counsellors without conquering his own self, and to conquer foes without conquering his counsellors, is soon vanquished himself and is ruined. He who conquereth his own self first, taking it for a foe, will not seek in vain to conquer his counsellors and enemies afterwards. Prosperity worshippeth greatly that person who hath conquered his senses and his counsellors, who inflicteth punishments on transgressors, who acteth after deliberation, and who is possessed of wisdom. Lust and wrath that dwell in the body are deprived of their strength by wisdom, like a couple of fishes ensnared in a net with close holes. Those two in consequence of which the gods shut the gates of heaven against one, who freed from worldly propensities is desirous of going thither, are excited by lust and wrath. That king who knoweth well how to conquer lust and wrath and avarice and boastfulness and pride, can own the sovereignty of the whole earth. That king who is desirous of gaining wealth and virtue and vanquishing his enemies, should always be engaged in controlling his passions. Influenced by lust, or from wrath, he that behaveth deceitfully towards his own kinsmen or others, can never win many allies. Uniting thyself with those chastisers of foes—the heroic sons of Pandu—who are all endued with great wisdom, thou canst, O son, enjoy the earth in happiness. What Bhishma, the son of Santanu, and that mighty car-warrior, Drona, have told thee is, O son, quite true,—Krishna and Dhananjaya are invincible. Seek thou, therefore, the protection of this mighty-armed one, this one that is not worried by exertion, for if Kesava becometh gracious, both sides will be happy. That *min,* who is not obedient to the wishes of wise and learned friends, always seeking his prosperity, only gladdeneth his enemies. O son, there is no good in battle, no virtue, no profit. How can it bring happiness then? Even victory is not always certain. Do not set thy heart, therefore, on battle. O thou of great wisdom, Bhishma and thy father and Vahlika (formerly) gave unto the Pandavas their share (of the kingdom) from fear. O chastiser of foes, never think of disunion with them. Thou beholdest today the fruit of that (peaceful) cession in the fact of thy sovereignty over the whole earth, with all its thorns removed by those heroes. Give, O chastiser of foes, unto the son of Pandu what is their due. If thou wishest to enjoy, with the counsellors even half (the empire), let their share then be given unto them. Half the earth is sufficient to yield the means of support unto thee and thy counsellors. By acting according to the words of thy well-wishers, thou wilt, O Bharata, win great fame. A quarrel with the sons of Pandu who are all endued with prosperity, who have their souls under complete control, who are possessed of great intelligence and have conquered their passions, will only divest thee of thy great prosperity. Dispelling the wrath of all thy well-wishers, rule thou thy kingdom as becometh thee, giving, O bull of Bharata's race, unto the sons of Pandu the share that belongeth to them. O son, persecution of the sons of Pandu for full thirteen years hath been enough. Augmented by lust and wrath, quench (that fire) now, O thou of great wisdom. Thou that covetest the wealth of the Pandavas are not a match for them, nor this *Suta's* son, who is exceedingly wrathful, nor this thy brother Dussasana. Indeed, when Bhishma and Drona and Kripa and Karna and Bhimasena and Dhananjaya and Dhrishtadyumna will be enraged, the population of the earth will be exterminated. Under the influence of wrath, do not, O son, exterminate the Kurus. Let not the wide earth be destroyed for thy sake. Of little understanding as thou art, thou thinkest that Bhishma, and Drona, and Kripa, all others will fight (for thee) with all their might. That will never happen, for as regards these, that are endued with self-knowledge, their affection towards the Pandavas and yourselves is equal. If for the sake of the sustenance they have obtained from the king (Dhritarashtra), they consent to yield up their very lives, they will not yet be able to cast angry glances upon king Yudhishthira. It is never seen in this world that men acquire wealth by avarice. Give up thy avarice then, O son, and desist, O bull of Bharat's race.'"

Section CXXX (130)

"Vaisampayana said, 'Disregarding these words of grave import, spoken by his mother, Duryodhana went away, in anger, from that place to the presence of wicked persons. And wending away from the court, the Kuru prince began to consult with Suvala's royal son, Sakuni, most clever in dice. And this was the resolution which Duryodhana and Karna and Suvala's son Sakuni, with Dussasana as their fourth, arrived at, 'This Janardana, quick in action, seeketh, with the king Dhritarashtra and Santanu's son, to seize us first. We, however, shall forcibly seize this tiger among men, Hrishikesa, first, like Indra forcibly seizing Virochana's son (Vali). Hearing that this one of Vrishni's race hath been seized, the Pandavas will lose their heart and become incapable of exertion, like snakes whose fangs have been broken. This mighty-armed one is, indeed, the refuge and protection of them all. If this grantor of wishes, this bull of all the Satwatas, be confined, the Pandavas with the Somakas will become depressed and incapable of any exertion. Therefore, disregarding Dhritarashtra's cries, we will seize even here this Kesava, who is quick in action, and then fight with the foe.' After those sinful men of wicked souls had come to this sinful resolution, highly intelligent Satyaki, capable of reading the heart by signs, soon came to know of it. And because of that knowledge, he soon issued out of the court, accompanied by Hridika's son (Kritavarman). And Satyaki addressed Kritavarman, saying, 'Array the troops soon. And accoutred in mail and with thy troops arrayed for battle, wait thou at the entrance of the court, till I represent this matter unto Krishna, unwearied by exertion.' Saying this, that hero re-entered the court, like a lion entering a mountain-cave. And he (first) informed the high-souled Kesava and then Dhritarashtra, and then Vidura of that conspiracy. And having informed them of that resolution, he laughingly said, 'These wicked men intended to commit an act here, that is disapproved by the good from consideration of virtue, profit, and desire. They will, however, never be able to actually achieve it. These fools of sinful souls assembled together, these wretches overwhelmed by lust, anger and yielding themselves upto wrath and covetousness, are about to perpetrate a highly unbecoming deed. Those wretches of little understanding and desirous of seizing the lotus-eyed, are like idiots and children desiring to seize a blazing fire by means of their garments.' Hearing these words of Satyaki, Vidura, endued with great foresight, said these words unto the mighty-armed Dhritarashtra in the midst of the Kurus, 'O king, O chastiser of foes, the hour of all thy sons is come, for they are endeavouring to perpetrate a highly infamous act, however incapable they may be of actually accomplishing it. Alas, united together they desire to vanquish this younger brother of Vasava, and seize this lotus-eyed one. Indeed, encountering this tiger among men, this invincible and irresistible one, they will all perish like insects in a blazing fire. If Janardana wisheth, he can send all of them, even if they fight in a body, unto the abode of Yama, like an enraged lion dispatching a herd of elephants. He will, however, never do any such sinful and censurable act. This best of persons, of unfading glory, will never deviate from virtue.' After Vidura had said these words, Kesava, casting his eyes on Dhritarashtra, said in the midst of those well-meaning persons, who listen to others' words, 'O king, if these (men) desire to chastise me by using violence, permit them to chastise me. O monarch, as regards my chastising them, for I dare chastise all of them together that are so excited with rage, I will not, however, perpetrate any sinful and censurable act. Coveting the possessions of the Pandavas, thy sons will lose their own. If they desire to perpetrate such a deed, Yudhishthira's object will then be (easily) accomplished, for, this very day, O Bharata, seizing these with all that follow them, I can make them over to the sons of Pritha. What is there that is difficult of attainment by me? I will not, however, O Bharata, commit in thy presence, O great monarch, any such censurable deed, that can proceed only from wrath and a sinful understanding. Let it be, O king, as this Duryodhana desireth. I give permission, O monarch, to all thy sons to do it.'

"Hearing these words (of Kesava), Dhritarashtra addressed Vidura saying, 'Quickly bring hither sinful Duryodhana, who is so covetous of sovereignty, with his friends, counsellors, brothers, and followers. I shall see if indeed, making one more effort I can bring him to the right path.'

'Thus addressed by Dhritarashtra, Kshattri once more caused unwilling Duryodhana to enter the court with his brothers, and surrounded by the kings (that followed him). King Dhritarashtra then addressed Duryodhana, surrounded by Karna and Dussasana and all those kings, saying, 'O wretch of accumulated sins, having for thy allies men of despicable acts, infamous is the deed that thou, uniting with sinful friends, seekest to do. Of little understanding, thou, infamy of thy race, one like thee alone can seek to do an act so infamous and disapproved by the good, however impossible it may be of being actually achieved. Uniting with sinful allies, wishest thou to chastise this invincible and irresistible one of eyes like lotus-leaves? Like a child wishing to have the moon, seekest thou, O fool, to do what cannot be done by the very gods, headed by Vasava with all their strength? Knowest thou not, that Kesava is incapable of being withstood in battle by gods and men and *Gandharvas* and *Asuras* and *Uragas*? Like the wind which none can seize of being seized with his hands, like the moon which no hand can reach, like the Earth which none can support on his head, Kesava is incapable by force.'

"After Dhritarashtra had said these words, Vidura (casting) his eyes on Duryodhana, addressed that vindictive son of Dhritarashtra, saying, 'O Duryodhana, listen now to these words of mine. At the gates of *Saubha*, that foremost of monkeys, known by the name of Dwivida, covered Kesava with a mighty shower of stones. Desirous of seizing Madhava by putting forth all his prowess and exertion, he did not yet succeed in seizing him. Seekest thou to apprehend that Kesava by force? When Sauri went to Pragjyotisha, Naraka with all the Danavas succeeded not in seizing him there. Seekest thou to seize him by force? Slaying that Naraka in battle, he brought away (from his city) a thousand damsels and married them all, according to the ordinance. In the city of Nirmochana, six thousand mighty Asuras failed to seize him with their nooses. Seekest thou to seize that Kesava by force? While only a child, he slew Putana and two *Asuras* assuming the shape of birds, and O bull of Bharata's race, he held up the mountains of Govardhana (on his little finger) for protecting the kine (from a continuous rain). He hath also slain *Aristha*, and *Dhenuka* and *Chanura* of great strength, and *Aswaraja*, and Kansa, the doer of evil. He hath slain Jarasandha, and Vakra, and Sisupala of mighty energy, and Vana in battle, and numerous other kings also have been slain by him. Of immeasurable might, he vanquished king Varuna and also Pavaka (Agni), and on the occasion of bringing (down from the celestial regions) the (heavenly flower called) *Parijata*, he defeated the lord of Sachi himself. While floating on the vast deep, he slew Madhu and Kaitabha, and in another birth he slew *Hayagriva* (Horse-necked). He is the maker of everything but is himself made by none. He is the Cause of all power. Whatever Sauri wisheth, he accomplisheth without any effort. Knowest thou not sinless Govinda, of terrible prowess and incapable of deterioration? This one, resembling an angry snake of virulent poison, is the never-ending source of energy. In seeking to use violence towards Krishna, endued with mighty arms and unwearied by exertion, thou wilt, with all thy followers, perish like an insect failing into fire.'"

Section CXXXI (131)

"Vaisampayana said, 'After Vidura had said this, Kesava, that slayer of hostile divisions, endued with great energy, addressed Dhritarashtra's son, Duryodhana, and said, 'From delusion, O Suyodhana, thou regardest me to be alone, and it is for this, O thou of little understanding, that thou seekest to make me a captive after vanquishing me by violence. Here, however, are all the Pandavas and all the Vrishnis and Andhakas. Here are all the Adityas, the Rudras, and the Vasus, with all the great Rishis. Saying this Kesava, that slayer of hostile heroes burst out into a loud laughter. And as the high-souled Sauri laughed, from his body, that resembled a blazing fire, issued myriads of gods, each of lightning effulgence, and not bigger than the thumb. And on his forehead appeared Brahman, and on his breast Rudra. And on his arms appeared the regents of the world, and from his mouth issued Agni, the *Adityas*, the *Sadhyas*, the *Vasus*, the *Aswins*, the *Marutas*, with Indra, and the *Viswedevas*. And myriads of *Yakshas*, and the *Gandharvas*, and *Rakshasas* also, of the same measure and form, issued thence. And from his two arms issued Sankarshana and Dhananjaya. And Arjuna stood on his right, bow in hand, and Rama stood on his left, armed with the plough. And behind him stood Bhima, and Yudhishthira, and the two sons of Madri, and before him were all the Andhakas and the Vrishnis with Pradyumna and other chiefs bearing mighty weapons upraised. And on his diverse arms were seen the conch, the discus, the mace, the bow called *Saranga*, the plough, the javelin, the *Nandaka*, and every other weapon, all shining with effulgence, and upraised for striking. And from his eyes and nose and ears and every part of his body, issued fierce sparks of fire mixed with smoke. And from the pores of his body issued sparks of fire like unto the rays of the sun. And beholding that awful form of the high-souled Kesava, all the kings closed their eyes with affrighted hearts, except Drona, and Bhishma, and Vidura, endued with great intelligence, greatly blessed Sanjaya, and the *Rishis*, possessed of wealth of asceticism, for the divine Janardana gave unto them this divine sight on the occasion. And beholding in the (Kuru) court that highly wonderful sight, celestial drums beat (in the sky) and a floral shower fell (upon him). And the whole Earth trembled (at the time) and the oceans were agitated. And, O bull of the Bharata's race, all the denizens of the earth were filled with great wonder. Then that tiger among men, that chastiser of foes, withdrew that divine and highly wonderful, and extremely varied and auspicious form. And arm-in-arm with Satyaki on one side and Hridika's son (Kritavarman) on the other, and obtaining permission of the Rishis, the slayer of Madhu went out. And during the uproar that then took place, the Rishis, Narada and others vanquished, for repairing to their respective places. And this also was another wonderful incident that happened. And seeing that tiger among men leave the court, the

Kauravas with all the kings followed him, like the gods following Indra. Sauri, however, of immeasurable soul, without bestowing a single thought on those that followed him, issued from the court, like a blazing fire mixed with smoke. And he beheld (at the gate his charioteer) Daruka waiting with his large white car, furnished with rows of tinkling bells, decked with golden ornaments, and endued with great speed, the clatter of whose wheels resounded like the rumbling of the clouds, and which was covered all over with white tiger-skins, and unto which were harnessed his steeds Saivya (and others). And there also appeared, mounted on his car, that favourite hero of Vrishnis, the mighty car-warrior Kritavarman, the son of Hridika. And that chastiser of foes, Sauri, who had his car ready, was about to depart, king Dhritarashtra addressed him once more and said, 'O grinder of foes, thou hast seen, O Janardana, the power I wield over my sons! Thou hast, indeed, witnessed all with thy own eyes. Nothing now is unknown to thee. Seeing me endeavour to bring about peace between the Kurus, and the Pandavas, in fact, knowing the state (in which I am), it behoveth thee not to entertain any suspicion regarding me. O Kesava, I have no sinful feelings towards the Pandavas. Thou knowest what words have been spoken by me to Suyodhana. The Kauravas and all the kings of the Earth, also know, O Madhava, that I have made every endeavour to bring about peace.'

"Vaisampayana continued, 'The mighty-armed Janardana then addressed Dhritarashtra, Drona, grandsire Bhishma, Kshattri, Vahlika, and Kripa and said, 'Ye have yourselves witnessed all that hath happened in the assembly of the Kurus, *viz.*, how wicked Duryodhana, like an uneducated wretch, left the court from anger, and how king Dhritarashtra also describeth himself to be powerless. With the permission of you all, I shall now go back to Yudhishthira.' Saluting them, that bull amongst men, Sauri then mounted his car and set out. And those heroic bulls amongst the Bharatas, those mighty bowmen, *viz.*, Bhishma, Drona, and Kripa, and Kshattri, and Aswatthaman and Vikarna, and that mighty car-warrior Yuyutsu, all began to follow him. And Kesava, on his large white car, furnished with rows of tinkling bells, proceeded then, in the very sight of the Kurus, to the abode of his paternal aunt (Kunti).'"

Critical Essays

Aesthetics of the Mahābhārata

Traditional Interpretations

Radhavallabh Tripathi

> Though the Mahābhārata describes a society distracted by deceit and intrigue and though the story is reeking with war and the spirit of war, the author clearly declares himself against the politics of power and looks upon the state not as an organisation of force but as a partnership in *dharma*. The modern apostles of the doctrine that the state is an end in itself with no higher duty than to maintain itself, will not find support for their views in it. The view that the end of the state is to organise and establish dharma, that its powers are strictly limited by unalterable laws which it can only enforce, has a greater appeal to he cultivated conscience of our times. The author refuses to be stampeded by transient moods and agitations of the time but approves of the principle that righteousness exalteth a nation.
>
> — S. Radhakrishnan (2008: xi–xii)

In the tradition of Sanskrit literature, each text generally begins with spelling out its purpose and order of chapters including an index of contents. In this way, a text defines its own category and themes at the very outset. The author of the *Mahābhārata* also adheres to this norm. It is said in the beginning of this great epic that 'the characteristics of this text have been defined here itself' (*Ādiparvan* 1.48).

In this process of defining itself, the following generic and specific terms have been used in the *Mahābhārata: upajīvya, itihāsa, ākhyāna* or *ākhyānavariṣṭha, kāvya, pañcamaveda,* and *bhāratadruma*. These terms also present the concept of the *Mahābhārata* as an epic poem.

In the tradition of *alaṅkāraśāstra* (literary theory in Sanskrit) the *Mahābhārata* has been defined as a *lakṣyagrantha* (a sourcebook for the *lakṣaṇas* or theories and definitions) and an *ārṣakāvya* (a *kāvya* or poem composed by a *ṛṣi* or seer). This essay examines the significance of these categorizations in understanding the nature of the unique aesthetic experience that the *Mahābhārata* leads us into.

Mahābhārata as *Upajīvya*

The term *upajīvya* means that which sustains, enlivens or functions as a source. The *Mahābhārata* claims that it should be classed as an *upajīvya kāvya:* 'This text will become an *upajīvya* for all the great poets, like Parjanya (rains, god of rain) for all the beings' (*Ādiparvan* 1.92)

Curiously enough, the term *upajīvya* has not been referred to in well-known Sanskrit dictionaries like *Amarakośa* and *Śabdakalpadruma*. The latter, however, includes *upajīvikā* and refers to *upajīvya* as its synonym (*Śabdakalpadruma*, vol. 1: 252). *Vācaspatyam* provides exhaustive notes on *upajīvya* and *upajīvikā*. Whereas the latter is defined just as a source of livelihood that sustains, *upajīvya* has been treated as a broader concept. It has been explained as the substratum, i.e., some thing that is taken recourse to, for existence of knowledge, for livelihood and other things. It is *prayojaka* (motivator) of *svasattā* (one's own existence) and *prayojaka* of *svajñāna* (knowledge of the self) (*Vācaspatyam*, vol. 2: 1207).

Considering the aforementioned explanation of *upajīvya*, we can say that the creators of the *Mahābhārata* visualized it as something that would sustain the traditions of knowledge and the society. The significance of the term *upajīvya* has been missed in the present studies on the *Mahābhārata* and the authors writing histories of Sanskrit literature have mostly referred to the *Mahābhārata* as an *upajīvya kāvya* only to bring out its impact on the literary tradition. An *upajīvya kāvya*, as envisaged in the *Mahābhārata* itself, would also set norms to be followed, establish trends and set traditions. The *Mahābhārata*, therefore, proclaims its role as an *upajīvya kāvya* in the following manner: 'This *ākhyāna* has become an *upajīvya* for all the good poets, just as a good lord becomes an *upajīvya* for all the servants desirous of progress' (*Ādiparvan* 2.241).

The *Mahābhārata*, as an *upajīvya kāvya*, not only presents the worldview, paradigms and standards for the Indian way of life, but also serves a source of literary criticism. The *ācāryas* (masters or theorists) of *alaṅkāraśāstra* have, therefore, rightly chosen the term *lakṣyagrantha* for the *Mahābhārata*. Ānandavardhana, a great savant of literary theory, remarks: 'The connoisseurs have been finding the attestation of the literary theories in the *lakṣyas* like the *Rāmāyaṇa* and the *Mahābhārata*' (*Dhvanyāloka, vṛtti* on 1.1).

The *Mahābhārata* in this way also spells out the criteria of literary analysis to be applied to itself. In fact, it was basically through the process of the composition of the *Mahābhārata* that the whole scenario of literary theory in the first millennium CE underwent a revolutionary change. The theory of *śāntarasa* and, finally, *śānta* as a *mahārasa* (greatest of the *rasas*) or *mūlarasa* (basic *rasa*) could be conceived because of the *Mahābhārata*.

It has been suggested in the text as well as in the commentaries on it that the *Mahābhārata* encompasses everything that sustains or nourishes a nation, or everything that should be cherished by it. This all-embracing nature of the text is also upheld in the oft-quoted maxim: *yanna bhārate tanna bhārate* (that which is not in *Mahābhārata*, is not to be found in this country of Bhāratavarṣa'). Again, by the way of self-appraisal, the *Mahābhārata* also declares: 'Whatever has been said here with regard to the four goals of human life can be found elsewhere, but whatever has not been said here will not be found anywhere else' (*Ādiparvan* 56.33).

Mahābhārata as *Itihāsa*

Both the *Rāmāyana* of Valmiki and the *Mahābhārata* are regarded as *itihāsas*. The term *itihāsa* is generally translated as 'history'. But it is not exactly analogous to the concept of history. While defining itself as *itihāsa*, the *Mahābhārata* also clarifies the idea of an *itihāsa*. An *itihāsa* is supposed to be as eternal as the Vedas. One of the vedic *saṁhitās* proclaims: 'Just like the four Vedas, the *itihāsa, purāṇa, gāthā and nārāśaṁsī* also came out from the Supreme Being' (*Atharvaveda* XV.6.11). The Upaniṣads also treat *itihāsa* on a par with Veda itself (*Bṛhadāraṇyaka Upaniṣad* IV.1.2).[1] The particle *iti* ('thus') in *itihāsa* denotes its capability of leading to a clear perception. Abhinavagupta, in his commentary titled *Abhinavabhāratī* on Bharatamuni's *Nāmyaśāstra* (I.15), gives a twofold interpretation to the term *itihāsa*. *Iti* denotes the visualization through direct perception—the past being visualized as if it is happening in the present. There is a stray verse quoted in *Vācaspatyam* providing the standard definition of *itihāsa*: 'The *itihāsa* comprises an account of past happenings and also preaches the way for the attainment of the *puruṣārthas* (four goals of human life)' (vol. 1: 924).

An *itihāsa* text thus presents a continuum of past, present and future. It is both prescriptive and descriptive. It is supposed to define the *puruṣārthas* and also the way for their attainment. The emphasis in this view of an *itihāsa* text is on the description of what ought to be, rather than on what was or has been and, as an *itihāsa*, the *Mahābhārata* is a poem of 'being and becoming'.

Applying the criterion for qualifying as an *itihāsa* to itself, the *Mahābhārata* claims that it is not just a documentation of the practices that have prevailed and are likely to continue, but also unravels the mysteries, records whatever is valuable, and creates a repository of knowledge systems (*Ādiparvan* 1.45-48).

With its discourse on the four goals of human life, an *itihāsa* text attains the status of an *āgama* (scripture). The *Mahābhārata* proclaims that 'it is the essence of the *itihāsa* that would form the best of the *āgamas* as it is imbrued with subtle meanings (*sūkṣmārtha*) and major concepts (*pradhānārtha*)' (*Ādiparvan* 2.31-33).

In this tradition, *itihāsa* is to be treated on a par with the Vedas, and is regarded as an important discipline to be studied like the Vedas. The *Mahābhārata*, in fact, equates itself with the Vedas (*Ādiparvan* 1.19). *Lokavṛtta* or the circle of society at large is said to be the subject for treatment in *itihāsa* (*Nyāyabhāṣya* IV.1.61).

The concept of *itihāsa*, in this way, incorporates cultural narrative of epic dimensions, a grand discourse as well as history of ideas, history of philosophy, together with cosmology. And all this should be visualized to make it relevant to a contemporary audience, as suggested by Abhinavagupta.

The tradition of the *alaṅkāraśāstra* classifies the *Mahābhārata* as an *ārṣa mahākāvya* (an epic composed by a seer). Viśvanātha was the first to use this term for the *Mahābhārata* (*Sāhityadarpaṇa* VI.304). An *ārṣa mahākāvya* is imbued with the vision of a seer. Having visualized the past, present and future of a country and the continuum of time in a flux, the seer presents the destiny of a nation and society and enables us to see it.

Mahābhārata as *Ākhyāna*

Ākhyāna means a narrative. It formed an essential subject in the curriculum of ancient *gurukulas* or *āśramas*. The Upaniṣads mention *ākhyāna* as one of the disciplines to be studied, along with the Vedas and the Vedāṅgas (six disciplines required for the study of the Vedas). *Ākhyāna* actually formed a part of the curriculum in the Upaniṣadic period (*Chāndogya Upaniṣad* VII.2.4).

The *Mahābhārata* describes itself as an *ākhyāna* and *ākhyānavariṣṭha* (greatest of the *ākhyānas*) (*Ādiparvan* 1.16). It further says that a person does not become wise unless he studies this *ākhyāna* (*Ādiparvan* 2.235).

Ākhyāna stands in close relationship with *upākhyāna,* which can be defined as an epic within the Epic, or a discourse within a grand discourse. Technically, as Bhoja puts it, an *upākhyāna* is a tale retold by one of the characters of an *ākhyāna* for enlightenment of another character, whereas an *ākhyāna* has been defined as a grand narrative to be presented by way of recitation of a text, songs and *abhinaya* (*Śṛṅgāraprakāśa* XI.331). Invariably, it has a relationship with the four Vedas: it is supposed to substantiate the Vedas. It is a narrative recording the achievements and history of an important dynasty. Teaching of the *ākhyāna* was regarded as necessary as the teaching of the Vedas and Vedāṅgas. As the *ākhyāna* forms a part of the collective memory of a community or society, it is told and retold again and again and the literary tradition subsists on it. As the *Mahābhārata* itself proclaims: 'Poets have been telling the *ākhyāna* of the *Mahābhārata* earlier, others are narrating it now-a-days and still some others will narrate it in future' (*Ādiparvan* 1.24; 2.390). Further, an *ākhyāna* is supposed to substantiate the Vedas, and the study of Vedas in itself is incomplete unless the *ākhyāna* is not included as a part of the curricula (*Ādiparvan* 2.235).

The *ākhyāna* was also an important part of Vedic rituals. Vedic rituals had two features: invocation of the divine and representation of the human creativity. The latter included recitation of *gāthās* (a lyrical form) and *nārāśaṁśīs* (heroic tales), as well as that of *ākhyāna*. A later Vedic text, *Aitareya Brāhmaṇa* (XXXIII.6.18), records the Śunaḥśepa *ākhyāna* or the story of Śunaḥśepa which was to be recited by the *hotṛ* priest during the performance of the *Rājasūya yajña* or royal consecration.

In the *Aśvamedha yajña* or horse sacrifice, the horse having been sent out for *digvijaya* (conquest of various kingdoms in all the directions), various *ākhyānas* named *Pārilava ākhyānas* (series of stories) were recited continuously for a year completed in 10 days, and thus, in each *Aśvamedha*, a total of 36 *ākhyānas* were recited. The *Rāmāyaṇa* of Valmiki (I.11.21, 12.1) records a gap of one year after the horse was left to wander during the course of the *Aśvamedha* performed by king Daśaratha, but does not specify the activities that went on in the *yajñamaṇḍapa* (pavilion for the sacrifice) till the horse returned. The *Aitareya Brāhmaṇa* (III.25.1) also mentions the *ākhyānavids* (narrators well versed in *ākhyānas*) who can recite the Sauparṇa legend.

Mahābhārata as *Kāvya* and *Veda*

Kāvya, in general, is a literary composition. The authors of the *Mahābhārata* conceived the text as a *kāvya*. The *Mahābhārata,* while defining itself as a *kāvya,* claims that it is a *kāvya* which even the *kavis* (poets) would find difficult to comprehend (*Ādiparvan* 1.97-98). Thus, the word *kāvya* would not just mean an ordinary poem in this context; it is to be treated on a par with the Vedas or *mantras,* and a *kavi* is not just an ordinary poet, but a seer. Describing the *Mahābhārata* as a *kāvya,* the authors of the epic claim: 'This poem is embellished with pious words, with human and divine conventions, it is enjoined with various meters and it is dear to the scholars' (*Ādiparvan* 1.26).

The *Mahābhārata* is also called the 'fifth Veda' or *Kārṣṇya Veda* (a Veda created by Kṛṣṇadvaipāyana Vyāsa) (*Ādiparvan* 3.20). The application of the term 'Veda' to the *Mahābhārata* is not merely a eulogy. The tradition provides the logic of conferring the status of the 'fifth Veda' to the epic. The study of *itihāsa* was taken up by the *Sūtas* in the same way as learned *Brāhmaṇas* recited the Vedas. The *itihāsa* was to be recited before an assembly of *dvijas* (twice-born) (*Anuśāsanaparvan* 90.26). The 88 sages led by Śaunaka are described as devout listeners of the *itihāsa* and *purāṇa* being narrated by a *Sūta*. The invariable link between the Vedas and the *Mahābhārata* is established by Yāska, the author of *Nirukta* (treatise on etymology) who adjusts some of the portions of the Vedas as *itihāsa* and *ākhyāna*. Kauṭilya too uses the term *Itihāsaveda* (*Arthaśāstra* I.3.2) and prescribes it as a part of the curriculum to be studied by a King. Manu also prescribed the daily study of *itihāsa* and *ākhyāna* (*Manusmṛti* III.232).

Tree as Metaphor for *Mahābhārata*

The authors of the *Mahābhārata* itself view the poem as a tree (*bhāratadruma*). The metaphor is extended to make the *Karṇaparvan* analogous to flowers, plucked and spreading their fragrance in the *Śalyaparvan*, and finally yielding the great fruit in the *Śāntiparvan*, with the *Mausalaparvan* forming the end of the tree of *Mahābhārata* (*Ādiparvan* 1.106-107, 120).

The two main characters of the epic are also visualized as two different trees: the tree of *manyu* (wrath) on one hand, and the tree of *dharma* on the other, represented out of wrath, Karṇa is its trunk, Śakuni its branches, Duḥśāsana its fruits and flowers, and the weak king Dhṛtarāṣṭra its root. Yudhiṣṭhira is a great tree created out of *dharma*, Arjuna is its trunk, Bhīma its branches, the two sons of Mādrī its fruits and flowers, and Śrīkṛṣṇa, the *Brahman* (Supreme Being), and the *Brāhmaṇas* (those who have knowledge of *Brahman*) its roots' (*Ādiparvan* 1.65, 66). This metaphor of the whole epic poem as a tree is in consonance with the traditional perception of literature. Bharatamuni, while defining the relationship between the diverse components of poetry, explains them beautifully through the metaphor of a tree: 'Just as a tree grows out of a seed, and from the tree come out the flowers and fruits, in the same way, *rasa* is the foundation and from *rasa* all the *bhāvas* (emotional states) find an arrangement' (*Nāṭyaśāstra* VII.38). Abhinavagupta, commenting on this stanza, says: 'A *kāvya* is tree, the performance by the actors is the flower and the relish of its *rasa* by the spectators is fruit'. In our cosmic view also, the Universe is viewed as a tree.

A beautiful verse in praise of the *Mahābhārata* is traditionally recited before the recitation of the *Bhagavadgītā*. It imagines the epic as this unblemished lotus blossom that the words of Vyāsa, the son of Parāśara, constitutes. "The intense fragrance of that flower is the deep meaning of the *Gītā*. Various stories and sub-stories are its petals. And this lotus blossoms as we address Lord Kṛṣṇa Hari through discourse by Him and about Him. Good and wise people buzz around this lotus like bees, drinking daily and repeatedly the nectar from its heart. May this *Mahābhārata*-lotus destroy the dirt we gather in this degraded age of Kali". This metaphor captures both the purity and the perfume, the aesthetic relishability (nectar, *rasa*) and the ethical attractiveness of this epic poem, which makes honest wise men addicted to the honey it bears.

Mahābhārata as a Text of Śāntarasa

Contrary to the views of many Western scholars and modern critics,[2] the *Mahābhārata* is viewed as a homogenous text in the Indian literary tradition. Also, there is a unity of design that is envisaged in the terms used to describe this epic. In this way, the concepts of the *upajīvya kāvya, itihāsa, ākhyāna* or *ākhyānavariṣṭha, kāvya, Pañcamaveda* or *Kārṣṇyaveda,* and *Bhāratadruma* are logically linked together. There is unity in its structure and design because the whole text culminates in the realization of the *puruṣārthas* and finally the fourth *puruṣārtha,* i.e., *mokṣa* (salvation). To understand the aesthetics of the *Mahābhārata,* we have to take into consideration the concept of *rasa* (aesthetic experience) and its relationship with *puruṣārtha* (aspirations of human life). Each *rasa* should culminate in one of the *puruṣārthas.* Even *śṛṅgāra* (erotic) *rasa* not only yields *kāmapuruṣārtha,* but may also lead to the attainment of other *puruṣārthas,* viz., *dharma* or *artha.* Bharatamuni, therefore, defines three types of *kāma*: *dharmakāma, arthakāma* and *mokṣakāma* (*Nāṭyaśāstra* XXII.96). Ānandavardhana, in his *Dhvanyāloka*

(IV *udyota*), says that *śānta* is the dominant *rasa* in the *Mahābhārata*. He also holds *śāntarasa* as a vehicle for salvation. Abhinavagupta establishes the supremacy of *śāntarasa* by arguing that it is a vehicle for *mokṣa puruṣārtha,* and *mokṣa* is the supreme amongst all the four *puruṣārthas* (ibid.).

If the purpose of whole poem is the realization of *mokṣa,* then *śānta* ought to be its dominant *rasa.* The logic of the whole poem culminating in the experience of *śānta* can be better understood when we consider the concept of *rasa* according to Ānandavardhana and Abhinavagupta. The *rasas* like *vīra* (heroic) and *raudra* (terrific) do occur in the *Mahābhārata,* but *bībhatsa rasa* (disgust) becomes more conspicuous than these.

Bharatamuni identified four *rasas* as the *mūla* (basic) *rasas*: *śṛṅgāra, vīra, bībhatsa,* and *raudra.* Out of each of these, four subsidiary *rasas* are generated. Thus, *hāsya* (comic) is born out of *śṛṅgāra*; *adbhuta* (wonder) out of *vīra*; *bhayānaka* out of *bībhatsa*; and *karuṇa* (pathetic) out of *raudra.*

This concept of basic and subsidiary *rasas* has its own logic as the four basic *rasas* are invariably linked with the four *puruṣārthas,* i.e., *śṛṅgāra* to *kāma, vīra* to *dharma, raudra* to *artha,* and *bībhatsa* to *mokṣa.* The *bībhatsa rasa* is of two types: *kṣobhaja* (generated by anguish) and *udvegī* (born out of uneasiness). The former leads to disillusionment which clears the path to salvation.

Through the aesthetics of the *bībhatsa rasa,* therefore, the spectator or reader undergoes the experiences of anguish, uneasiness and disgust which may finally make him liberated from the mundane and the earthly. Abhinavagupta is right in suggesting that the experience of the *bībhatsa rasa* would thus lead to *śānta* and to salvation. The *kṣobhaja* type of *bībhatsa* is also called pure (*śuddha*) and leads to liberation (*mokṣa*).

The aesthetics of the *Mahābhārata* does not rest on *tanmayībhavana* (rapture). It is just opposite of the aesthetics of ecstasy. It is the aesthetics of distance and detachment. The text itself accepts that it is not about pleasure and happy times. It claims that it is going to describe something sad and awful. Vyāsa, at the very outset of the narrative, approaches Satyavatī, his mother, and tells her that most unhappy times are approaching:

> Gone are the times of happiness
> the terrible times are nearing in,
> each coming day is going to bear
> more and more horror
> and the youth of the earth
> has already been exhausted. (*Ādiparvan* 119.6)

It is true that the *Mahābhārata* presents the deepest moments of crisis in history and in human life raising perennial questions of existence. But there is this warning note which resounds again and again in its texture. The sense of utter waste persists. After emerging victorious in the great war, Yudhiṣṭhira says: 'The whole world appears empty and hollow and no longer pleases me. They are all gone—the friends and kin—and my army is wasted away' (*Śāntiparvan* 26.2-3). Arjuna, the great hero of the *Mahābhārata* war, loses face in a pathetic debacle at the hands of petty robbers and is unable to rescue the ladies of the Yādava family. But the *Mahābhārata* does not end in this utter dejection and sense of helplessness. The deep anguish and disgust that the heroes like Yudhiṣṭhira and Arjuna feel paves the way for *śānta rasa* and *mokṣa*.

Therefore, the tradition does not hold the *Mahābhārata* as an epic of genocide, as it is viewed by the modern scholarship.[3] Also, neither is it understood as a tragedy ending in utter dejection, again quite unlike the way it is understood by the critics of today.[4] We find that rising from the feeling of dejection, both the great heroes, Yudhiṣṭhira and Arjuna, approach Bhīṣma and Vyāsa respectively and receive the final discourse on *dharma* and the way to salvation. The saga of struggle between two branches of the same dynasty is invested with a higher purpose of life and fulfillment of aspirations of human beings. There is no feeling of joy and sensuous pleasure at the end of the narrative. Ironically enough, both Ānandavardhana and Abhinavagupta, two of the greatest masters of *rasa—dhvani* system in the *alaṅkāraśāstra,* therefore, agree that the *Mahābhārata* has a *virasāvasāna* (an ending devoid of *rasas*). Ānandavardhana says that this ending sans *rasa* produces a feeling of dejection. But this leads to renunciation as well at the same time. Therefore, the keynote of the *Mahābhārata* lies in *mokṣa*. Vyāsa, a person of supreme intelligence, with a view to save the humanity drowned in illusion, imparting the light of knowledge himself, says: 'Just as the world order without an essence, goes disarray, the feeling of renunciation takes over' (*Śāntiparvan* 168.4). Ānandavardhana hints at two levels of *rasa*-realization here: *samanaska* (with attachment) and *vimanaska* (without attachment, dispassionate). There is *rasa* through empathy in former; the latter involves aesthetics of distance and disillusionment.

Commenting on Ānandavardhana's thesis, Abhinavagupta says: 'Annihilation of each other by the people of Vṛṣṇi race, the calamity inappropriately befalling on the Pāṇḍavas and the killing of Kṛṣṇa by a hunter—through all these episodes, the *Mahābhārata* has an ending that is devoid of *rasa*' (*Dhvanyāloka* IV.5).

Not only does Ānandavardhana hold the *virasāvasāna* as the culmination point of this great epic, but he also says that the *Mahābhārata* is a *śāstra* and has been brought to end with complete disillusionment or detachment because a *śāstra* (scripture) should be in a form of a discourse on some *puruṣārtha*. The *Mahābhārata* has *mokṣa* as the *puruṣārtha* and *śānta* as its dominant *rasa*. Despite tremendous emotional scenes, there is *vimanaskatā* or annihilation of all pleasurable sensations.

Ānandavardhana also informs that there has been a tradition of interpreting the *Mahābhārata* in this way. Its author, the great and wise Vyāsa, wrote it with an intention of rescuing the people from the abyss of ignorance in which they were weltering, and leading them to emancipation.

All other *puruṣārthas* are subservient to *mokṣa* and all other *rasas* subsidiary in relation to *śānta rasa*. The opponents of this theory would possibly raise the question: how can one decide that only *mokṣa* and *śānta rasas* are conspicuous in the text, when the text itself declares in the very beginning that all the *puruṣārthas* are to be delineated in it. Ānandavardhana says that there is an inherent focus on *mokṣa* in the text and it is not proclaimed directly, but suggested by the very presence of Śrīkṛṣṇa as the *sanātana tattva* (eternal element). The very feeling of a sheer 'colossal waste' and uselessness of all human efforts would generate the inclination towards renunciation.

The fact that the author of the *Mahābhārata* has named one of the *parvans* as *Śāntiparvan* is a strong evidence for corroborating the theory of Ānandavardhana and Abhinavagupta. The understanding of the *Mahābhārata* requires a paradigm different from the prevailing norms of aesthetics in the later tradition of Sanskrit literary theory.

Notes

1. *Upaniṭṣaṃgraha,* 111.
2. Modern orientalists failed to appreciate the *Mahābhārata* as a coherent homogeneous poem. M. Winternitz went to the extent of calling it a 'literary nonsense'. To quote him: 'The Mahābhārata as a whole is a literary nonsense. Never has an artist's hand tried—and it would have been really impossible—to unite the conflicting elements into a unitary poem. Only theologicians and commentators without poetic leanings and clumsy copyists have at last welded together into a disorderly mass the actually non-combinable parts coming down from different countries' (Winternitz 1987: 305).
3. 'One of the themes is repeated, large scale but inconclusive human destruction. The business at Kurukshetra is just one in a series of near genocides' (Brodbeck and Black 2007: 8).
4. 'It is not Śānta but Duranta—the tragic sense—that prevails in MB' (Sharma 2009: 33).

Political Formations and Cultural Ethos

Sheldon Pollock

Production and Reproduction of Epic Space

[. . .] Narrative has an internal spatial logic, a "semiotic domain around which a plot coalesces and self-organizes," as one scholar puts it, though literature does not merely receive and reproduce this domain secondhand but helps to create it. In addition to literature's narrative mapping of a particular world, literary forms themselves are "place-bound" and have their "peculiar geometry . . . boundaries . . . and favorite routes."[1]

It is these two other properties—the space that has meaning for Sanskrit literature qua literature and the space of its literary forms—that now need to be addressed. It would be instructive to examine these for Sanskrit literary culture as a whole and to show the varieties of spatial logic present in premodern South Asia.[2] . . . Our focus here will be the Sanskrit *Mahābhārata:* investigating the space of literary content and the space of literary form in premodern India's most sustained and profound discourse on power brings us into direct contact with a vision of cosmopolis as a political order that was as influential as any in shaping thought about and practice of polity during the first millennium. It is not often recognized just how significant a feature spatiality is for the *Mahābhārata,* both internally in the story it has to tell and externally in the kinds of literary-cultural practices that ensured the text's reproduction and promoted its circulation. Whatever other interests it may have, and there are many to be sure, the *Mahābhārata* seems especially concerned with creating a conceptual macrosphere of culture-power in the same way as its custodians were concerned with consolidating this sphere in the world of thought and action.

Everything about the *Mahābhārata,* from its history as a text to the history of its impact on South Asian culture, is huge and complex. There is little hard evidence about the origins of the work in its monumental form (eighteen books, and something on the order of a hundred thousand verses according to its own calculation). Even a cursory analysis of the manuscript data available in the critical edition reveals that the majority of the books were transmitted not orally but in reasonably stable form based on written archetypes. These cannot have come into being much before the beginning of the Common Era and are very likely of a much later date. This written transmission was vastly complicated by the fact that the text circulated as part of a living culture and grew and changed as dramatically as any living cultural phenomenon has ever done, producing a text-critical problem as large and intricate as any in world literature.

The genre to which the *Mahābhārata* belongs, and therefore the kinds of meanings traditional readers and listeners found in it, is not much easier to unravel than its textual history. It represents itself for the most part as *itihāsa,* an account of "the way things indeed were." However much modern scholarship may complicate the factuality of that record, many serious minds of medieval India concerned with telling the truth about the past took as Year One on their calendars the date of the war described by *Mahābhārata* and of the Kaliyuga that the war was believed to have inaugurated. Yet the *Mahābhārata* was not only *itihāsa,* it was also *kāvya.* For many later writers (as their encomia of poets show, and as Rājaśekhara's tale of Poetry Man confirms), Vyāsa, the supposed author of the *Mahābhārata,* was a poet second only to Vālmīki. Eventually the *Mahābhārata* came to also be viewed as a transcendently authoritative moral discourse; one ninth-century literary theorist conceived of the work as "moral discourse with the aura of literature." The last important medieval editor and commentator of the *Mahābhārata,* at the end of the seventeenth century, could thus say,

> To the objection that one should not comment on or recite the *Mahābhārata* as if it were a sacred text because it is a human creation . . . I respond: whether or not simpletons like us can find the Vedic sources from which the *Mahābhārata* is derived, it is derived from Vedic sources. The entire body of moral discourse remembered *(smṛti)* that was composed by Manu, Vyāsa, and the other omniscient seers is precisely like the Veda insofar as it is the enunciation of those who know the Veda. It should therefore be treated like scripture *(āgamayitavyam)* and commented upon and recited accordingly.[3]

Such different textual identities—history, poetry, moral law, and scripture—entailed for traditional readers and listeners quite different protocols of interpretation, and medieval Indian literary theory is unequivocal on the various kinds of meaning communicated by various textual types. The additional complications that arise when the *Mahābhārata* (as also the *Rāmāyaṇa*) is subsumed under the European idea of epic, especially when epic is assessed within the context of modern European discourses on nation and novel, need separate analysis.

Of a complexity commensurate with its manuscript history and genre identity is the *Mahābhārata*'s very content. If the *Rāmāyaṇa* is rightly said to have become a veritable language for talking about the world, then the *Mahābhārata* became a veritable library of the world, for around the main narrative are piled high many volumes of lore and doctrine contributed by Indian thinkers and storytellers over centuries. The work famously celebrates its own encyclopedism, declaring near the start that "whatever exists in the world is to be found in the *Mahābhārata* and whatever is not there does not exist." Nonetheless, the text, over the course of tens of thousands of verses, never loses sight of the narrative core—the struggle between two sets of cousin-brothers for succession to rulership in the Kuru capital, Hastināpura—or of the central problematic upon which it is so adamantly insistent, the antinomy of political power:

> *arthasya puruṣo dāso dāsas tv artho na kasya cit /*
>
> Man is slave to power, but power is slave to no one.[4]

The dilemma of power—in the starkest terms, the need to destroy in order to preserve, to kill in order to live—becomes most poignant when those whom one must kill are one's own kin. That is why the *Mahābhārata* is the most harrowing of all premodern political narratives in the world: the *Iliad,* like the *Rāmāyaṇa,* is about a war far from home, the *Odyssey* about a post-war journey home, and the *Aeneid* about a war for a home. The *Mahābhārata* is about a war fought at home, and in any such war, both sides must lose.

The spatial interests of the *Mahābhārata* exert the same kind of structuring force on the narrative as do its political interests, and this is so because the two are mutually constitutive: the political exists in space, and what exists in space is unavoidably related to the domain of power, whether as something inviting or something resisting incorporation. Thus the plotting of an epic geosphere, far from representing just another among the *Mahābhārata*'s myriad concerns, forms one of its central subjects. Power here is figured, in essence, as the command of space, however we are to understand the idea of command (and the difficulties of a satisfactory understanding should not be minimized), and the space to be controlled is thus a fundamental concern of power. The latter point merits particular scrutiny because it merited the *Mahābhārata*'s own scrutiny. Over and over the narrative maps a coherent supraregional domain, a zone within which political action was held to be operative and meaningful. In fact, such mapping presents itself at every important narrative juncture in the text—exemplifying in this something of Bakhtin's "chronotope," but with the chronotope's politics of space more clearly visible than Bakhtin himself may have understood.[5] Here are several key instances:

In preparation for his consecration as *cakravartin,* "wheel-turning emperor," the act that determines the course of the entire rest of the tale, Yudhiṣṭhira, the eldest of the Pāṇḍavas, sends out his four brothers to conquer "the four directions"—not "in the four directions" but the whole known world that had political meaning: Arjuna to the north, to defeat the people of Ānartta, the Kāśmīrakas, the Bāhlīkas, and others; Bhīma to the east, to defeat the people of Videha, Magadha, Aṅga, Vaṅga, and Tāmralipi; Sahadeva to the south, to defeat the people of Tripurā and Potana, plus the Pāṇḍyas, Drāviḍyas, Coḍrakeralas, and Andhras; and Nakula to the west, to defeat the kings of Marubhūmi, Mālava, and Pañcanada, as far as the Pahlavas.[6]

At the moment of greatest tension, on the eve of the war, Dhṛtarāṣṭra, the blind king who is uncle to the Pāṇḍavas and father of their rivals led by Duryodhana, muses in private with his confidant, Sañjaya. This scene has been preceded by a series of increasingly desperate and ultimately fruitless delegations sent by both sides in hopes of averting war, and the mustering of forces, which "has turned the whole orb of Jambūdvīpa, as far as the sun shines, into an armed camp." Dhṛtarāṣṭra believes catastrophe is inevitable, being convinced of the fact (however perplexed by it) that kings are always prepared to kill each other for possession of the earth: "O Sañjaya, these brave kings, who delight in war. . . are ready to give up their life for land. . . What virtues must this earth possess, Sañjaya! Speak to me of them." He asks about the different continents and in particular about Bhāratavarṣa—"object of my son Duryodhana's craving, of the greed of the sons of Pāṇḍu, and of my own attachment"—and the regions and cities from which the countless soldiers have gathered for war. After describing the seven "family mountains" of Bhāratavarṣa, from Mahendra to Malaya, and the many great rivers from the Narmadā to the Kāverī, Sañjaya lists the multitude of *janapadas*, "people-places," beginning with the lands of the Kurus and Pāñcālas and proceeding in more or less clockwise order through a hundred or more locales, from Śūrasena, Kaliṅga, Kuntala, Kāśikośala, and Cedivatsa to the people-places of the south and west, ending with those of the Huṇas (Huns), Tukhāras (Tocharians), and Pahlavas (Parthians) in their mountain fastnesses.[7]

After the war, the Pāṇḍavas perform the horse sacrifice, thereby asserting their political authority over whatever space the sacrificial horse wanders through unchallenged. As a result the supralocal domain is plotted again, this time extending from Trigarta, Prāgjyotiṣa, Maṇipūra, Magadha, Vaṅga, Cedi, Kāśī, Kosala, Āndhra, and Draviḍa across to Gokarṇa, Prabhāsa, Dvārakā, Pañcanada, and Gandhāra.

If the Pāṇḍavas' political power has now been confirmed, both the war and the new and meaner Kali Age it has inaugurated have sapped their strength and will: "Cursed be the law of power," they declare, "that has left us dead in life." They eventually renounce sovereignty and begin the *mahāprasthāna,* the Great Departure. They proceed first to the Lauhitya River (the Brahmaputra) in Bengal to the east, then "travel by way of the northern coast of the ocean to the southwest quarter," head for Dvārakā and thence to Mount Himavān, the great Sand Ocean, and Mount Meru. The journey is sketched in broad strokes, but the text takes care to note that the Pāṇḍavas, at the end of their "skein of journeys," have performed one last circumambulation of the earth for the possession of which they had earlier destroyed their family.[8]

Thus at every turning point of the main narrative—the royal consecration before the war, the survey of a world soon to be at war that is the very object of that war, the reaffirmation of dominion after the war, the ritual death march at the end of the story—the *Mahābhārata* continually insists on *placing* the action and thereby producing a specific macrospace, one with a uniformity, coherence, and salience that manifest themselves everywhere in the narrative. No doubt this space is sometimes rendered unfamiliar, confused, or exoticized. When the four brothers set out on their conquest in support of Yudhiṣṭhira's claim to sovereignty, Sahadeva conquers "Rome, Antioch, and a city of the Greeks" in the south beyond the land of the Tamils, which for its part is sometimes represented not just as the political domain of the Pāṇḍyas, Drāviḍas, and Coḍrakeralas but (if the names are to be taken literally) as the habitation of "One-Legged," "Camel-Eared," and other fantastic peoples.[9] But what should claim our attention above all is the very fact of the presence of this spatial representation in the *Mahābhārata,* not its precision according to later cartographic standards. There exists, the narrative insists, a recognizable geosphere where the *Mahābhārata*'s communicative medium, the Sanskrit language, and its message, the possibility as well as predicament of a sole royal power, have application. It is a space that has coherence, however blurred at the edges, and political content, however unrealizable the tragic tale shows it to be. The movements of the heroes are movements through a familiar world and rarely beyond it (they are always turned back from proceeding into the unfamiliar, as when Arjuna arrives at the northern reaches of Harivarṣa and the land of the Uttarakurus, where humans die if they enter and war cannot occur, 2.25.8 ff.). And this movement is typically inseparable from the political project they advance. One of the last images the work leaves on the mind's eye bears this double dimension: to abandon political power in the Great Departure is to sever one's ties to this macrospace, and to do that is to prepare for death.

The *Mahābhārata*'s narrative construction of a supraregional domain was complemented, or perhaps better, enacted, by a range of material-cultural practices relating to the text, including the spread and distribution of manuscripts, the creation of editions, and the various modes of popular dissemination. These practices accomplished two things at once. First, they reproduced narrated space by their location in and circulation through actual space, thereby investing the narrative with a new degree of actuality and cognizability. Second, they reasserted the symmetry of the political and cultural spheres, endowing the transregional cultural formation that found expression in Sanskrit with a political imagination of transregional scope.

The most obvious and concrete correlate between the fictional plotting of a macrospace and its factual reproduction lies in the diffusion of *Mahābhārata* manuscripts. It is striking how closely this followed the boundaries of the circuit represented in the narrative itself. Manuscripts of the work are found in Kashmir, Nepal, Bengal, Tamilnadu, Kerala, Maharashtra, Gujarat, western Panjab, and everywhere in between—but only there. Nothing suggests that there ever existed a central Asian or Burmese or Sri Lankan recension of the *Mahābhārata*. Like other kinds of Sanskrit literature, the *Mahābhārata* no doubt did circulate across wider southern Asia from an early period. Manuscripts of the work were donated to temples in Cambodia as early as the sixth century, and individual verses were incorporated as quotations in a Javanese *kawi* text of about the tenth century. But in neither instance did these manuscripts ever become part of a tradition of textual reproduction, any more than there existed a tradition of primary creativity in *kāvya* beyond the inscriptional variety (an enigma of Sanskrit culture in Southeast Asia . . .). The text was evidently studied and would eventually play a major role in the vernacularization process, especially in Java, but nothing indicates that it ever functioned as a component of a developing, productive literary culture that found expression in Sanskrit.

The *Mahābhārata* manuscripts are written in a wide variety of regional scripts. (That a truly transregional form of writing, Devanagari, would not come into wide use until the fourteenth or fifteenth century, at end of the cosmopolitan period, is only another of the wonderful incongruities of the Sanskrit cosmopolis.) Today we tend to think of these scripts as having been illegible outside their regions, but in fact there was far more intercommunication between them, at least among specialists, than can be assumed by the usual method of extrapolating from the conditions of modernity, under which an earlier "multiscriptism" (like an earlier multilingualism) has been much reduced. Manuscripts of the *Mahābhārata* written in Malayali (in the far southwest) and in Sharada (in the far northwest), the two scripts typically taken as the limit cases of cross-regional intelligibility, can easily be shown to have been mutually influential. Moreover, although manuscripts are classifiable into regional traditions, regionalism here pertains entirely to differences in local writing systems. No regionalization of any consequence, in point of dialect or in the particulars of material or social or even religious life, can be detected in any recension or version. To the degree that regional versions can be said to exist at all[10]—and the idea is not entirely modern but was known to editors in medieval times—they mark distinctions without differences. That is, while the text was undoubtedly expanded or contracted in one recension or another, this was unaccompanied by the least hint of localization. In short, the unmistakable impression given by hundreds of medieval manuscripts copied time and again for centuries on end is that the *Mahābhārata,* just like Sanskrit itself, existed in a quasi-universal transregional space and spoke across this space in an entirely homogeneous voice—until of course this voice became truly regional and new vernacular *Mahābhāratas* were created.

The transregional scope and character of the manuscript tradition were recapitulated in the great premodern editions of the *Mahābhārata* in both the locations of their production and the geocultural logic informing their text-critical procedures. There will later be occasion to note the ideological conjuncture of philology and nationalism that marked the *Mahābhārata* critical-edition project that began in Pune in the 1920s. But that was not the first time in South Asia that an edition of the *Mahābhārata* was deliberately created, albeit premodern editions differed markedly in critical method, social context, and cultural-political purpose from what was to come later.

There is a tendency, especially among scholars who deny the Pune critical edition any authenticity, to think of the so-called Nagari vulgate as a kind of natural formation, akin to an alluvial deposit at the mouth of the *Mahābhārata* tradition. It is of course nothing of the sort but, on the contrary, a conscious construction by Nīlakaṇṭha Caturdhara, a Maharashtrian Brahman who worked in Vārāṇasī in the last quarter of the seventeenth century. He tells us in his introduction that he gathered "many manuscripts from different regions and critically established the best readings." He did a substantial amount of editing in the process, since his text differs markedly from that of Devabodha, the earliest commentator whose work is extant, and who sometime in the eleventh century established a text affiliated with the Kashmiri tradition. The opening section of Devabodha's *Jñānadīpikā* (Light of Knowledge) makes no clear statement of critical methods, and it is not easy to infer what these may have been from the available portions of his work. But Nīlakaṇṭha's explicit acknowledgment of the transregional dissemination of manuscripts, and with it the tacit recognition that these are all versions of the same text and must be compared with each other to pierce through the darkness of ignorance and attain textual truth, are important markers of both a general theory of textuality as well as an understanding of this particular text's mode of being. Far from being peculiar to Nīlakaṇṭha, these beliefs were shared by every editor who cared to explain his method.[11]

[. . .] A conceptual supraregion of a particular shape and content was thus produced and continually reproduced across a real supraregion, not just narratively, in the very story the *Mahābhārata* tells, but also concretely, in the broad diffusion of manuscripts and the dispersed points of production for medieval annotated editions of the text, as well as culturally and linguistically, in both what the "regional" recensions say and how they say it. It was also demonstrated materially in the widespread existence of endowments for the continual performance and explication of the work. And most of this activity was promoted by the kinds of kings whose ideal types are the subject of the story. Given the relatively stable language and cultural content of the *Mahābhārata,* the mega-space recreated by textual dissemination and performance was a homogeneous one, where all regional differences were elided. And given the narrative substance and core concerns of the *Mahābhārata,* this space was projected above all as a political space, presupposing the transregional intelligibility and acceptability of a uniform logic of power and polity.

Moreover, the particular modalities of communication that marked the dissemination of the Sanskrit form of the work across all of South Asia without interruption for more than a millennium—oral performances on the basis of hand-written texts—constituted a method and a scale of inculcation of transregional political sensibilities probably without parallel in premodern world culture. The mode of understanding generated by this kind of dissemination was no doubt different from the conceptual-political effects induced by the print texts of modern mass culture, but it need not, by any means, have been less potent. And while no unitary collective subjectivity may have been evoked among listeners and readers by the narrative itself, nonetheless the text was for centuries reproduced everywhere in the very world produced by the text itself, and every such actual place was thereby incorporated into the text's supralocal cosmopolitan conceptual space.

The text was also being read and performed, however, far away from the world apparently constructed by the text. This might be taken as an instance of how far the circulatory space of the Sanskrit cosmopolis exceeded its conceptual space. A more just, if less intuitive, understanding requires conceiving of South Asian space itself as exceeding its concrete landmass. What is so remarkable and deeply suggestive about the actual ways of being in the Sanskrit cosmopolis is that its conceptual space could be reproduced so easily and repeatedly in worlds located outside its apparent physical boundaries. As we saw, this was recognized clearly and explicitly as early as the seventh century: as Xuanzang put it, "People of distant places with diverse customs generally designate the land that they admire as India." Although it may not have engendered a tradition of textual reproduction in Java or Khmer country of the sort found across the subcontinent, the *Mahābhārata* was a decisive cultural force in both places: it was central to the development of *parwa* and *kakawin* literature in the one case, and in the other its narrative found frequent cultural expression in everything from conventional epigraphical allusions to plastic representations on bas reliefs on temple walls. The list of epic linkages in Southeast Asia could be vastly expanded. In what is today Laos, for example, a grant was made by an overlord named Somaśarman instituting "daily uninterrupted readings" of the *Mahābhārata* (which, in its "complete" form, was gifted to a temple along with manuscripts of the *Rāmāyaṇa* and *purāṇas*) at the very time that a Pallava king half a world away was establishing a similar endowment for the perpetual recitation of the text.[12] One effect of the geopolitical energies and associations of the epic in regions that were apparently excluded from the epic's space—at least according to a positivistic cartographic understanding—was to prompt them to reconfigure such a space of their own: if the epic did not include their worlds in Bhāratavarṣa, they would include Bhāratavarṣa in their worlds by wholesale toponymic transformation.

Thus across Southeast Asia a thorough-going reconstitution of the cognitive landscape occurred, where not only natural features like mountains and rivers but also regions and kingdoms were identified with names borrowed from the *Mahābhārata*. As late as the sixteenth century, in a description of the Javanese pilgrimage circuit titled the *Tantu Panngelaran,* the story is recounted how, at the origin of the island, the gods, having created men and women, moved Mount Meru from India to Java and took up their dwelling there. The Khmers, according to one compelling argument, saw themselves as living not in some overseas extension of India but inside an Indian world, one populated by the gods and heroes as depicted, above all, in the *Mahābhārata.* That such a world was indeed recreated in Cambodia is richly demonstrated by the distribution throughout the country of the various "self-manifested signs" or "luminosity signs" *(svayaṃbhūliṅga, jyotirliṅga)* of the god Śiva, comparable to the twelve that plot out a kind of Śaiva space in the subcontinent; by the "new Kurukṣetra" that was founded, according to an inscription that cites verses from the epic itself, by King Devānīka in Vat Phu in the late fifth century and known to be in existence as late as the eleventh; and by the stunning half-mile-long frieze on the outer galleries of Angkor's main entrance, where panels narrating the great battle on the field of the Kurus are suggestively juxtaposed to those depicting the marching armies of Sūryavarman II. Not only was the reordering, or, more correctly, the epicizing, of Southeast Asian space common, it may have been directionally inflected. In Laos there appears to have been, in the west and east respectively, a Mālava and a Daśārṇa region—ancient toponyms in India for what are today Malwa and the region stretching east from Sagar district in Madhya Pradesh—while Champa to the east in what is now central Vietnam and Dvāravatī to the west on the Thai peninsula complement the epic's Campā in today's Bengal and Dvārakā in Gujarat.[13] A similar directionality could be found in central Java: Through the plains of Kedu, where the great monuments of Indo-Javanese culture are located, there ran a Gaṅgā River joining with a second river at a town called Prāgāwatī (Prāyāgavatī). The plains are bounded by mountains, Himalaya-like, to the north; the great Buddhist shrine Borobodur was built in a place comparable in orientation to the Buddhist *stupa* of Barhut in central India; while to the far west there was a region known as Malaya (Malayu). As one of the most insightful of the early generation of Javanists put it, "There was intentional effort made to create in that part of Java . . . a replica of the Holy Land of India."[14] Clearly, space in the cosmopolitan sphere was infinitely fungible, with multiple exemplars of the same mountains, rivers, and regions. During the age of epic reproduction, geoculture possessed, in a real if quite unfamiliar sense, no singular "home" and "abroad," no hard inside and outside, no stable center and periphery, since home and inside and center could be recreated everywhere.

Concomitantly, and in an equally real if unfamiliar sense, India's own geography during the cosmopolitan period did not exist as we now think of it, nor as home, inside, and center, and so should no more be seen as the donor for these representations than the rest of the world should be seen as their recipient. India itself was a site under construction; what was taking place in Southeast Asia was occurring simultaneously in the subcontinent as well. In the far south, cities, regions, political zones, mountains, and rivers were being named for celebrated northern sites: Mathurā (Maturai), Pātaliputra, Mālava, Magadhaimaṇḍala (near Salem), Cedimaṇḍala (on the banks of the Penner), with a southern Kailāśa (Teṅkailās) in Kerala and Gaṅgā rivers seemingly everywhere. The Indianization of India itself at the level of geography was of a piece with virtually every other aspect of the growth of the Sanskrit cosmopolis, where similar cultural practices in everything from inscriptional eulogies to cosmocratic urban designs manifested themselves across the transregion such that it is often impossible to say who was lender and who was borrower.[15]

In the regions to the north and west of the subcontinent a rather different situation presents itself. Certainly the *circulatory* space of the Sanskrit cosmopolis at different times in the history of the formation included large parts of western and central Asia: some of the oldest surviving manuscript fragments of Sanskrit literature have been found there (in what is now Xinjiang province of China, for example), and certainly texts of the Sanskrit knowledge systems, especially medicine, circulated across the region. But, as noted earlier, this area was never included in the conceptual space of the *Mahābhārata* and, correspondingly, was not in the zone of dissemination for its manuscripts. Instead, the region seems to have been slotted into the fantasy world of the "Northern Kurus" and the like; in addition, no toponymic transformation seems to have occurred there. The presence of limits to a quasi-universal cosmopolitan world is no simple thing to explain. The space into which the Sanskrit cosmopolitan order did not extend was occupied by early Persianate culture to the west, Tibetan and Chinese to the north and east. Historical parallels—such as the barrier formed by Greek culture against the expansion of the Latin cosmopolitan order in the eastern Mediterranean, certainly not beyond Mesopotamia—suggest that, perhaps to the same degree that cosmopolitan cultures abhor and fill vacuums, they also seem to map out spheres of influence that do not overlap.

However much we may be persuaded of the coherence of epic space and its reproducibility in the cosmopolitan thought-world of premodern Asia, it is one thing to bring to light its shape or even to show that geocultural representations bore some conceptual political content, and another altogether to understand how that space related to the world in which real power was actually exercised.

Notes

1. Moretti 1998: 5.
2. For a preliminary analysis of Sanskrit literary culture in spatial terms see Pollock 2003: 102 ff.
3. Nīlakaṇṭha's commentary on the *Mahābhārata* p. 2, column 1.16; column 2. The *Bṛhatsaṃhitā* (c. 550), the Aihoḷe inscription (634), and the *Rājataraṅgiṇī* (c. 1150) all use a Kaliyuga dating system, among others, commencing (discrepantly) after the battle of Kurukṣetra. The *Mahābhārata* is *śāstrarūpe kāvyacchāyānvayini* in *Dhvanyāloka* 4.5, p. 530.
4. *MBh* 6.41.36; cf. vv. 51, 66, 77.
5. Bakhtin 1981: 84–258.
6. *MBh* 2.23–29 (cf. 2.4).
7. *MBh* 6.1.8; 6.5.3–5, 21; 6.9.1–2; 6.10.64–66 (reading *pahlava* for *pallava;* the *MBh*'s geography here is identical with that of the *Padmapurāṇa* 3.6–7, a version of the longer recension noted in chapter 5.1, see Kirfel 1931:3).
8. For the wanderings of the sacrificial horse see *MBh* 14.73–85; Yudhiṣṭhira's exclamation is found in 15.46.8; and reference to the brothers' final *prādakṣiṇya* in 17.1.44 and their course in 17.1.31–2.2.
9. *MBh* 2.28.49. "Roma" may refer to Constantinople (founded 324), but even then the location remains problematic. An expansion among southern manuscripts, at the point where the text describes the barbarous beings (found even in the sober Varāhamihira, see chapter 5.1), seeks to restore the civility of the southern region (see Reich 1998: 69).
10. Grünendahl 1993 importantly reconsiders the logic and reality of "regional versions" of the *MBh.* On regionality and recension see also Pollock 2003: 108 ff.

11. The quotation is from Nīlakaṇṭha's commentary on the *Mahābhārata*, introduction, v. 6. On Nīlakaṇṭha's see Minkowski forthcoming; on Devabodha, Sukthankar 1944: 274. An analysis of Devabodha's influential interpretive practice—the identification of the *tātpārya*, or essential purport, of every section of discourse (this would be imitated by later commentators for centuries, especially Arjunamiśra)—merits more study than De's few words (1944: ix).
12. *ISC*: 30 (*IK*: 19): . . . *aśeṣaṃ bhāratam dadat* | *akṛtānvahaṃ acchedyāṃ sa ca tadvācanāsthitim* ||
13. It is unclear what to make of the four traditional divisions of Champa: Amarāvatī (Quang Nam), Vijaya (Binh Dinh), Kauṭhāra (Nha Trang), and Pāṇḍurāṅga (Phan Rang), see Wheatley 1983: 396. On Java, see Lombard 1990: 13–14, who also cites Groslier 1979: 179 on Khmer country, and cf. Wolters 1979: 437–39 for the argument on the Khmers. For the twelve *jyotirliṅgas* see chapter 5.1 (the *svayaṃbhūliṅgas* are listed in a late commentary, cf. Gopinatha Rao 1971 2.1: 83 ff.); for Devānīka's inscription, see chapter 3.2. Some Chinese pilgrims, such as Yching (fl. 700) saw Pa-nan (Funan) as the southeast corner of Jambūdvīpa (Pelliot tr. *BEFEO* 3: 284; cf. de Casparis 1956: 185). Southeast Asian historical geography has been a magnet for sometimes eccentric interpreters of Ptolemaic toponyms with a curious lack of methodological candor. Among these G. E. Gerini is probably to be numbered, but his notion of the distribution of Southeast Asian regions in a similar "topographical order" to India, or "toponymic mimicry," retains interest (1909: 121). The most serious account since Coedès is Wheatley 1983, though a view of the whole is not easy to derive from his work.
14. Stutterheim 1939: 79–83. He might have also mentioned Java's Kalinga (and possibly its Madura) in the eastern part of the island, though we need (once more) to bear in mind how confused is the historical geography of early Java and how uncertain the identification of some of the toponyms.
15. Until toponymic duplication receives the detailed study it merits see Raghavan 1943, from which a number of my instances are taken. The recreation of Bhāratavarṣa in late-medieval Maharashtra in the pilgrimage circuits of the Mahānubhāvas, or the equation in Cōḻa records of the Gaṅgā and the Kāverī, may be pointing toward something rather different: the miniaturization of the cosmopolitan within the new vernacular worlds (chapters 9.3; 10.1, 3).

Draupadī's Question

Alf Hiltebeitel

If hearing *Nala* lifts its listeners' spirits, it would be not only because it holds up mirrors, but because it raises questions. Or, more exactly, it mirrors certain questions and keeps them alive. At the Pāṇḍava-Kaurava dice match, having bet all his wealth and brothers, Yudhiṣṭhira is prodded into losing himself and then Draupadī. The wager lost, Duryodhana orders that Draupadī be brought to Dhṛtarāṣṭra's house as the slave (*dāsī*) of her new masters.[1] Draupadī asks the messenger a question, refuses to come with him, and challenges him to ask it in the dicing hall, which he does. Draupadī's question is a *praśna,* and as Shulman observes, "The Epic is fond of such *praśnas*: this is the term Draupadī uses when she tries to save herself and her husbands at the dice-game. . . . There, as elsewhere in the text, the *praśna* points to a baffling, ultimately insoluble crystallization of conflict articulated along opposing lines of interpretation" (1996, 153). Draupadī's question unsettles the authorities, brings forth higher authority where it is silenced or absent, and opens the question of authority to multiple voices, including her own and the poets'.[2] The sabhā is the epic's ultimate setting for constructing, deconstructing, and rethinking authority.[3]

We have already made some observations about this question and the scene that provokes it: that it has to do not only with the self of King Dharma (Yudhiṣṭhira), but the "subtle" self or essence of dharma, and that the scene provokes two expressions about what is the "highest dharma." To Bhīma, about to burn Yudhiṣṭhira's arms, Arjuna says the highest dharma is to remember not to overstep one's eldest brother (*bhrātaraṃ dhārmikaṃ jyeṣṭhaṃ nātikramitum arhati*; 2.61.8cd)—a somewhat troubling point, since he says this to his own older (if not eldest) brother Bhīma. And for Vidura, it is speaking what is applicable to dharma when one knows it (61.80). As Biardeau puts it, for Vidura, leaving Draupadī's question unanswered puts the dharma itself at stake.[4] I have also suggested that the question hovers over the entire *Mahābhārata*: that no one ever resolves it, and that Yudhiṣṭhira will still be trying to figure it out at the very end. With this has gone the suggestion that it also has something to do with love as it is tested in Draupadī's marriage to Yudhiṣṭhira as one of her five husbands.

Draupadī is not the first to raise one aspect of her question. This is first voiced by Vidura, who incarnates Dharma, but whose authority is undercut by his having a low caste mother: the wager of Draupadī may be invalid, he says, since "I think she was staked when the king was no longer his own master (*anīśa*)" (59.4). Vidura's words are part of a warning of disaster, but he says them to Duryodhana, who ignores them, having already ordered that Draupadī be led away and enslaved in the house of his father. It is the question's insolubility and the impasses it opens that provoke the two violent scenes of Draupadī's hair-pulling and disrobing. Let us follow the question as it unfolds through these events.

A. Hair Pulling

It is Draupadī who raises the actual question, which emerges as her fourth in a series. When Duryodhana's "usher," whose approach to Queen Draupadī is compared by Vaiśampāyana to a dog's (60.3), tells Draupadī she is to come with him as a slave, she asks three questions in a burst: "How do you speak so, an usher? What Rājaputra would wager his wife? The king was befooled and crazed by the dicing. Was there nothing else for him to stake?" (5). In these questions, she sounds angry, incredulous, and then sarcastic. But when the usher has explained the betting sequence, with Yudhiṣṭhira having bet himself before he bet her (6), she uses her wits: "Go to the game. Having gone, ask in the sabhā, what did you lose first, yourself or me (*kiṃ nu pūrvam parājaiṣtr ātmānam māṃ nu*)? Having learned that, then come to take me" (7). Draupadī formulates her question in a way that opens up two things that might work in her favor. She definitely wants the question raised "in the sabhā," where she can expect it to be treated "in court" as a case of "law," dharma. And, whether cleverly or inadvertently—and if we grant that she is clever to address the court, she is probably being clever here too—in asking Yudhiṣṭhira a question whose answer she has already obtained, she makes it clear at least to readers that her question is about more than it says. Listening in, we may ask whether Yudhiṣṭhira too can read behind her words, even though he will only hear those she has imparted to the usher. Draupadī seems to give him a precious riddle. For although one is forced to translate, "What did you lose first, *your*self or me?" what she also says, literally, is, "What did you lose first, self or me?" Several scholars have followed up the legal side of Draupadī's question, but few have recognized its obvious philosophical import as a question about the nature of the self,[5] and none have discussed it.

Returning to the court, the usher doesn't change Draupadī's question in any essentials, but quotes her on a further question before he repeats the one we have heard: "'As the owner of whom did you lose us' (*kasyeśo naḥ parājaisīr*)? So queries Draupadī. 'What did you lose first, (your-)self or me' (*kiṃ nu pūrvam parājaiṣīr ātmānam atha vāpi māṃ*)?" Here, "Yudhiṣṭhira did not stir, as if he had lost consciousness (*niśceṣṭo gatasattva ivābhavat*), and made no reply . . . whether good or ill." The questions snowball even as their meanings double: "As owner of whom?" or, "As master, or lord (*īśa*), of what?" One may ask, did Draupadī really ask this new question? In effect, the "usher" joins Draupadī's question with Vidura's observation that Yudhiṣṭhira was "not his own master or lord" (*anīśa*) when he bet her. "As if" Yudhiṣṭhira had lost consciousness. Had he? If so, for how long? If not, of what do Draupadī's words make him conscious? One has much to ponder already.

Duryodhana has some reason to be surprised at Draupadī's response, for as Mehendale points out, when he had first ordered her to be taken to the Kaurava quarters, he "and probably everyone in the Assembly" assumed "that Draupadī had lost her status as a free woman. But now, for the first time, he realizes that Draupadī does not agree to this position. . . . He tacitly admits that her question is justified" (1985, 183). Seeing also the potential to catch Yudhiṣṭhira in a lie, he says, "Let Kṛṣṇā Pāñcālī come here and ask the question herself. All the people here shall hear what is her word and his" (60.10).[6] The usher goes back to Draupadī. Finding her in what van Buitenen calls "the king's lodgings" (*rājabhavanam*), he tells her apologetically that she is summoned. Draupadī reflects: "So now the All-Disposer disposes, touching both who are touched, the wise and the fool. He said, 'In this world dharma is alone supreme.' Protecting, he will dispose peace." We are not told who the "he" is whom she quotes: the All-Disposer? Viṣṇu-Kṛṣṇa? Dharma? Yudhiṣṭhira? No one says such precise words in the epic, either earlier or later. The name sounds fitting for Viṣṇu or Kṛṣṇa, while the words sound more like Yudhiṣṭhira, and as if she is quoting him, as Damayantī does Nala. In any case, at this point the Critical Edition text itself becomes contestable. As Edgerton, the *Sabhāparvan* editor, sees it, Draupadī seems to come to the sabhā twice: first, with a "trusted messenger" (*sammatam dūtam*) sent for her by Yudhiṣṭhira (14); then, with Duḥśāsana. This second arrival would occur when the usher balks at approaching Draupadī a third time after a northern "interpolation" has returned him a second time to the sabhā (531* line 6 *apud* 2.60.13). But these movements are uncertain. What is clear is that she is accosted by Duḥśāsana in what van Buitenen calls a "dwelling" (*veśman*; 19), and that she then runs from this place toward the women around Dhṛtarāṣṭra. There Duḥśāsana grabs her by the hair (21-22).

It is tempting to adopt Edgerton's view that, "Clearly we have here parts of two entirely different versions of the story," and his inclination to drop the two verses concerning Yudhiṣṭhira's messenger, which involve a change of meter, as an interpolation. He is certainly right that "attempts to smooth over the inconsistencies" are indeed interpolations.[7] And he is also right about the ludicrous effect produced by some northern manuscripts to put the second of these verses, the famous description of Draupadī's arrival in the sabhā before Dhṛtarāṣṭra, into Yudhiṣṭhira's mouth as a command: "In a single garment, a waistcloth below, weeping, having her period, having come to the sabhā, she came before her father-in-law" (2.60.15), is turned into Yudhiṣṭhira's order, "Come before your father-in-law in a single garment, a waist-cloth below, weeping, having your period!" Not only is this preposterous marital cruelty out of character; it makes Yudhiṣṭhira speak when we have been told he is mindless and silent. Indeed, such a command would answer Draupadī's question prematurely: having bet himself, Yudhiṣṭhira would exemplify by this command that he still retains his husbandly rights over Draupadī. No such cruelty or authorly stupidity need be imagined, except that someone did *change* the text by imagining it. Clearly someone who didn't like something about Draupadī's question wanted to settle it in favor of an extreme male arrogance.

It is indeed surprising that the epic poets lend to this confusion by using such imprecise terms (*bhavana, veśman*) to describe the places of Draupadī's movements near or within the sabhā. But I think the Critical Edition gives us a readable text that is better for what it has removed, and not necessarily a conflation of "two entirely different versions of the story." As it stands, while the usher is still with Draupadī, Yudhiṣṭhira sends his trusted messenger, but we don't know the message. Left to do this silently, as if by a signal, Yudhiṣṭhira could still be thought of as appearing witless. Draupadī comes to the sabhā in front of Dhṛtarāṣṭra. Duryodhana then, "gleeful" at what he sees in the faces of the assembly, tells the usher, who could quite naturally have come back to the sabhā with Draupadī (and the "trusted messenger") unmentioned, says, "Bring her right here, usher. Let the Kurus speak to her visibly." Terrified by Draupadī's anger, which he has already glimpsed, the usher, "abandoning his pride," asks what he should say to Kṛṣṇā. Duryodhana, rash and thinking the usher to be afraid of Bhīma, which he is not, tells Duḥśāsana, who *should* be afraid of Bhīma, he has nothing to fear from "our powerless rivals," and orders, "Fetch and bring Yājñasenī yourself." "Then the Rājaputra [Duḥśāsana] rose up, having heard his brother, eyes red with wrath," and entered that "veśman of the great chariot warriors" (60.16-19). This appears to be an area off to the side of the sabhā to which the

Pāṇḍavas would have repaired after the dicing, and where Draupadī seems to have gone, and not evidence of a second story in which Draupadī is still in "the king's lodging." I would be just as happy to drop the two verses about Yudhiṣṭhira's trusted messenger and the first description of Draupadī's bloodstained appearance in the sabhā, since the former is awkward by any reckoning and the latter reiterated endlessly. But it seems better not to ignore them, and to consider them among the "more difficult readings."

In any case, Duḥśāsana now drags Draupadī's hair, and doesn't stop to ask or answer questions. "Come, come, Pāñcālī, you are won, Kṛṣṇā . . . . Enjoy the Kurus (*kurūn bhajasva*)" (60.20). She runs toward the Kaurava women's quarters, but Duḥśāsana rushes after her; "He seized by the long black flowing hair the wife of the Indras among men," and led her to the sabhā. While she was being dragged, "she spoke softly, 'I'm having my period now! I have one garment, fool! You cannot lead me to the sabhā, you non-Ārya!' But forcefully holding her down by her black (*kṛṣṇa*) hair, he said to Kṛṣṇā, 'Cry out for help (*trāṇāya vikrośa*) to Kṛṣṇa and Jiṣṇu, to Hari and Nara. I will lead you for sure. *Be* in your period, Yājñasenī, in a single garment or with no garment. You are won at dice and made a slave. With slaves one delights as one wishes'" (60.22-27). Duryodhana has summoned Draupadī to let her raise her question, which includes the question of her slavery, but Duḥśāsana simply calls her "slave" (*dāsī*) "time and again."[8] She answers, "You whose conduct is non-Ārya, of cruel acts, don't unclothe me, don't drag me" (30). It is the cruel and non-Ārya Duḥśāsana who orders Draupadī, "Be in your period," not Yudhiṣṭhira.

Duḥśāsana's taunts are also a prelude to what follows: the disrobing and Draupadī's "cry for help" to Kṛṣṇa, or more exactly to Kṛṣṇa, also known as Hari, and to Arjuna, also known as Jiṣṇu and Nara. *Trāṇa* stands here for more than just "help": Draupadī's *trāṇāya vikrośa* will be her "cry for salvation."

B. Disrobing Draupadī, Redressing the Text

Draupadī now gets to ask her question in the gambling hall, furious at her mistreatment, dragged and tossed about by Duḥśāsana, hair disheveled, menstrual blood spotting her single garment, taunted as a dāsī. During all this she challenges the men in the court "who have studied the śāstras" to consider her question, which she frames in a surprising statement about dharma and Yudhiṣṭhira that we may read, I suggest, as her assertion of faith that things have not gone totally awry: "The king, son of Dharma, is firm in dharma; dharma is subtle, to be understood by the adroit (*dharme sthito dharmasutaśca rājā/ dharmaśca sūkṣmo nipuṇopalabhyaḥ*; 60.31ab)." Her husbands are "inflamed" by her "side-long glances" (*kaṭākṣa*; 35cd), which hurt them more than the loss of kingdom or riches. But we find that although the subtlety of dharma is admitted right and left, none of the śāstra-knowing men are adroit enough to answer her question, which they bandy about from every angle.

Bhīṣma responds first, as he should since he is the senior śāstric authority on such matters: "Because of the subtlety of dharma, dear, I am unable to solve your question the proper way (*na dharmasaukṣmyāt subhage vivaktum/ śaknomi te praśnam imaṃ yathāvat*)" (60.40ab). He equivocates twice, first over the issue of the wife as property and then over more legalistic subtleties that border on the ethical and the philosophical: "One having no property cannot bet another's, but considering that a wife is under a husband's authority (*asvo hyaśaktaḥ paṇitum parasvam/ striyaśca bhartur vaśatāṃ samīkṣya*) . . ." (40cd). The property issue is itself philosophically coded; one could translate, "One with no 'his' cannot bet another's 'his.'" But while Bhīṣma seems to know this, he contents himself with the inconclusivities of dharma as "law": "Yudhiṣṭhira could abandon the whole abundant earth before he would abandon truth. And 'I am won' was said by the Pāṇḍava. Therefore I cannot decide this. Śakuni is second to no man at gambling. The son of Kuntī was free to choose with him. The great-souled one does not consider him deceitful. Therefore I cannot speak to your question." Bhīṣma sticks to the surface of *what has been said,* which, as a good "lawyer," is all that is admissible as evidence in the sabhā as court. Yet we know that silences refute and extend this admitted evidence: we know that Yudhiṣṭhira knows at least that Śakuni cheats, although he may not know how he does so or whether he does in any particular instance;[9] and we know that there can be more to truth than what is said, and that what is said is precisely where dharma is subtle, where there is more to dharma than meets the eye, more than language can express. There is thus something unpleasant here."[10] Bhīṣma's equivocality amounts to an equivocation, a refusal to honor this "more," as Draupadī herself suggests, refuting his points term for term, but rather too interpretatively,[11] and insisting on an answer to her question (45): words that come with tears.

These are greeted with insults from Duḥśāsana and an outbreak of dissensions on both sides. Among the Pāṇḍavas, in a scene we have noted, Bhīma now denounces Yudhiṣṭhira for treating Draupadī worse than an ordinary gambler treats a whore: although he is "the master (*īśa*) of all we possess" (61.4), he has "gone too far" in staking Draupadī: "I shall burn off your arms! Sahadeva! Bring fire!" To which Arjuna replies that while Yudhiṣṭhira has kept to the Kṣatriya's dharma of meeting a challenge, Bhīma "oversteps" his "highest dharma" of not overstepping his eldest brother.

As the hair pulling turns into the second violation of the disrobing, the responses to Draupadī's question become polarized. In the epic's only expression of pro and con views, Karṇa joins in a carefully constructed debate with Vikarṇa, an otherwise obscure[12] youngest brother of Duryodhana, whose name, in this context, suggests a contrived opposition: Vikarṇa as "good demon" and Karṇa as the Sun god's son gone demonically awry.[13] Vikarṇa takes what seems to be a compassionate view, although as Shah points out, this "defence does not turn out to be a defence at all but a mere debate on technicalities. His arguments do not in any way contradict the general belief that the wife is her husband's property" (1995, 31). Says Vikarṇa, the throw is null for three reasons: (1) Draupadī was staked after Yudhiṣṭhira bet himself; (2) it was only due to the prodding of Śakuni that Yudhiṣṭhira bet her; and (3) the "faultless" (*aninditā*) Draupadī is "common to all the Pāṇḍavas" (*sādhāraṇī ca sarveṣām pāṇḍavānām*; 61.23-24). Karṇa, outraged at such assertions by a mere youth, offers a close rebuttal:[14] (1) it is irrelevant when she was wagered: Yudhiṣṭhira could bet her because Draupadī is "included within his total property" (*abhyantarā ca sarvasve draupadī*; 32); (2) Śakuni may have prodded Yudhiṣṭhira, but he did it audibly and her wager was allowed by all the Pāṇḍavas (*kīrtitā draupadī vācā anujñātā ca pāṇḍavaiḥ*; 33); and (3), the twist on which everything turns, being "common to all the Pāṇḍavas," Draupadī cannot be "faultless" at all: "Or if you think it was through adharma that she was led into the sabhā in a single garment, hear my final word. One husband per wife is ordained by the gods, O scion of Kuru; but she, whose submission is to many, is for certain a whore."[15] A whore is common to all and protected by none—a reminder that Bhīma cannot protect Draupadī even though he denounces Yudhiṣṭhira for treating her worse than a whore.

More than this, recalling Duḥśāsana's taunt—"*Be* in your period, Yājñasenī, in a single garment or with no garment"—Karṇa continues: given that she is a whore, "leading her into the sabhā is not strange, to my mind, whether she is wearing a single garment or even naked. . . . This Vikarṇa is a very childish speaker of wisdom. Duḥśāsana! Strip the clothes of the Pāṇḍavas and Draupadī (*pāṇḍavānāṃ ca vāsāṃsi draupadyāś cāpyupāhara*)."

Once again, the textual contestation is especially rich. How was Draupadī protected by inexhaustible sarees? The Critical Edition makes it an unexplained wonder, and Edgerton, as the *Sabhāparvan*'s editor, thinks "cosmic justice" is "apparently implied" (1944, xxix). Or was it the story Duḥśāsana's words anticipate, and which everybody knows, including, as we shall see, Draupadī and Kṛṣṇa *later* in the Critical Edition, that Draupadī prayed to Kṛṣṇa? Let us look at the apparatus. Based on the Critical Edition's own criteria, Edgerton's judgment that "the evidence of the manuscripts is entirely conclusive" (1944, xxviii) is warranted, and it seems that the passage is an interpolation. Yet a reexamination of northern and southern variants provides a case where the editorial protocols may yield a nugget, though not necessarily the one that Edgerton imagined. Indeed, they may require us to reopen the question.

Edgerton's comments focus mainly on matters of style and continuity, but he also cannot avoid some of the theological implications of the presumed alterations:

> No prayer by Draupadī; no explanation of the miraculous replacement of one garment by another; no mention of Kṛṣṇa or any superhuman agency. It is apparently implied (though not stated) that cosmic justice automatically, or "magically" if you like, prevented the chaste Draupadī from being stripped in public. It is perhaps not strange that later redactors felt it necessary to embroider the story. Yet to me, at least, the original form, in its brevity, simplicity, and rapid movement, appeals very forcefully. (ibid., xxix)

Within the context of the passage itself, the Critical Edition's accumulated evidence leaves no grounds to refute these conclusions. The reconstituted text has continuity without Kṛṣṇa's intervention, and the tendency of later redactors (both northern and southern) to embroider the story is evident. Southern and northern variants of Draupadī's plea differ significantly, and both recensions provide what Edgerton calls "prime" and "excellent" manuscripts that entirely omit it.[16] Rarely does the epic offer a better passage in which to examine a process of textual layering.

One must, however, still be cautious. The reconstituted text is a twentieth-century reconstruction, and not proof of an "original." One must thus admit that, with no known original, Edgerton's choice could merely typify the eagerness of the Critical Edition's editors to excise bhakti by stripping the text. The manuscript evidence of variants could be no more than a collection of embellishments upon something that is indeed fully acknowledged elsewhere in the Critical Edition. At their base, Kṛṣṇa's intervention could be implied all along, but be told with different images and words of invocation that reflect the story's popularity. *Mahābhārata* poets often imply more than they tell, as when Draupadī's hair is called a "path" that the Pāṇḍavas followed to victory (12.16.25)—without it ever being clear what Draupadī did with her hair (Hiltebeitel 1981, 200-1). Moreover, just as the whole disrobing scene is omitted at some Draupadī festival drama cycles because of its inauspicious near-exposure of the goddess's impure (menstruating) nakedness (Hiltebeitel 1988, 228-29), it is possible, as analog, that late sectarian copyists might have omitted Kṛṣṇa's part in rescuing Draupadī to rescue *him* from "textual contact" with her impure single garment. What makes certain manuscripts "excellent" in the eyes of the Critical Edition editors is not any proof of their antiquity, but precisely their relative usefulness in shortening the Critical Edition text.

These cautionary remarks take us in opposite directions, but they are not contradictory: at a charged point, a text can be both expanded and contracted. Indeed, the Critical Edition cannot itself solve the problem, since, as has been indicated, it admits two powerful passages that explicitly recall Draupadī's prayer to "Govinda"! One has Kṛṣṇa recall her appeal in a message of warning to the Kauravas:

> This old debt will not glide off from my heart, that Kṛṣṇā cried out, "O Govinda," when I was far away.

And a second has Draupadī keep Kṛṣṇa mindful of this debt herself:

> Five great warrior sons are born to me by five heroes who are lawfully as related to you as Abhimanyu is, O Kṛṣṇa. Yet I, a woman, was seized by the hair when I went to the sabhā while Pāṇḍu's sons were watching and you were living, O Keśava. While the Kauravas, Pañcālas and Vṛṣṇis were living, I became a slave of sinners, placed in the middle of the sabhā. While the apathetic, motionless Pāṇḍavas looked on, when I said, 'Save me, O Govinda,' you were longed for in my mind (*nirāmarṣesvaceṣṭeṣu prekṣamāṇeṣu pāṇḍuṣu/ trāhi māṃ iti govinda manasā kāṅkṣto 'si me*). (5.80.23-26)

To retain the argument that the Critical Edition reconstitutes the original disrobing scene, one would have to argue either that the reconstituted *Sabhāparvan* passage has a textual autonomy from the critically reconstructed *Mahābhārata* as a whole, or that the two *Udyogaparvan* references to Kṛṣṇa in the scene reflect a later stratum of the text. Such arguments are possible, and the latter is probably the one that could have been expected of Edgerton, had he read ahead. But there is no compelling evidence that the *Udyogaparvan* recollections are any later than the *Sabhāparvan* episode they surely recall. Indeed, they are very sparse, condensed, and unelaborated. Draupadī and Kṛṣṇa—the two principal "witnesses"—recall virtually the same thing, each in the other's company: each says Draupadī called upon "Govinda" to save her; Kṛṣṇa recalls that Draupadī appealed to him from afar. Although neither mentions Draupadī's clothing, it is certain, at least for the second passage, that the disrobing scene is the setting.[17] If we are to contemplate originals, it is hardly more likely that Kṛṣṇa's intervention was unknown at an early stage of the text than that it was known.

In any case, the rich variations must have a history. The reconstituted text now reads (2.61):

> 40. Then Duḥśāsana, O king, forcibly tore off Draupadī's garment in the middle of the sabhā, and began to undress her.
>
> 41. But whenever one of Draupadī's garments was removed, O king, another garment like it repeatedly appeared.
>
> 42. Then there was a great shout of approval there, a terrible roar from all of the kings, having watched the greatest wonder in the world.

It is after verse 40 that most of the variations occur. The main southern variant, to which shorter additions were frequently made, has the distressed Draupadī repeatedly call out "Govinda" and "Kṛṣṇa" (*govindeti samābhāṣya kṛṣṇeti ca punaḥ punaḥ*), and then recite a one-*śloka* prayer that several versions refer to as a song (*gītā*) taught to her by the sage Vasiṣṭha (547* and 548*, *apud* 2.61.40). Draupadī's repetition of the name "Govinda" at this point provides a Sanskrit counterpart, and possible source in the southern recension, for her cry "Govinda" at this point in Villiputtūr's Tamil *Makāpāratam,* and in Draupadī cult possession rites (Hiltebeitel 1988, 280-81 and n. 38). The song taught by Vasiṣṭha also includes the name Govinda:

> Holder of the conch, wheel, and mace, whose residence is Dvārakā, Govinda, Lotus-Eyed, protect me who has come for refuge.

One sees here a fully articulated and intentionally highlighted bhakti theology, probably colored by Śri Vaiṣṇava overtones. The fact that the invocation "Govinda" is mentioned in both *Udyogaparvan* passages, however, means it is not restricted to the southern recension.

The chief northern variant (543*), familiar from the Roy and Dutt translations of the *Mahābhārata* from the Vulgate, and commented upon by Nīlakaṇṭha, is actually found "in only a few Devanāgarī manuscripts" (Edgerton 1944, xxix). It is, however, much longer than the main southern variant, and has many more contextual references to other facets of the *Mahābhārata*. Here Draupadī refers to Kṛṣṇa as "Beloved of the Gopī folk" (*gopījanapriya*; 543*, line 2; also 542*, line 1), one of the few allusions to Kṛṣṇa's childhood among the cowherders in the epic. Although we should no longer assume that such allusions are late or interpolated, this one's explicitness in referring to the Gopīs themselves is quite possibly an indication that the passage was worked up by poets familiar with the *Harivaṃśa*, or the work of still later Paurāṇikas or north Indian bhakti sectarians.

The passage also goes to bizarre lengths to achieve a kind of literalism in bringing Kṛṣṇa to Draupadī's aid. At his residence in Dvārakā, "having heard the words of Yājñasenī, Kṛṣṇa was deeply moved. And having abandoned the couch where he slept, the benevolent one came there on foot out of compassion."[18] To cover the roughly eight hundred miles from Dvārakā to Hāstinapura "on foot" (*padbhyām*) to rescue Draupadī at a moment's notice is more than would normally be required even of a deity, not to mention a literary convention. In this, the passage is like another that the Critical Edition relegates to an appendix. While the Pāṇḍavas are in exile, the sage Durvāsas visits Hāstinapura, where Duryodhana goes all out to gratify him and finally obtains a boon from him. Visiting the Pāṇḍavas in the forest when they've finished a meal and Draupadī has just lain down to rest, Durvāsas demands food for himself and his thousand disciples. What can Draupadī do but pray to Kṛṣṇa? "With you as protector, O lord of gods. in every distress there is no fear, as formerly when I was set free from Duḥśāsana in the sabhā."[19] Leaving Rukmiṇī's bed, Kṛṣṇa comes immediately, and after some frivolities at Draupadī's expense, takes some "vegetable and rice" (105) left over from the meal and miraculously makes it stuff Durvāsas and his throng's stomachs. Thinking they might anger the Pāṇḍavas by having to refuse the meal, Durvāsas decides to leave, and adds: "I fear still more, O Brahmans, from men who take refuge at the feet of Hari" (line 21). As Sukthankar says,

> With this story disappears one of the very few episodes . . . in which Śrī Kṛṣṇa is represented as hearing from a distance, as it were by clairaudience, or divine omniscience, the prayers of his distressed devotees and as either coming instantly to help them in person or providing invisibly the means of their rescue or safety. The other . . . [episode is] the disrobing of Draupadī. . . They undoubtedly represent a later phase of Kṛṣṇa worship.
> (1942, xiii n. 1)

All things considered,[20] it seems prudent to agree with Sukthankar that there may be a relative lateness to passages that *elaborate* on Kṛṣṇa's answering from afar, as in the Durvāsas episode and the northern variant of the disrobing scene where he arrives "on foot." But there are still textual grounds to suspect that he can do so mysteriously.

Immediately following the statement that Kṛṣṇa came "on foot" to veil Draupadī with sarees, there is a curious verse (544*). It is found extensively in the northern recension, sometimes after the long rapid-travel passage just cited, but more often directly after verse 40, with the long passage omitted. It shows its anomalous character by being the only verse among all those that recount the scene, whether accepted or rejected by the Critical Edition, that is in the *triṣṭubh* rather than the *śloka* meter. Theologically, however, it is consonant with a śloka verse (553*, *apud* 2.61.41) that is also found widely in the northern recension, and almost uniformly in the same manuscripts as 544*. It would thus appear that verses 544* and 553* together constitute the oldest variant, or perhaps the "original interpolation," in the northern recension. Set into the reconstituted text, the altered passage would read as follows:

> 40. Then Duḥśāsana, O king, forcibly tore off Draupadī's garment in the middle of the sabhā, and began to undress her.
> 544* Yājñasenī cried out for salvation (*trāṇāya vikrośati*) to Kṛṣṇa, Viṣṇu, Hari, and Nara. Then Dharma, concealed, the magnanimous, having a

multitude of garments, covered her.
41. Whenever one of Draupadī's garments was removed, O king, another garment like it repeatedly appeared.
553* Thereupon garments of many colors and whites appeared, O lord, by hundreds, due to the protection of Dharma.[21]

In verse 544* Draupadī does invoke Kṛṣṇa under the first three names mentioned, but the fourth—Nara—usually refers to Arjuna. Here Draupadī is doing almost exactly what Duḥśāsana has said she could do in the nonproblematic Critical Edition verse cited above. In anticipation of her stripping, he taunts, "Cry out for salvation (*trāṇāya vikrośa*) to Kṛṣṇa and Jiṣṇu, to Hari and Nara" (60.26). But the help in verse 544* seems to come not from Kṛṣṇa or Nara, but from Dharma. And in verse 553*, her rescue is even more clearly "due to Dharma's protection" (*dharmasya paripālanāt*) alone, with no mention of any other figure. Indeed, Draupadī has counted on the protection of Dharma from the beginning (see above, n. 13).

As noted, Dharma incarnates in Vidura and sires Yudhiṣṭhira: the one, the first to raise an aspect of Draupadī's question and the first to continue pressing for an answer to it immediately after the miracle (61.51c-57); the other, silenced by it and left most to ponder it. To be sure, Dharma, like Nara, could refer to Kṛṣṇa as Viṣṇu, for whom such a name is possible. But in the epic Dharma is more a deity on his own whom we have come to know. Indeed, the "concealed" (*antarhita*) Dharma who rescues Draupadī here is certainly reminiscent of the Dharma who disguises himself as a Yakṣa and a dog to test Yudhiṣṭhira in encounters with death. Yet "Dharma/dharma's protection" would also seem to have an impersonal connotation here. The two verses identifying dharma/Dharma as the source of the miracle were perhaps what Edgerton had in mind when he spoke of "cosmic justice" automatically rescuing the chaste Draupadī. Justice (*dharma*) may be set in motion by a prayer to Kṛṣṇa, but it is available to Draupadī precisely because she is just, virtuous, herself.[22] I think this is apt, yet I think we must also consider the implication that the "concealed dharma" operates here as well as through the ignored Vidura and the silent Yudhiṣṭhira.

If these verses are our oldest variant, or "original interpolation" in the northern recension, then it is reasonable to suspect that they could have proved devotionally uninspiring to later northern poets, who could have sought uniformity in the ambiguous references to Kṛṣṇa, Nara, and Dharma by prefacing verse 544* with a long and explicit plea to Kṛṣṇa culminating in the totally unambiguous but ridiculous assertion that he came to Draupadī's rescue "on foot." If one must guess at a chronology, the southern recension's simple devotional "song" is probably later than the verses invoking Dharma and earlier than Kṛṣṇa's fancy footwork and the reference to the Gopīs. As to the verses invoking Dharma, they are *probably* (if they are the original interpolation), but *not necessarily* (if they are the oldest variant), younger than the *Udyogaparvan* recollections of Draupadī's cry to Govinda, which cannot be called interpolations. This leaves us with the question of whether one can profitably argue for a priority between the reconstituted passage that makes no mention of Kṛṣṇa and the critically accepted texts that do, so briefly, under the name "Govinda." I doubt that one can. Lipner links Draupadī's cry to Kṛṣṇa with "popular versions," and says that "in the final analysis" it is dharma that vindicates her (1994, 207 and 344, n. 8). But Kṛṣṇa's intervention cannot be attributed to "popular versions": the "original interpolation" seems to have been unpopular, and the Critical Edition knows the story elsewhere. Moreover, the Critical Edition has Draupadī call not only on dharma but on the All-Disposer. If the All-Disposer alludes directly or indirectly to Kṛṣṇa, he may be working with dharma all along.

One may ask, what does all this textual variation on Draupadī's cry for salvation have to do with her question? But we need only recall that Karṇa's order to strip her is the outcome of his cruel answer to it. We have already found such connections in *Nala*: the body stripped—to any degree (see n. 32)—is a self laid bare. As Nala is stripped, so is Yudhiṣṭhira. For each, their project becomes that of restoring themselves, their kingdoms, and their marriages. But the women are never stripped. Damayantī retains half a sari, and Draupadī receives endless sarees. For the one a fraction is left by her husband, for the other an infinity is received from . . . what?

The textual variations are different commentaries on what saves the heroine who asks about the self of the hero, not only to save herself but to save him, or them. As in *Nala,* it is a question of the self, as ātman, only with the royal hero and not with the heroine. These two heroines have other refuges, one of them being their fidelity, another being riddles. Other than that, what saved Draupadī? Was it God who comes from afar? on foot? even in his absence? Was it the All-Disposer, or Dharma—one of whom, she says earlier, will bring peace? Dharma as law? as justice? as reduced to a question left for those who embody it—the ignored Vidura and the silent Yudhiṣṭhira—still to keep alive? The variants give all the answers but the last, which I think we must nonetheless still keep pending.

Although Vidura says a question raised in the sabhā requires an answer lest dharma be injured (see n. 5), his words are greeted with silence, and Karṇa orders Duḥśāsana to take the dāsī away to the "houses" (*gṛhān;* 61.81)! But Draupadī stands her ground, saying she will abide by the answer given (62.4-13). Bhīṣma equivocates again (14-21), this time concluding, "I think Yudhiṣṭhira is the authority on this question, whether she is won or not won, so he can give utterance himself (*api svayaṃ vyāhartum arhati*)" (21)—which Duryodhana seems to appreciate. Indirectly daring Yudhiṣṭhira, he taunts Draupadī to get a response from him or, if he will not speak, from another of the Pāṇḍavas: "Let them declare in the midst of the nobles for your sake, Pāñcālī, that Yudhiṣṭhira is not a master. Let them all make Dharmarāja, a liar (*kurvantu sarve cānṛtaṃ dharmarājam*), Pāñcālī, (and) you will get free from servitude" (25). So cued, Bhīma now says that Yudhiṣṭhira *is* their master (*īśā;* 32-33), which would leave Draupadī a dāsī; but his answer is ignored. Karṇa insults the dāsī some more, and Bhīma flares up. Again Duryodhana taunts Yudhiṣṭhira to answer, now addressing him directly, and shows Draupadī his bared left thigh, goading Bhīma to vow to break it (63.1-16). Again Vidura says the dharma requires an answer, now more urgently than ever, and seems to suggest his own view of the impasse as a kind of mirage: "A stake that one who is not his own master plays would be won as in a dream, I think."[23]

Finally Arjuna seems to pick out of Vidura's gloom the implication that Draupadī is not lost: "The king was formerly our master in the betting (*īśo rājā pūrvam āsīd glahe naḥ*), Kuntī's son, the great-souled king Dharma. But whose master is he whose self is vanquished (*īśas tvayaṃ kasya parājitātmā*)? Realize this (*taj jānīdhvam*), all you Kurus" (63.21). Arjuna's words are but another question, one that leaves Draupadī's question hanging. As his question closes the debate on Draupadī's question, it leaves two matters open: not only whether Yudhiṣṭhira has been his own master, but whether indeed his self has been vanquished. Arjuna's opinion, which is of course the opposite of Bhīma's, probably registers what is closest to the dharma's unacceptable truth. But it settles nothing, for at this very moment jackals bark and donkeys bray (23).[24] These terrible omens sound at Arjuna's words.[25] This is probably because he is doing the very thing he had told Bhīma not to do: he is overstepping his eldest brother, indeed, his two elder brothers, since he is also disagreeing with Bhīma. Whatever the truth of his words, they are an unacceptable truth that cannot be the truth of the story, and are as ominous as the omens that greet them. For were they taken as final, they would be the very thing Duryodhana wants to hear, even at the cost of freeing Draupadī: that Yudhiṣṭhira is a liar.

At last these omens prompt Dhṛtarāṣṭra to offer Draupadī the boons that allow her to choose Yudhiṣṭhira's freedom and that of all her husbands, plus their weapons. And Karṇa recognizes that she has been the Pāṇḍavas' salvation (*śānti*) and their boat to shore (64.1-3). As Kṛṣṇa will later confirm, "Kṛṣṇā lifted up the Pāṇḍavas, as also herself, as with a ship from a swell in the ocean" (5.29.35).

C. The Question within the Episode

Let us now look at the implications of Draupadī's question: first, mainly within the episode itself, and then at what lies behind and follows from it at other points in the epic. Even as she is dragged into the sabhā decrying the Kuru's loss of dharma that brings her there, she attests to Yudhiṣṭhira's firmness in dharma and her knowledge that "dharma is subtle" (60.31-33). Yet the dharma is also what subjugates her there in the sarcastic words of Karṇa: "There are three who own no property: a slave, a student, and a woman are nonindependent *(asvatantra)*. You are the wife of a slave, his wealth, dear—without a master, the wealth of a slave, and a slave (yourself)" (63.1). These words resonate with a famous verse in *The Laws of Manu* (9.3) that describes women as "nonindependent" (*asvatantra*). Draupadī challenges this, speaking about, and perhaps for, women as a class: "These Kurus stand here in the hall, lords of their daughters and daughters-in-law, all considering even my word—answer this question of mine the proper way" (61.45). The men are challenged to consider a question that questions their "ownership" of women.[26] It is by appealing to dharma around a question that brings both overt and hidden questions to life that she can save herself and the Pāṇḍavas.

Śakuni, Yudhiṣṭhira's deceitful opponent, delivers the probing verse: "There is surely your dear lady (*priyā devī*), one throw unwon. Stake Kṛṣṇā Pāñcālī. Win yourself back by her (*tayā 'tmānam punarjaya*)" (58.31). "Your dear lady," *priyā devī*. . . . The first meaning of *devī* is of course "goddess," which would be an overtranslation but hardly an overestimation of the lady. More than this, *devī* is the goddess as "she who plays" (Biardeau 1985, 17), and Pāñcālī is a name for Draupadī, used with heightened frequency in this scene (ibid., 11, 13-14), meaning "the puppet." As Yudhiṣṭhira sets to wager her, he speaks from what feels like a reverie: She is not too short or too tall, not too black or too red—I play you with her (*tayā dīvyāmyahaṃ tvayā*). . . ." Doll-like, iconic, she is bet and lost, and Yudhiṣṭhira will say nothing until her question frees him. Once in the forest, Draupadī will say we are all puppets, our strings pulled by the Creator—to which Yudhiṣṭhira will reply that she is eloquent with passion, but heretical. As Pāñcālī, Draupadī is thus the doll or puppet who speaks, who even recognizes herself as such; as *devī*, she is the lady who is played who also plays.

But there is more to Yudhiṣṭhira's words as they turn from reverie to silence: ". . . Eyes like the petals of autumn lotuses, a fragrance as of autumn lotuses, a beauty that waits on autumn lotuses—the peer of Śrī in her beauty. Yes, for her noncruelty (*ānṛśaṃsya*), her perfection of form, the straightness of her character (*śīla*), does a man desire a woman (*yām icchet puruṣaḥ striyam*). . . . Her waist shaped like an altar, hair long (*vedimadhyā dīrghakeśī*), eyes the color of copper, not too much body hair . . . such is the woman, king, such is the slender-waisted Pāñcālī, whom I now throw, the beautiful Draupadī" (58.33-37). It is important that Draupadī is not in the sabhā to hear these words; they are not for her to hear but for Yudhiṣṭhira to remember. We now see that while it is his hearing Damayantī tell Nala, "Ānṛśaṃsya is the highest dharma, so I heard from you" (3.67.15cd; see p. 228 above), that begins Yudhiṣṭhira's long and painful education about ānṛśaṃsya, it is this unforgettable scene—the first to use the term in connection with him, and with he himself, like Nala, the speaker—that grounds "noncruelty" for him, we might say above all, in the big and little cruelties of his marriage.

It is clear that in all this talk about betting oneself, Draupadī's question is a philosophical one about the nature of self, compounded by legal issues of *mastery*, *lord*ship, *property*, *own*ership, and slavery in the hierarchical context of marriage, and symbolized around the figure of the ultimate lord, master, and owner, the king, in relation to a subjecthood and objecthood of the queen, his wife. These themes are discernible in the Sanskrit,[27] as are those we have noticed in *Nala* of possession of self versus possession by the madness of dicing, and, one senses, the theme of love and abandonment, of love between six people in one and the same marriage tested to the breaking point especially in Bhīma's and Arjuna's different expressions of near-insubordination. Listen to what Yudhiṣṭhira says when he bets himself just before he wagers Draupadī: "I am left, so beloved of all my brothers. Won, we shall do work for you when the self is itself a deluge" (*upaplave*, 58.27). Slipping into his loving reverie, Yudhiṣṭhira descends into silence once he has lost her. Here we see Draupadī's question from a new angle. Yudhiṣṭhira's loss of self *appears*—it is only described so by others—to be a loss of consciousness, like Nala's. Yet is he unconscious? What is the nature of the "self at stake" in Draupadī's question?

Here we seem to be in an agonistic multidialogical situation that reverberates with Upaniṣadic scenes in which fathers and sons, gurus and disciples, and even men and women churn the oppositional languages of rivalry and status to release the saving knowledge of what is one.[28] Gārgī, whose questions to Yājñavalkya are like arrows; Yājñavalkya to Maitreyī, renouncing the world and saying goodbye forever to his dearer-than-ever "knowledge-discoursing (*brahmavādinī*)" wife: "not for love of the husband is a husband dear, but for love of the ātman . . . ; not for love of the wife . . ." We should not forget the limits such dialogues impose on the women speakers.[29] But here, where only one of the partners is speaking and the other is silent, the speaker is the woman. Does she speak, at least for now, for both of them, while Yudhiṣṭhira cannot, or will not, speak for himself?

As *Nala* has demonstrated, in the *Mahābhārata*, the language of such questions and answers is compounded by proto-Sāṃkhya-Yoga and bhakti (see chapter 6, § B). Al Collins (1994, 3-4) shows how a sovereign self, male (*puruṣa*), replicates itself in other selves through a "scale of forms" that "presents a problem for male identity formation." Man (and, for that matter, woman), as mind-ego-intellect, is feminine matter, *prakṛti*, living—ultimately unconsciously—"for the sake of puruṣa," of "man" as conscious self or soul. As Collins says, "The problem is not limited to kings" who top this "scale of forms," "but is universal: it is highly dangerous to claim to be a self" (1994, 4). This well describes Yudhiṣṭhira's predicament; no wonder he is silent. Should he claim to be a self who wagered Draupadī first, he simply lies and loses her forever. If he claims to be a self who wagered her after he lost himself, he—or his brothers—might keep her, or maybe just compound their slavery, but he lies about having lost himself.

Indeed, should he claim, like Nala, that in betting and losing his wife, "I myself was not its doer," the self he wagered would be counterfeit, making him a more deceiving gambler even than Śakuni.[30] If *Nala* can lift the Pāṇḍavas and Draupadī's spirits, it cannot retrospectively provide Yudhiṣṭhira with Nala's excuses. No matter how tempted a reader might be to say that Yudhiṣṭhira was "possessed by Kali," who is incarnate in Duryodhana, or even that he was just crazed by the dice (see above, n. 7), Yudhiṣṭhira could not help himself by saying such things, since unlike Nala, he bet his wife.

Buddhists have a story about Aśoka—a king, indeed an "emperor," who topped the scale of forms—that invites reflection here. The "great quinquennial festival" (*pañcavārṣika*) described in Buddhist sources involved, as an extravaganza of imperial *dāna* (gifting), the "custom of divestment and then reacquisition of the royal clothes and jewels" (Strong 1983, 94). In the *Aśokāvadāna,* Aśoka announces he is ready to give away vast wealth to the sangha and bathe the bodhi tree.

> This, however, hardly represents the totality of his assets. There follows, therefore, a comic scene in which Aśoka's young son Kunāla indicates with a hand gesture to the crowd that he will double the amount. The crowd laughs and Aśoka is forced to "outbid" his son by tripling his original offer; Kunāla quadruples it. This goes on until finally, Aśoka, retaining only the state treasury, makes a total gift to the sangha of his whole kingdom, his harem, his ministers, his self, and his son Kunāla. This is the ultimate potlatch, and Kunāla, finding himself part of his father's gift, cannot very well outdo him.
>
> Then, however, having given everything away to the sangha, . . . [Aśoka] buys it all back, . . . and thereby redeems from the sangha his kingship, his wives, his ministers, his son, and his self. (95-96)

The summary is Strong's, who may have been reminded that Marcel Mauss called the *Mahābhārata* dice match "the story of a monstrous potlatch" (see chapter 1, n. 2). But Strong's translation of the episode shows that it is not so comic. It begins, "Now at that time Kunāla's eyes had not yet been put out." Aśoka laughs at the first outbidding, but is "irritated" by the second. When he learns his opponent is Kunāla, it is in perhaps both humors that he makes the encompassing bid that includes "my self, and Kunāla": that is, *both* their selves. He thereby dissolves or nullifies their mock-rivalry by his subsuming wit (264-68). Aśoka loves Kunāla, but is "too attached to his son's eyes," which "resembled a fully blossomed blue lotus." When Kunāla is cruelly blinded by his stepmother, who resents his rejection of her ardor towards him, and fears he might kill her, she lets Kunāla think that it is Aśoka who has ordered the blinding. As a blind minstrel, Kunāla then reconciles with his father, but he cannot save his stepmother from Aśoka's cruel execution, even though saying that he loves her provides the "act of truth" by which he regains his sight (268-85). It is between losing his first and second eyes that Kunāla is enlightened about the impermanence and emptiness of self, making it clear that we have been hearing about Buddhist *non*selves in this contest: fathers and sons, husbands and wives, again hard truths from the dialogical situation.

But what about Draupadī? Biardeau, also insistent that a Sāṃkhya problematic underlies *Mahābhārata* portrayals of heroines, argues that the heroine-goddess represents prakṛti as unconscious matter, blind ignorance given to "obstinacy"; matter that unknowingly yet somehow inerrantly works on behalf of puruṣa (1984, 263) through "blind initiatives"; heroines whose ignorance is unknowing in particular about dharma.[31] Unlike Kunāla, such a dim Draupadī would have no sight to begin with and none to get back. The epic poets do touch on Sāṃkhya themes, but this reading is one-sided. Biardeau says nothing about ignorance when it is a question of a heroine's "knowing time and place," or exhibiting her ingenuity in posing riddle-questions that prompt a hero's anagnorisis and draw him out of his concealment, riddles about intimacies and pains of love that are a lifeline allowing him *and her* to use their wits, to "play for time," and thus to give time its play. Draupadī certainly knows enough about dharma to question it. It is not just her obstinacy that makes her persist. Her timely "strategy for survival," her "delaying tactics" amidst the craven Kauravas, have "paradoxically . . . involved a concerted effort to freeze time," or better suspend it, by language that undercuts and literally eludes the grasp of patriarchal authority in the "men's court."[32] Yudhiṣṭhira *appears* to be silent: is it that he reads her "signs" and leaves her this chance to play for time?[33]

That is my sense of things, although as we shall see, if it is true, it may work at the dice match without working for all things, since time does eventually run out. Let us touch on a few defining incidents in the relationship of Yudhiṣṭhira and Draupadī over the long haul to see what such an interpretation would entail.

D. Before and After the Question

Once the Pāṇḍavas marry Draupadī, they establish themselves, with Kṛṣṇa and Vyāsa's help, in their new half of the kingdom at Indraprastha (1.199.26-28). Kṛṣṇa then leaves for Dvārakā (50), Vyāsa recedes back into the text, whereupon Nārada "by chance arrived" (*ājagāma yadṛcchayā*; cf. chapter 2, n. 61). He sees the Pāṇḍavas sitting on five thrones with one queen, and once Draupadī has left the room, he tells them a story to impress them with the need to avoid a breach between them. Two demons, Sunda and Upasunda, were safe in the boon that death could come to them only if they killed each other. Nonetheless, they did so over Tilottamā, whom the celestial architect Viśvakarman had fashioned at the gods' bidding to Śrī-like perfection—from diamonds and all the world's most beautiful things (203.12-17), a truly perfect doll with no prior attachments—to tempt the pair to their own destruction. Having heard this story, which is not that flattering to Draupadī, the Pāṇḍavas make a compact (*samayam*): "Anyone who would see one of the others while he is sitting together (*sahāsīnam*) with Draupadī must live in the forest for twelve years as a celibate (*brahmacārin*)."[34] We soon learn that "sitting together" is a euphemism and that Nārada, as usual, is prompting as much trouble as he is precaution.

All goes well for a while, but after a "long time" the idyll ends. A Brahman comes crying to Arjuna that thieves have made off with his cows; unless the thieves are apprehended and his cows returned it will be a rebuke to Pāṇḍava rule. Arjuna says, "Don't fear," but faces a dilemma: the Pāṇḍavas' weapons are "where Dharmarāja Yudhiṣṭhira was with Kṛṣṇā." It would be great adharma, thinks Arjuna, for the king were he to overlook this, whereas by protecting the Brahman "it would establish the nonheresy (*anāstikyam*) of all of us in the world." He convinces himself to bravely face death in the forest to avoid this adharma, and in rapid order, "having followed the king in entering (*anupraviśya rājānam*), taking leave, grabbing his bow, delighted (*saṃhṛṣṭaḥ*)," Arjuna "addressed the Brahman, 'Come quickly'"(205.1-19). Catching these thieves is no problem, but there is one upon his swift return: Arjuna tells Yudhiṣṭhira, "The compact is completely overstepped by my seeing you (*samayaḥ samatikrānto bhavat saṃdarśanān mayā*). I will go dwell in the forest. That was surely the compact we made" (24). Yudhiṣṭhira, hearing this "disagreeable word unexpectedly (*sahasā vākyam apriyam*)," tries to smooth things over: "What you did, O hero, in following my entry (*anupraveśe*) is not disagreeable (*apriyam*). I forgive it entirely. It is not a transgression in my heart (*vyalīkaṃ na ca me hṛdi*). Surely the younger following the entry of the elder (*guror anupraveśo*) is not an offense. The breach of the rule is the eldest's following the entry of the younger (*yavīyaso 'nupraveśo jyeṣṭhasya vidhilopakaḥ*)" (26-27). But Arjuna holds to principle: "'One should not observe dharma through fraud.' So I have heard from *you*! I will not waver from truth. By truth I took the weapon." Off he goes to dwell in the forest for twelve years (29-30).

One begins with the obvious question: why did the Pāṇḍavas keep their weapons in the bedroom? But the poets never even ask it, much less answer it. A Draupadī cult analogy is useful again. It is as if the bedroom is like a Draupadī temple, where the Pāṇḍavas *and* Draupadī's weapons are stalled, to be taken out for festival processions, including one reenacting Arjuna's defense of the kingdom of Virāṭa against a cattle raid. But more immediately, the weapons in the bedroom are the Pāṇḍavas' tokens of virility, and Arjuna wants his back.

I have translated the repeated use of *anu-pra-viś-* as "follow in entering," for it certainly carries sexual connotations in the context of the Pāṇḍavas' tenuous marriage protocols. That Yudhiṣṭhira and Draupadī are not just "sitting together" is underscored in the Oriya *Mahābhārata* of Sāralādāsa, in which the complaining Brahman is revealed as Agni:

> Agni came in the guise of an unidentified brahman and insisted on meeting Yudhiṣṭhira who was with Draupadī in her harem (bedroom). As a sign for that Yudhiṣṭhira left his foot-wears by the side of the door. But Agni, in the form of a dog, lifted those foot-wears. Arjuna, being ignorant of this, went inside the bedroom and saw the coition of his brother and Draupadī. (Misra 1995, 144-45)

It does not take much to realize that if the younger may follow the entry of the eldest but not vice versa, Arjuna *may* find something problematic in Yudhiṣṭhira's having this turn with Draupadī, since these events would transpire after at least one previous cycle of passing Draupadī down by order of seniority, with the result that Yudhiṣṭhira would have "followed in entering" after the turn of *his* youngest brother Sahadeva: indeed, after all four of his younger brothers. Moreover, considering that Yudhiṣṭhira is first called not just the "eldest" but the "guru," Arjuna's "gazing" is a kind of "violation of the teacher's bed" (*gurutalpa*), one of the worst of sins. Indeed, given that a guru and eldest brother are equivalent to a father, Arjuna sees an approximation of the "primal scene."

Moreover, *anu-pra-viś* also means attack: Yudhiṣṭhira and Draupadī are vulnerable when Arjuna "completely oversteps" his compact by "seeing" them. Having by his own admission "completely overstepped" his eldest brother at this first test of their marital concord, it is not hard to see that it foreshadows his warning to Bhīma not to do the same at the dice match, and his finally doing the very same himself.

Of course the poets do not say such things. Yet we know that this scene ends the Pāṇḍavas and Draupadī's idyll, and it seems Arjuna is quite eager to end it. Once the "delighted" Arjuna has invaded the bedroom, stood his ground on the principle of the compact, and left for his twelve years of "celibacy," Draupadī will not again see the man who won her until he has married three other women and brought one of them home: the "auspicious" Subhadrā, sister of Kṛṣṇa, who seems to become his "favorite."

For all six partners, then, it is enough to say that the happy freshness of their honeymoon is over. For Draupadī and Yudhiṣṭhira in particular, it ends with their own intimacy interrupted by the brother who not only won Draupadī, but whom she now comes to start missing in this first of what will be Arjuna's many absences and estrangements.[35] Again, the poets do not have to tell us that Yudhiṣṭhira bends so far to keep Arjuna around, at least in part, to keep Draupadī happy, and that when he claims to find nothing "disagreeable" in his "heart" about Arjuna's interruption and gaze, that his heart would be troubled. They do not have to tell us that if Draupadī begins to find her multiple marriage emotionally less satisfying than it was to this point, she will have no one to blame but Yudhiṣṭhira, who upheld the mother's word that made her polyandry happen.[36] Draupadī will wait until Arjuna has returned with Subhadrā to have her one son with each Pāṇḍava. The five are born a year apart and Arjuna's is named third (1.213.72, 79), so Arjuna must have again taken his turn after his two older brothers. But the account is perfunctory.

So much for what comes before Draupadī's question. The next passage of interest comes early in the forest book in the long exchange between Yudhiṣṭhira and Draupadī that includes what I have called Draupadī's puppet speech. It is the nadir of their relationship, coming between the dice match and Arjuna's departure (at Yudhiṣṭhira's behest) to obtain divine weapons, which itself sinks the remaining Pāṇḍavas in the misery that prompts their hearing of *Nala*. More specifically, it comes between Yudhiṣṭhira's reverie about Draupadī's "noncruelty" with his descent into silence while she raises her question, and their hearing of Damayantī's message-reminder to the estranged Nala that, in Nala's words, "Noncruelty is the highest dharma." The exchange between Yudhiṣṭhira and Draupadī highlights this quality of ānṛśaṃsya. It prompts Yudhiṣṭhira's first expression of how he understands it, and, moreover, how he contextualizes it in relation to intimacy.

Draupadī—introduced here as "dear and beautiful, a scholar (*paṇḍitā*)[37] and a faithful wife (*pativratā*)" (3.28.2)—begins by observing that the cruel (*nṛśaṃsa*) Duryodhana is not unhappy about their suffering (3); Yudhiṣṭhira should act like a Kṣatriya, all of whom have anger, and not like a Brahman (34). Yudhiṣṭhira defends himself:

> Truth is better than falsehood, noncruelty than cruelty (*satyaṃ cānṛtataḥ śreyo nṛśaṃsāc cānṛśaṃsatā*). Even to kill Suyodhana,[38] how can one like me give reign to anger, which has many faults and is shunned by the respectable (*sādhuvivarjitam*)? . . An angry man does not see his task correctly, full-hipped one. The angry man considers neither task nor limit (*maryādā*). . . . If there were no one among men having forbearance like

> the earth, there would be no peace (*saṃdhi*) among men, for war has its root in anger. If the oppressed were to oppress, if one hit by his guru were to strike back, it would be the destruction of beings and adharma would be broadcast. . . . Were fathers to strike their sons and sons their fathers, husbands to strike their wives and wives their husbands, then in such an angry world there would be no birth, Kṛṣṇā (*evaṃ saṃkupite loke janma kṛṣṇe na vidyate*); know that the birth of creatures has its root in peace (*saṃdhi*), lovely one. In such (a world), all creatures would quickly perish, Draupadī. Therefore, wrath is for the destruction of creatures and nonexistence. But since those who possess forbearance like the earth are seen in the world, the birth of beings and existence is carried on. In every distress, beautiful one, a man should be forbearing, for forbearance is declared the existence and birth of beings. . . . Suyodhana is not capable of forbearance and so finds none. I am capable of it and thus forbearance finds me. That is the conduct of the self-possessed (*etad ātmavatāṃ vṛttam*). This, forbearance and noncruelty, is the eternal dhama, and that I truly do. (3.30.15, 18, 25-26, 28-32, 49-50)

Draupadī won't buy this: "In this world a man obtains prosperity neither by noncruelty and dharma, nor by patience, uprightness, nor tenderness" (31.2). Their suffering, she says, is brought on by Yudhiṣṭhira's putting dharma before the rest of them, betting his brothers and her away with his kingdom. His words make her think they are like puppets being played by a capriciously hurtful divine child (30-39). Yudhiṣṭhira tells her it is heresy (*nāstikyam*) to censure the good heavenward ship of dharma (32.1 and 22), or salvation that comes to the devoted mortal by the grace of the highest deity (40).

I suppose Yudhiṣṭhira is a frustrating husband. But at the heart of his argument, he reveals what he is about, and what he seems to think Draupadī should be about. It was, after all, Draupadī's *ānṛśaṃsya* that Yudhiṣṭhira recalled just before he wagered her and descended into silence. That was out of her hearing, but it seems that without mentioning his words at that moment, *ānṛśaṃsya* is the quality, along with "forbearance" (*kṣama*), that he would like to remind her of now. He tells her it is the maintenance of these two qualities, noncruelty and forbearance, that sustains existence and the birth of beings. Indeed, the *saṃdhi* which these qualities make possible is not just "peace," but "connection," which, in the context here, implies the peace to have sexual connection without cruelty or interruption.

This theme has by now been richly developed. When Yudhiṣṭhira's great-grandmother Satyavatī prepared to tell her son Vyāsa to rescue the Kuru line by siring sons with his half-brother's two widows, she said, "Because beings cry out (*anukrośāc ca bhūtānām*) and for the protection of all, having heard what I say, you must do it with noncruelty (*ānṛśaṃsyena*)" (1.99.33)—as noted (see chapter 2, § C.2), a strange thing to tell an "author" about characters he is about to make love to and father, and we must wonder how well he listened, considering the outcome. We have also seen Pāṇḍu, Yudhiṣṭhira's father, cursed because he lacked the "noncruelty" (*ānṛśaṃsya*) to wait until two Ṛsis-turned-deer were finished with their pleasure.[39] But most of all, the theme has come into focus because Arjuna has interrupted Yudhiṣṭhira and Draupadī in the bedroom. Did Arjuna show forbearance and noncruelty? Probably not, even though he is portrayed as opposing cruelty (2.61.7; 3.142.15, 25; 254.13; 4.61.21)—without, however, the term *ānṛśaṃsya* in these cases, which so often distinguishes Yudhiṣṭhira. But if Arjuna was hasty and cruel (couldn't he have knocked?), and even eager for some escapades, we understand why Yudhiṣṭhira would never say so, especially to Draupadī, and why he would take such pains to say that what Arjuna did was "not disagreeable."

But there is something more in Yudhiṣṭhira's words. His conduct of forbearance and noncruelty is, he claims, that of "one who is self-possessed" (*ātmavat*). Is it possible that he is answering Draupadī's question? Has he learned something from the dicing? Is he hinting that he had not really lost himself, but could not say so? That in some sense, his silence meant that he thought he understood her question? He is quite convincingly self-possessed now, and it would not be unreasonable to propose that while he appeared to have "lost consciousness" during the time Draupadī raised the question, he knew enough—perhaps just enough—to "keep to himself" while she played for time.

Draupadī and Yudhiṣṭhira have a few more ups and downs. The bedroom scene is no doubt echoed in the *Karṇaparvan* in one of the many surprising features of the insult-exchange between Yudhiṣṭhira and Arjuna over Arjuna's delay in killing Karṇa while Yudhiṣṭhira nurses his wounds away from the action, but still, of course on the battlefield. Says Arjuna, "Lying on Draupadī's bed (*draupadītalpasaṃstho*) you insult me, and I am to kill great warriors for your sake?" (8.49.83ab; Reich 1998, 235, translating). Once again, Arjuna finds Yudhiṣṭhira in Draupadī's bed; once again, it is a question of Arjuna using his weapons. But this time there are insults. And when the war is over, Draupadī severely upbraids Yudhiṣṭhira once again, now for wanting to abandon the kingdom he has just won, which would turn all their suffering to nought. He is like a eunuch, she says, like a Kṣatriya without a rod (*daṇḍa*) (12.14.12-14); he is like a madman whom his brothers, were they not crazy themselves from following him, should bound with the heretics (*nāstikyaiḥ*); or he should be treated with drugs (32-34). Yet she speaks these words to him as one who "always took pride, especially in Yudhiṣṭhira, and was ever cherished by the king."

But we hasten to the end. Heading north on their ascent to heaven, self-restrained and rapt in yoga (*yogayuktāḥ*), the Pāṇḍavas and Draupadī see the great peak Himavat (*himavantam mahāgirim*). Crossing even beyond it (*apy atikramantas*), they see an "ocean of sand" (*vālukārṇavam*) and the great mount Meru (17.2.1-2). The ascent combines with cosmological images of the yogic journey, delivered with an appropriate rapidity. To follow Witzel (1984, 228-29), Himavat is often called *giri* or *uttara giri* in Vedic texts, where it may be seen as what remains at dawn on the northern horizon of the "spotted rock," the revolving upside-down subterranean mountain of the night sky studded with stars not contained in the Milky Way. If the image holds for the epic, the Pāṇḍavas and Draupadī's journey now heads backward from Himavat into the night and forward into a post-Vedic yogic cosmology. Beyond Himavat is an "ocean of sand": a likely image of the stars, which the travelers are said only to *see*, not to cross by walking. And beyond this they *see* (again with no mention of actual footwork) Mount Meru, which is no real mountain but the cosmic mountain by which the totality of the universe is projected as measurable, perceivable, and knowable. While they are holding to their yoga, moving quickly, Draupadī's yoga is ruined and she falls to the ground. Asked by Bhīma why she fell, Yudhiṣṭhira replies, "Her partiality for Arjuna was especially great (*pakṣapāto mahān asyā viśeṣeṇa dhanaṃjaye*). That is the fruit she now enjoys" (17.2.6). Yudhiṣṭhira and his brothers (including Arjuna) travel on, leaving her body behind with that thought, which might reopen the whole book on Yudhiṣṭhira, yet will not be his last about her.

His brothers fall, and Yudhiṣṭhira is left with the dog. Indra comes to take him to heaven, but because of his "noncruelty" Yudhiṣṭhira won't leave the dog. The dog turns into Dharma in his own form (17.3.16),[40] who congratulates Yudhiṣṭhira for his "capacity to cry out (*anukrośa*) toward all beings" (17), and tells him that he can now reach his heavenly worlds in his own body, a nonpareil feat (20, 27). The gods provide him a chariot to heaven, where Nārada welcomes him among the royal Ṛṣis. But seeing heaven without his brothers, Yudhiṣṭhira wishes to go where they are. Indra discourages him: "Why do you still draw on human affection (*mānuṣyakaṃ sneham*)? . . . The human heart (*mānuṣo bhāvaḥ*) still touches you, lord of men. This is heaven!" (31-33). Yudhiṣṭhira replies that he wants to be where his brothers are, "where my dear Draupadī is, the best of women, the great dark one (*bṛhatī śyāmā*) rich in spirit, character, and virtue (*buddhisattvaguṇānvitā*)" (36).

This verse, which emphatically ends the *Mahāprasthānikaparvan*, yields this singular compound. It is used only one other time in the epic, where it introduces Āstīka as one whose name means "there is," and who has these same qualities "even as a child."[41] "Rich in spirit, character, and virtue" is van Buitenen's translation for the description of Āstīka (1973, 108), and I have transferred it to Draupadī. But it can hardly be all that is meant, even if one keeps it a copulative compound as "rich in insight, goodness, and virtue." *Guṇa* in the singular is unlikely for "virtue,"[42] but is regularly used in the epic as a proto-Sāṃkhya term. Indeed, *guṇa, buddhi,* and *sattva* are all proto-Sāṃkhya terms with Upaniṣadic prehistories and resonances across the *Mahābhārata.* It is tempting to understand this language as describing Draupadī and Āstīka as characters who represent and provoke awareness. One could thus translate it as "having the sattvic quality (*guṇa*) of insight."[43] The juxtaposition of "great dark one," feminine, with *buddhi* may hint that Draupadī evokes the dark *pradhāna,* primal matter or prakṛti, which, transformed into buddhi, serves to discipline the five senses and bring about the awakening of puruṣa.[44] There would seem to be something to ponder in Yudhiṣṭhira's final description of the character of his wife.

As the epic's last book, the *Svargārohaṇaparvan,* now opens, Yudhiṣṭhira's resolve hardens. Seeing Duryodhana shining in heaven, he is affronted. He blames Duryodhana for the war and the mistreatment of Draupadī in the sabhā, and doesn't want to be in a heaven with him (18.1.1-10). Nārada, smiling, tells him that here enmities cease; Yudhiṣṭhira should not think of what was done at the dice match, the pain (*parikleśa*) done to Draupadī and the other pains that followed: "This is heaven! There are no enmities here, lord of men" (11-18). But Yudhiṣṭhira still protests, and says he prefers to see the afterworlds of his brothers (including Karṇa), his allies, and Draupadī; "Where they are is my heaven. To my mind this is not heaven" (20-2.12). The gods reply, "If that is where your faith (*śraddhā*) is, son, you may go without delay," and order a celestial messenger, "Show Yudhiṣṭhira's friends (*yudhiṣṭhirasya suhṛdo darśaya*)" (2.13-14). Yudhiṣṭhira's "faith" lies in seeing his *suhṛds*: "those who are dear to his heart."

The messenger takes Yudhiṣṭhira on the foul and slippery path to the edge of hell (*naraka*). There he hears the piteous cries of his brothers, Dhṛṣṭadyumna, Draupadī, and Draupadī's sons asking him to stay for a time, since he brings them comfort (2.16-33).

> Yudhiṣṭhira then reflected (*vimamṛśe*), "What now is the effect of destiny (*kasyedānīṃ vikāro 'yam*) by which these have gone to hell? . . . Am I asleep? Am I waking up? I do not seem to understand. Ah, this is a mental twist. Or maybe it is the wandering of my mind." So King Yudhiṣṭhira reflected in many directions, overwhelmed by sorrow and grief, his senses agitated by thought (*cintāvyākulitendriyaḥ*). Then the king, the son of Dharma, intensely gave way to anger, and Yudhiṣṭhira then censured (*garhayāmāsa*) the gods and also Dharma. (42-50)

Yudhiṣṭhira's final contest with his father Dharma holds strong echoes of Naciketas' contests with his father *and* Yama in the *Kaṭha Upaniṣad,* which introduces proto-Sāmkhya-Yoga language in profusion, especially when Yama gives Naciketas his third boon and describes the ascent to heaven. Yudhiṣṭhira, living out such an ascent, is back to the question that was raised about him in the sabhā: was he conscious or crazed? Now he asks it of himself, compounding it with more proto-Sāṃkhya-Yoga language about the wanderings and "generated products" of thought as he contemplates the vision before him. His "censure" or "accusation" of Dharma (or dharma) comes from these uncertain thoughts, and has no finality, as Indra soon indicates.[45] Yudhiṣṭhira has only glimpsed that he has more to awaken to, and that it is Dharma who keeps putting him through these cruel and intolerable tests.

Despite the foul smell, Yudhiṣṭhira determines to stay where he is, and sends the messenger back to the gods to tell them so. But the gods are soon there and the stench, the underworldly Vaitaraṇī river, and the gloom (*tamas*) disappear with their arrival. Indra comforts Yudhiṣṭhira: He should not make himself angry; he has had to see hell because he killed Droṇa by fraud. For similar reasons the others also experienced hell. Indra invites Yudhiṣṭhira to see them now, freed from sin in their radiant celestial bodies, and to take his supreme place among the greatest of the royal Ṛsis (18.2.52-3.25). Without Yudhiṣṭhira's having moved an inch, Indra announces what has opened before him: "This is the sacred celestial river, O Pārtha, purifier of the triple world, the heavenly Gaṅgā (*ākāśagaṅgā*), O Indra among kings. Having plunged there, you will go; having bathed there, your human heart will go away (*te bhāvo mānuṣo vigamiṣyati*). Your grief gone, without troubles, you will be freed of enmity" (3.26-27). This is now twice that Indra speaks of Yudhiṣṭhira's "human heart," first to tell him he is still "touched by it" when he prefers his family's worlds to those of heaven, and now, once he has found his family, to tell him his human heart will "go away." Indra now seems intent on limiting the discussion of what will go away with Yudhiṣṭhira's human heart to the pangs of grief and enmity, since this time he does not mention the ties of affection (*sneha*) that he mentioned before.

But Dharma knows where Yudhiṣṭhira's heart is: "Even as Indra was speaking to that Indra-among-Kauravas Yudhiṣṭhira, Dharma, visibly possessing his own form, addressed his own son. 'Aho, greatly wise king, I am pleased by your devotion to me, your truthful speech, forbearance, and restraint. This is the third test I have made for you, king. Nothing, Pārtha, makes you swerve from your own heart'" (18.3.28-30).[46] Dharma reveals that he was indeed behind the Yakṣa's questions, the dog's devotion, and now this, Dharma's final test, which is of Yudhiṣṭhira's human heart, and by which Yudhiṣṭhira is now "purified" (*viśuddha*; 31-34). Unlike Yudhiṣṭhira's thoughts, his heart cannot swerve. Unlike the Muni who abandons the dog with the human heart, Yudhiṣṭhira does not swerve because he has the virtues Dharma has just mentioned, plus those exemplified in both of the prior tests, and surely also in this one: *ānṛśaṃsya* and *anukrośa*. What Yudhiṣṭhira saw, Dharma continues, was an illusion displayed by Indra; hell must be seen by every king. His brothers (including Karṇa) "did not deserve hell for long. And the Rājaputrī Kṛṣṇā did not deserve hell, Yudhiṣṭhira. Come, come, best of Bharatas. Sec the triple-world-going Gaṅgā" (34-37). These are the last words that pass from this strange father to his son, mixing tenderness with what is almost another cruelty—that is, it seems (and here Dharma contradicts Indra), Draupadī did not deserve hell at all—neither the one Yudhiṣṭhira has just seen her in nor those he put her through. We can assume, I think, that Yudhiṣṭhira has always known this, which is perhaps how Dharma can utter these last words without their being a fourth test. We can also assume that Yudhiṣṭhira does not think Draupadī deserved hell for preferring Arjuna.

Yudhiṣṭhira has not gone anywhere during this conversation, so the celestial Gaṅgā is still before him: "He went together with Dharma and all the gods. Having plunged into the sacred purifying divine river sung of by the Ṛṣis, the king abandoned the human body (*tanuṃ tatyāja mānuṣīm*). Having assumed a celestial appearance (*vapus*), Dharmarāja Yudhiṣṭhira, immersed in this water, was without enmity, his anguish gone" (18.3.38-40). His body is gone; even his enmity and anguish (*saṃtāpa*). And his human heart is supposed to go too. But we have just noted how Dharma's last words leave an impression about Draupadī, which it now seems is the last thing Yudhiṣṭhira carries with him.

In heaven, he sees Govinda and his brothers, each in turn in their radiant celestial forms (4.1-6). But when he sees Draupadī, something powerful happens that has been easy to miss. Seeing her garlanded with lotuses, seated in heaven with the splendor of the sun, "suddenly King Yudhiṣṭhira was wishing to question her (*athainām sahasā rājā praṣṭum aicchad yudhiṣṭhirah*)" (8). But Indra, impatient again with lingering affections, cuts him off by telling him about Draupadī's divine origins,[47] and then points out the heavenly abodes of Draupadī's sons, and those of Karṇa, Abhimanyu, Bhīṣma, Droṇa, and many others, who, having abandoned their bodies, won heavens by meritorious words, thoughts, and deeds (9-19).

Quickly, in answer to a question of Janamejaya's that closes the *Mahābhārata*'s inner frame and the "whole story of the Kurus and Pāṇḍavas" (18.5.25), the next and last thing we hear about Yudhiṣṭhira comes amid a long list of the characters who dissolve into divine forms: he "entered Dharma" (*dharmamevāviśat*) along with Vidura (5.19). And we are back in the Naimiṣa Forest (although it isn't mentioned here) to close out the outer frame with Ugraśravas telling Śaunaka how Janamejaya was "pleased" to end his snake sattra after the arrival of Āstīka (26-29). Thirty more verses about Vyāsa, the text, and the merits of its recital finish the epic.

So Yudhiṣṭhira wants to ask Draupadī a question, but he never gets to ask it.[48] This is a tenacious human heart. It goes on questioning into the swirl of its dissolution. I retain the imperfect—*aicchat*, "he was wishing to question her"—because this is the perfect moment for a verb of incompletion. Although Yudhiṣṭhira and Draupadī have their end, the question has no finality, because not only did he not get to ask it or she to answer it, but we will never know what it was. Past, present, and future thus open up with this "imperfect moment." And with all the echoes of the sabhā in these two final parvans, and in particular Nārada's insistence that

Yudhiṣṭhira should not think of the pain done to Draupadī at the dice match and the other pains that followed, and Dharma's comment that she did not deserve hell, we remain within the rules of this playful text if we suspect two things. First, that a trouble Nārada sees and seems to try to avert is only something that is bound to happen: that our best clue to what Yudhiṣṭhira is thinking about is what Nārada has told him not to think about. And second, that if Dharma knows his son, he knows him to be good at riddles. In any case, whatever Yudhiṣṭhira wants to ask Draupadī, he is reminding us of Draupadī's question.

Writing about the epic dice match as a recharged piece of the Vedic Rājāsūya sacrifice, whose "dead letter" the masterful poets dramatically revive to carry forward the ambiguities of their "point, counterpoint" story, van Buitenen gives us one of his most memorable insights: "the epic is a series of precisely stated problems imprecisely and therefore inconclusively resolved, with every resolution raising a new problem, until the very end, when the question remains: whose is heaven and whose is hell?" (1975, 29). This design is one of deferral.[49] The question Yudhiṣṭhira doesn't get to ask comes even after this, and is the *Mahābhārata*'s very last deferral. Indra distracts Yudhiṣṭhira into the glorious higher worlds of personal dissolution, and Vaiśampāyana and Ugraśravas rapidly tie up the text. Yudhiṣṭhira will never answer Draupadī's question and he will never ask her his own.

Notes

1. 59.1; 60.4, following Mehendale 1985, 182, who clarifies that the second verse explains the first: when Duryodhana orders the "usher" to "bring Draupadī," it is to Dhṛtarāṣṭra's house, not the sabhā.
2. Cf. Suzuki 1989 on the "metamorphoses" of epic heroines beginning with Helen, and "woman as a figure that questions" (3). Given Homer's poetic voice and vision (40, 54-55), Helen in particular interrogates the authority of the epic's heroic code (28, 33) that scapegoats women in the name of men's heroic struggles.
3. See Lincoln 1994, 12: had he discussed India, the *Mbh* "court" scene would have to have been the obvious counterpart to his choices from Greece, Rome, and Germanic sources, especially for his interest in

"authorized speech and significant silence" (9-12, 25-27, 51-53, 55-56, 75), stripping (25), and questions raised about women (90-102). See also Higonnet 1994 on the "erasure of women from the history of war literature" (160); Hess 2001 on the continuing praśna literature built on questions about, or of, the *Rām.*

4. 1985, 10, with reference to 2.61.52: "dharma is harmed (*pīḍyate*)" if it is unanswered.
5. Although I will not pursue the comparison, Yudhiṣṭhira is put into the position of raising for himself and the others in the court, including incarnate demons, the Pascalian/Faustian question of what it means to have "wagered one's soul" (see Hiltebeitel 1987).
6. Ganguli's translation catches an important sense here: "Let everyone hear in this assembly the words that pass between her and Yudhishthira" ([1884-96] 1970, 2:189). Duryodhana wants to play them off against each other. But they won't fall for it.
7. Edgerton 1994, xxxi-xxxii: *531 (as already noted, giving the usher a second return to the sabhā); *532 (clarifying that Draupadī has arrived in the sabhā in front of Dhṛtarāṣṭra, with the implication that when Duḥśāsana goes for her, she is no longer at "the king's lodgings"); *533 (giving her a "residence" [*bhavanam*] where Yudhiṣṭhira's trusted messenger can find her).
8. Quoting Mehendale (1985, 185), for whom her slavery is the whole question. Not also the repeated uses here of the name Yājñasenī, basically "She whose army is connected with the sacrifice," cf. Hiltebeitel 1988, 194, 338, 392.
9. Shulman 1992. Indeed, at the start of the game, Yudhiṣṭhira says, "Śakuni, don't defeat us by crooked means and cruelly (*amārgeṇa nṛśaṃsavat*)" (2.53.3).
10. Cf. Biardeau 1985, 20: Bhīṣma remains obstinately mute, "recusing himself" not only before Draupadī but Ambā; Karve 1974, 14: "in the court where he sat as the eldest he did not lift a finger to halt the indignity to a woman"; the most callous and indifferent of all *Mbh* men toward women, Bhīṣma exhibited "an almost inhuman treatment" toward them (11-14, 25); Mehendale 1985, 194: "his attitude . . . was unbecoming of him; and since Draupadī was not only insulted with abuses, she was also a victim of molestation, his attitude must be judged unpardonable . . . ; improper . . . ; he should have told Duḥśāsana he was in the Assembly of civilized Kṣatriyas and not in the den of hooligans." Even Thakur 1992, 141-47, gives his hero no excuses here.
11. Or "pathetically" (Lipner 1994, 206). Yudhiṣṭhira was an innocent who did not wake up until he'd lost all, and thus cannot be said to have had any choice, she says (60.43-44)—as if she could perhaps still hope that

it was a vast right-wing conspiracy.

12. Though "considered to be one of the four important (*pradhāna*) Kauravas" (Mehendale 1985, 194, n. 1, citing 1.90.62), this is his sole moment, one for which the Tamil Draupadī cult elevates his profile (Hiltebeitel 1988, 235-36, 272-77).
13. Mehendale 1990 and Dhavalikar 1992-93, 525, n. 8, take me to task for my appeal to "nature mythology" in Hiltebeitel 1980a. I accept Mehendale's criticism of my attempt to extend the color symbolism of Draupadī's garments to an evocation of the colors of the three guṇas (288), but the Draupadī-Karṇa/Earth-Sun correlations are simply part of the poets' stock of tropes. Mehendale's argument combines a realism about the epic's past (287; cf. n. 6 above) with a determination to require metaphor to meet the tighter requirements of allegory (286).
14. Mehendale 1985, 185-86, contra Hiltebeitel 1980a, 98, on this breakdown and my phrase "point for point rebuttal" (softened here), sees Vikarṇa making two points: (1) Yudhiṣṭhira lost Draupadī by his gambling addiction, one of the four addictions that lead one to abandon dharma; (2) Śakuni prompted him, with varied repercussions that include my point one. That Mehendale combines my first and second points is trivial, but his neglect of the third suggests that he finds Karṇa's response to it distasteful (cf. 1985, 179, n. 3, on "incidents one would be ashamed to repeat" that he opines to be "unauthentic," and below, n. 32). I omit his first point because it makes no argument that Draupadī has not been lost and because Karṇa ignores it. Indeed, it would be an untenable argument for Yudhiṣṭhira and the Pāṇḍavas, from whom Duryodhana, most crucially, has invited concurrence. In finding it "difficult to agree" that Karṇa offers a close rebuttal, Mehendale thinks Karṇa's whole reply, dismissed as "not important," "must belong to some other version . . . in which Yudhiṣṭhira loses [everything] . . . not piecemeal, but in a single game in which he staked" all at once (186; cf. 1995a, 35, n. 3). For a four-point breakdown, including Vikarṇa's addiction argument, cf. Mehendale 1995a, 34; Söhnen-Thieme 1999, 150.
15. 61.34-35: *manyase vā sabhām etām ānītām ekavāsasam/ adharmeṇeti tatrāpi śṛṇu me vākyam uttaram// eko bhartā striyā devair vihitaḥ kurunandana/ iyaṃ tvanekavaśagā bandhakīti viniścitā.* Cf. Shah 1995, 90 and 1.114.65: Kuntī, rejecting Pāṇḍu's request, after Arjuna's birth, that she take on further divine mates to provide him more sons, scolds him for not recalling the "law" that a fourth union (implying levirate) makes a woman "loose" and a fifth makes her a "whore" (*bandhakī*)—or for Lipner, a "slut" (1994, 206).
16. Edgerton refers here to the northern Śāradā codex and to two southern manuscripts, one in Grantha script and one in Malayalam (ibid., xi and xxix).

17. The first could recall Kṛṣṇa coming to Draupadī's aid to fill her cooking pot, discussed below, but this is unlikely since the CE rejects it. Bhattacharya 1995, 188-90, fails to mention these passages in arguing that Draupadī's disrobing is itself an interpolation.
18. 2.543*, lines 10-11: *yājñasenyā vacaḥ śrutvā kṛṣṇo gahvarito 'bhavat/ tyaktvā śayyāsanam padbhyāṃ kṛpayābhyagāt.* We would seem to have here an allusion to Kṛṣṇa as Viṣṇu-Anantaśāyin, the lord who wakes from sleeping on the serpent-couch to recreate the universe and bestow boons (cf. Hiltebeitel [1976] 1990, 106-7).
19. *Āraṇyakaparvan,* App. I, No. 25, lines 86-87.
20. Along with a debasement of the "Śaivite" Durvāsas with his horde of followers, the shift in tone seems to diminish the stature of Draupadī. Kṛṣṇa leaves the bed of Rukmiṇī, whom, rather than Draupadī, another presumably sectarian passage makes the incarnation of Śrī, leaving Draupadī an incarnation of Indra's wife Śacī (Hiltebeitel [1976] 1990, 62, n. 7).
21. *Nānārāgavirāgāṇi vasanānyatha vai prabho/ prādurbhavanti śataśo dharmasya paripālanāt.* Mehendale 1990, 288, noting that I rely on Nīlakaṇṭha in translating *virāga* as white (1980a, 107), prefers "having different colours": i.e., that some of the garments were "each one of a different colour" (*nānārāga*) and others multicolored. This is possible.
22. On dharma as having garments with which to "dress one with virtue," sometimes hypocritically, see Hiltebeitel 1980a, 101. Cf. Spivak 1988, 183; Biardeau 1984, 255: when Nala leaves Damayantī in the forest, he "implores the gods to protect her, knowing well that she is 'covered with *dharma—dharmeṇāsi samavṛtā*'" (3.248* line 2, after 3.59.21), here evoking this "original" dimension of Draupadī's disrobing in an interpolation.
23. 2.63.19ab: *svapne yathaitaddhi dhanaṃ jitaṃ syāt/ tad evam manye yasya dīvyatyanīśaḥ.* Cf. van Buitenen 1975, 152: ". . . if the stake is put up by one who does not own it!"
24. Mehendale deplores these omens, getting quite carried away: "The Indian tradition has touched a very low point in allowing the stanzas about bad omens to remain where they are for so long. We are unaware of the fact that in doing so we have tarnished the fair image of a person like Śrī Vyāsa" (1985, 193). Despite noting how well they are established in both the text and the Indian tradition (179-81), he wants to find them either "a figment of some interpolator's imagination" (193; cf. 181, 192) or that Dhṛtarāṣṭra, already convinced by Arjuna, ignored them when he decided to give Draupadī her boons (193).
25. Mehendale does not ask why they do so, requiring his explanations (see n. 52 above) as to why Arjuna's words have been "overlooked" (1985,

190). He rues that "[n]obody has ever sensed that what happened was due to Arjuna's reply" (189), and that Arjuna hit "the bull's eye" (192). But it is Mehendale who misses the point. Lipner, concluding correctly that "[t]he question remains open," cites Bhīma's and the jackals' contributions, but ignores Arjuna's (1994, 209).

26. On the contrary, Karve 1974, 87-90, gives an astonishing reading of Draupadī's question as her "greatest mistake": Draupadī "tried to show off her learning"; "by putting on airs in front of the whole assembly, she had put Dharma [Yudhiṣṭhira] into a dilemma and unwittingly insulted him"; "Draupadī was standing there arguing about legal technicalities like a lady pundit when what was happening to her was so hideous that she should only have cried out for decency and pity in the name of the Kshatriya code. Had she done so perhaps things would not have gone so far." Karve compares Draupadī here with Sītā, as does a woman interviewed by Mankekar who, after seeing both heroines portrayed on Indian national television, "felt Draupadī was 'Westernized' because the heroine questioned and challenged her elders on the propriety of their actions" (1993, 552).
27. The main terms covering these meanings are *īśa* and *anīśa*, which I have cited frequently, translating *īśa* as "master." At two points, Draupadī is also said to be "lordless" (*anāthavat*) or, as van Buitenen translates (1975, 141, 146), "without protectors" (60.24cd, 61.52b).
28. Cf. Witzel 1987a. One may ask whether Draupadī's question overreaches the limits of her knowledge (371-72). I would argue that it does not; see below on Draupadī and the question of *avidyā*, "ignorance," and her recognition as a "paṇḍit."
29. Cf. Falk 1977, 105-7, setting Draupadī and Yudhiṣṭhira's exchanges amid such male-female dialogical situations.
30. See Derrida 1991 and 1992, raising the questions of law, narrative, the aleatory, the gift of time, and of what may be counterfeit in a wager. "The gift must let itself be structured by the aleatory; it must appear chancy," dicey (1992, 122-23, 163). In effect, Draupadī's question is her added throw of the dice, as in a Telugu folk *Mbh* story of her playing the last throw herself (Hiltebeitel 1988, 238).
31. A key passage is 4.15.34: Yudhiṣṭhira tells Draupadī, when she protests being kicked by Kīcaka, "You are ignorant of time (*akālajñāsi*), you run about like an actress!" But one cannot generalize on these silencing words. Yudhiṣṭhira may be reminding her she *should* be "acting" like a Sairandhrī, "biding her time" while they keep their disguises; or perhaps of how by contrast she "played for time" in the sabhā. Cf. Biardeau 1997b, 38, 47.
32. I transpose these quoted phrases from Suzuki's description (1989, 75) of Penelope's "vigilant consciousness of the passage of time," her "strategy

for survival in Odysseus' absence, her delaying tactics against the suitors." Note too that "Homer's Helen" repeatedly "poses the question of her responsibility—a question that remains unanswered [not only] in the *Iliad*" (56) but to Penelope in the *Odyssey* (74-75). Cf. above, nn. 2 and 3.

33. See Shulman 1996, 151: In the epic dice match, with the certainty of losing, "one mostly fights for time." My thoughts on "giving time," the "aleatory," and on dharma as law and justice begin from that quote (from a 1991 draft of Shulman 1996) and Biardeau's discussions of *daiva* and the name Pāñcālī (see above at n. 56), variously enriched by Derrida 1991 and 1992, Grosz 1997, and Caputo 1997a, 160-229. "The gift gives, demands, and takes time . . . That is one of the reasons this thing of the gift will be linked to the—internal—necessity of a certain narrative [*récit*] or a certain poetics of narrative" (Derrida 1992, 41). See also above, nn. 10 and 61. For a different reading—Yudhiṣṭhira "ostentatiously declines to take any further part in the episode . . . once he knows" Draupadī is menstruating, so as to maintain male purity—see M. Brockington 2000, 4.
34. 1.204.28. Twelve years according to the CE. Van Buitenen 1973, 446, thinks one year was the "original duration," as does Oberlies 1995, 181. But Arjuna must not only go all around India; for nine months of this "year" he is near Maṇalūra for both the beginning *and end* of Citrāṅgadā's pregnancy with their son Babhrūvāhana (1.209.24).
35. As just noted, his return from this one with Subhadrā is especially bittersweet. Cf. 3.38.19-25: Draupadī's sadness on Arjuna's departure to obtain weapons; 3.142: missing him; 3.144-46: her forest hardships and "colorful frolics" (*krīḍitāni . . . vicitrāṇi*; 145.43) at the prospects of seeing him: 3.161.29: just back from heaven he sleeps beside the twins; 4.23.24 (see Hiltebeitel 1980b, 161): harsh and cryptic words during their estrangement while incognito; 14.89.1-10 (and Dumézil 1969, 164): she won't hear of his having any imperfection on his return from the year of guarding the Aśvamedha horse.
36. Kuntī says, "Share it [her] all equally" (1.182.1-4), thinking Draupadī is alms (Hiltebeitel 1988, 200). See Mohanty 1990, 279, on Pratibha Ray's Oriya novel *Jajnaseni* depicting Draupadī's final recollections "of her tortuous and suffering life." Nicely written and translated (Ray 1995), it has interesting twists on the marriage, in which Draupadī clearly favors Arjuna, has a rough first night with Yudhiṣṭhira, and wishes she were monogamous (28-83). The present bedroom scene is bowdlerized (she is massaging his feet) but with the other details intact; the surprise is that Draupadī wants to come with Arjuna into the forest as a celibate like Sītā—to which Arjuna cruelly replies that Sītā had only one husband (163-67).

37. That she is a "scholar" might reflect on the intelligence that lies behind her question that stumps all the experts in the sabhā, some of whom cite paṇḍits in their defense (30.16, 22; 33.56). This is probably the verse Karve has in mind when she says, "In the *Aranyakaparva* Dharma called her a 'lady pundit,' hardly a complimentary epithet in the eyes of the Kshatriyas of the Mahabharata" (1974, 90). See above, n. 26, on Karve.
38. Yudhiṣṭhira's euphemistic name for Duryodhana, implying that there is something "good" (*su*) about him.
39. . . . The theme and terms recur in the Mitrasaha story: a Brahman couple enjoy forest sex until Mitrasaha attacks the husband; "While the woman was crying out (*vikrośamāna*), the king most cruelly (*sunṛśaṃsakṛt*) devoured the husband" (1.173.14); she curses him to become the cannibal Kalmāṣapāda. The bereaved cry of a female *krauñca* bird upon seeing her mate slain in the act of love by a cruel hunter is also Vālmīki's inspiration in composing the *Rām*; see Leslie 1998.
40. Belvalkar 1959, *Svargārohaṇaparvan* Introduction, xxix, takes "Yamadharma" to have been Indra as well as the dog. Better, I think, the two gods cooperate throughout Yudhiṣṭhira's two last "tests" (see 18.3.2, 30; 3.34).
41. 1.44.19-20. Cf. 3.147.111: in answer to Hanumān's question, "Who is Hanumān?" Bhīma provides a parallel description of Hanumān as *buddhisattvabalānvita*, with *bala*, strength, instead of *guṇa*: perhaps "endowed with power of intellect and goodness," or "endowed with the sattvic power of the buddhi."
42. I thank James Fitzgerald (personal communication, 1996) for this point: "guṇa is not really the abstract noun 'virtue.'"
43. Fitzgerald (personal communication, 1996), calling it "one of many depressingly ambiguous compounds involving these terms," regards both as possible, and tentatively prefers the proto-Sāṃkhya one (for the reason cited in n. 42). But he offers and prefers a third: "to construe *buddhisattva* as a dvandva . . . in apposition to the guṇa(s) with which Draupadī is *anvitā*/ endowed": thus "endowed with the virtues of insight and bravery,"
44. On *buddhi* in the epic, I am most tempted here by one of Vyāsa's *Śāntiparvan* teachings to Śuka (12.246.9-15): "Vyāsa compared the human body to a city which was ruled by Queen Intellect; this queen has the mind as her counsellor who harassed the senses which were the citizens" (Belvalkar 1966, ccxiv-xv). Queen Intellect (*svāmini buddhir*, 9b) is also inviolable" (*durdharṣā*; 12a). The *BhG*, among other things, makes also Kṛṣṇa the embodiment of the buddhi-charioteer of *KU* 3.3-9, and Vyāsa's "buddhi is unlimited" (*vyāsenāmitabuddhinā*: 1.56.21; see Sutton 2000, 27). Kṛṣṇā Draupadī, Kṛṣṇa Vāsudeva, and Kṛṣṇa Dvaipāyana—the three Kṛṣṇas (see Hiltebeitel [1976] 1990, 60-76; 1984; 1985a)—thus all have this "darkly illuminating" sattvic quality. Cf. also Sutton, 171 (on Nārāyaṇa's

bestowal of buddhi on Brahmā to create the universe [12.337]); 344-47 (in relation to other faculties); and chap. 4 at n. 146; chap. 6 at n. 46; and chap. 8 for more on Śuka and the buddhi, especially at n. 64.

45. Shulman 1996, 160-64 reads this as a "curse" of Dharma/dharma that must include Yudhiṣṭhira himself, and a breakdown of the "battered" linguistically constructed world that Dharma has imparted to him. Granted dharma's fragility as linguistically constructed, I do not see how its breakdown carries if Dharma is doing a test. A separate issue: Yudhiṣṭhira is also not renouncing dharma in the fashion Kṛṣṇa recommends to Arjuna (*BhG* 18.66).

46. More literally, "You do not swerve from your own heart (experience, nature), Pārtha, by (any) means": or ". . . by means (of what comes) from your own heart (etc.)."

47. It is here we learn that she was "fashioned by the holder of the trident" (18.4.10), as mentioned in chap. 5, p. 187. Cf. Gellrich 1985, 235-36, on narrative ironies of distraction and interruption.

48. A few mss. have *draṣṭum* or *spraṣṭum* for *praṣṭum*: he wanted "to see" her or "to touch" her rather than "to question" her!

49. On deferred work and deferred speech, see Malamoud 1989, 68. One could see the *Mbh* as "an allegory of reading the Veda" in the sense Gellrich develops for Dante and Chaucer's "allegory of reading" the Bible (and other medieval books): "the allegory of the *Commedia* consists in the structure of temporal distance between the originary *liber* of God, envisioned in the sky at the end of the poem, and the book of written efforts to explain the experience of its meaning" (1985, 165); cf. 188-89: the "continually deferred" "origin" in *House of Fame*, 246: "not completing the narrative" of *Canterbury Tales*. As Gellrich seems to suggest (76-77, 180, 183, 200, 240-47), allegories of reading are also allegories of writing. See also chap. 2, n. 18. For Derrida on this topic, it is perhaps sufficient for now to recall that "difference defers-differs [diffère]" ([1976] 1994, 66).

Selections from The Sanskrit Hero: Karṇa in Epic Mahābhārata

Kevin McGrath

Karṇa Kaunteya

1. A Brief Life

Karṇa makes his first nominal entry into the *Mahābhārata* in the Ādi *parvan* where he is described, in *triṣṭubh* verse, via the metaphor of a tree. Ugraśravas, the poet who is the actual speaker of the *Mahābhārata* as we have it, is describing the poem and its origin.[1]

> I,1,65: *Duryodhana is a great tree, filled with resentment, Karṇa is the trunk...*

This metaphor of the hero as a tree recurs again many times in the poem.[2] As usual with the epic hero, the narration commences with a prolepsis, telling of what happened at the end.[3] He is thus mentioned by Dhṛtarāṣṭra, who casts him in the company of Duryodhana and Śakuni (I,1,95), the three who rigged the gambling match. Dhṛtarāṣṭra then sings a long monody of his grief in *triṣṭubhs*.[4] Karṇa is spoken of in the course of this lament as having set his mind, along with Duryodhana, on the attempted capture of Kṛṣṇa (I,1,119). He is described as refusing to fight and concomitantly rejecting Bhīṣma, the Kaurava commander. From the very start of the poem, Karṇa is cast in somewhat shadowy light.

* Excerpted from the chapters titled 'Karṇa Kaunteya' and 'Six Speeches' of Kevin McGrath's *The Sanskrit Hero: Karṇa in Epic Mahābhārata*, pp. 25–43 and pp. 142–153.

Karṇa is next mentioned in the course of the *Parvasaṃgrahaḥ*, where his ear-rings are taken by Indra (I,2,127). Then, he is described as mounting the chariot of Kṛṣṇa (I,2,148) and being, *anumantritaḥ*, 'consecrated'. He rejects Kṛṣṇa, however. This moment anticipates the Gītā, where Kṛṣṇa speaks to Arjuna: a crucial equivalence between these two heroes is thus established early on in the poem.

The Karṇa *parvan* itself is qualified as, *paramādbhutam*, 'extremely wonderful,' an epithet no other *parvan* receives (I,2,169). A few events from the final battle are given and Karṇa is then said to be killed. In chapter fifty-seven of the Ādi *parvan* we have the second reference to Karṇa's distinguishing characteristics: the ear-rings that cause his face to shine, and the breastplate he is born with that sets him apart from ordinary mortals.

I,57,82: *The one whose face shone with ear-rings, bearing a cuirass inborn.*

Heroes, unlike mortals, are not brought into the world simply: somewhere in their generation a deific presence is at play. This is the source of the ambiguity that distinguishes heroes from mortals and from deities: their lives occupy this space between two zones of the cosmos. The divine birth of Karṇa is first given in I,104,7 where Kuntī served the visiting *ṛṣi* Durvāsas so well that he gave her a favour in recompense, disclosing a mantra by which she could call upon any deity in order to conceive a son. This of course she does, consequently becoming pregnant as well as having her virginity sustained. She does not seem to tell her husband Pāṇḍu about this although she does explain to him the use of the mantras which Durvāsas taught her (I,113,34ff.)

She bore the *vīra*, the 'warrior', the best of weapon-bearers, who was distinguished by his innate breastplate and glowing ear-rings.[5] He is *amaraprabham*, 'glorious as an immortal' (III,292,4). It is noteworthy that he is called *sūta* even before he is adopted by the actual charioteer from whom he received this title. Here we see the poet assuming that his audience already knows the story; this is not really a case of anticipation.[6]

Kuntī then proceeds to expose the child, *kumāraṃ salakṣaṇam*, 'the marked boy', to the river Gaṅgā. He is retrieved by an *adhiratha*, a charioteer, and his wife Rādhā, and taken as their own. Karṇa receives from the *dvija*, 'twice born', the name Vasuṣena, because of his golden ear-rings and cuirass (III,293,12); the name is connected with his later liberality and with his progenitor the Sun, one of the Vasus. The audience never actually hears from whom he receives the name of Karṇa. He develops into a young man, 'venerating the Sun from noon onwards' (I,104,16), and he is a 'truthful man, heroic, praying', always generous to brahmins.

Gāndhārī, on hearing that Kuntī had produced a son, *bālārkasamatejasam*, 'whose splendour was like the sun that was newly risen', aborted her own pregnancy by Dhṛtarāṣṭra, which led to the production of Duryodhana and his ninety-nine brothers and single sister (I,107,25).

This abbreviated account of Karṇa appears in the preliminaries to the poem and highlights the important moments of his story prior to his physical presence in the narrative proper, which only begins with his appearance at the weapons trial in I,125. An audience would thus briefly hear all of his life before the character entered the story, beginning with his death, as sung of in Dhṛtarāṣṭra's lament.

From the most ancient hero Rāma Jāmadagnya he had received instruction in the martial arts; similarly from the teachers Droṇa and Kṛpa. Then, as a mature young warrior, Karṇa appears at the weapons trial and challenges Arjuna, a contest that will inform the rest of his life. At this point he makes his first association with Duryodhana and becomes an intimate advisor and is consecrated as a king of an eastern province.

When the question of legality arises as to whether Draupadī had been won or not in the rigged gambling session in book two, she herself having raised the 'point of order', *praśna*, Karṇa is vociferous and eloquent as well as insulting in defence of Śakuni's victory (II,62,26). Karṇa speaks well, this is one of his major qualities; he is not simply martially adept and an equal to Arjuna, but he also has the gift of address, including verbal attack. He, as a king should, gives his firm and well illustrated opinion on dharma as it pertains to this situation: what is correct behaviour and what is incorrect. He even goes on to say, indicating a knowledge of *śāstra,* that,

> II,61,35: *A single husband is ordained for a woman by the deities ...*

Subsequently he always fits the role of king well, frequently giving his view on policy or correct kṣatriya action.

Newly arrived in the forest, Yudhiṣṭhira, reviewing his enemies, describes Karṇa as,

> III,37,16: *Karṇa is passionate, always bristling, a great chariot-warrior, familiar with all weapons, invincible, covered by an adamant breastplate.*

The audience first hears of Karṇa in action during the Ghoṣayātrā *parvan* where he engages with *gandharvas* and is soundly beaten. Then, during the cattle raid against the Matsyas he skirmishes with Arjuna for the first time and is again beaten.

Indra, disguised as a brahmin, approaches him before the battle of Kurukṣetra and requests the ear-rings and cuirass. A true kṣatriya cannot refuse such a request and Karṇa cuts off his divine attributes. In return he receives from Indra a missile which is guaranteed to destroy its target, divine or human.

Immediately prior to battle commencing, Karṇa retires, having been insulted by Bhīṣma. He does not enter the fray until book seven. In book eight, the Karṇa *parvan,* he fights with Arjuna and perishes. Just before he dies Karṇa made several claims as to how dharma had failed him and as to how *daiva* or 'destiny' had triumphed. *Jayo daive pratiṣṭhitaḥ,* is what he had said earlier concerning this, which is now repeated several times again: 'victory depends on what comes from the deities' (VII,120,29).

2. The Name of Karṇa

One of the meanings of the word Karṇa signifies 'eared' or 'the ear-ringed one'.[7] Thus intrinsic even to his nominal being is this possession of ear-rings that denote invulnerability. When Kuntī had conceived her son, in the account given in book three, Sūrya appears as *āmuktakavacaṃ devaṃ kuṇḍalābhyāṃ vibhūṣitam,* 'a deity decorated with ear-rings and possessing a breast-plate' (III,290,5). Karṇa receives these as part of his identity as metonyms of his descent, because Kuntī, before agreeing to make love with Sūrya, makes him promise that the son born of the union would be *kuṇḍalī kavacī śūro* 'a hero with ear-rings and breast-plate' (III,291,17).[8] In fact it is the promise of the divine ear-rings and cuirass for her child that really seems to seduce Kuntī. Sūrya admits to her that Aditi herself bestowed the ear-rings upon him and that both they and the cuirass are *amṛtamayam,* 'made up of the immortal' (III,291,18). He promises to give her son these things, *te'sya dāsyāmi,* 'These I will give to him' (III,291,21).

In book five when Indra comes to him and begs to be given the ear-rings so that his son, Arjuna, Karṇa's chosen opponent, may win their imminent duel, Karṇa cuts them off. Without his ear-rings Karṇa is a hero who is 'without himself', that is, dead, or soon to be dead—the ear-rings being an emblem for his identity or life.[9] The epic poets make much of this economy of metaphor where the ear-rings are exchanged for fame and a spear, and then the spear is given up to a figure who wears ear-rings, in return for further renown.

No other players in the epic possess ear-rings that are so remarkable. Kings and *sūtas* sometimes display ear-rings, but there the quality stops; the poets take no further notice of the fact. One such character who is thus remarked is the *sūta* or poet Saṃjaya who sings much of the central part of the poem and who possesses the divine eyesight allowing him to be aware of what is occurring far away in the distance; he is called, *kuṇḍalī,* 'the one with ear-rings'. Another is Jayadratha, whose decapitated head is described as possessing ear-rings *sakuṇḍalam,* (VII,121,26).[10] Also ear-ringed is Ghaṭotkaca, a demon *rākṣasa* who is instrumental in making Karṇa even more vulnerable than he is. His ear-rings are *bālasūryābhe,* 'like a young sun'. Interestingly, in the next line he is described as also possessing a cuirass, this one being 'broad and very bright and of brass or white metal' (VII,150,10). . .

In book three, Indra, the progenitor of Arjuna, appears before Karṇa in order to divest him of his signs of invulnerability so that Arjuna will triumph in the forthcoming duel. Immediately prior to this, Karṇa's own father, the Sun, Sūrya, comes to him in order to warn him about what Indra is up to. Karṇa dismisses Sūrya's warning saying that for him to be able to give something to Indra, the chief of the deities, will only bring him fame. For the chief immortal to come and beg from him can only elevate Karṇa in terms of renown. He goes on to talk at length about the importance if not the priority of fame over anything else.

Indra then appears, disguised as a brahmin, and Karṇa hands over his jewels and breastplate, removing them bloodily with a knife. In return he receives a missile, *śakti* that is unerring in its flight.[11] Thus, although he is no longer invincible, he retains the potential capacity to destroy Arjuna, as well as earning the superlative honour of having bestowed a gift upon the chief of the celestials. Later on, through a similar act of great liberality, Karṇa also relinquishes the missile.

When Karṇa had cut away his natural breast-plate he received the patronymic, *vaikartana,* from *vikartana,* the Sun, 'divider' or 'distributor', but it can mean 'the one who cuts'. When he does this cutting, all the deities and celestials are present and roar aloud and flowers fall from the sky (III,294,36). This is something that only occurs once again, that is, at the end of his life in book eight (VIII,63,60). Thus, these two instants, where there is a loss of im/mortality, are being emphatically indicated by the poets.

Not long after this Karṇa briefly skirmishes with Bhīma, the father of the *rākṣasa* Ghaṭotkaca. In this engagement he loses an ear-ring to one of Bhīma's arrows. There is a triple polyptotonic play on the noun here, for the kind of arrow that is used is called a broad arrow or *karṇin.*

VII,114,3: *He pierced Karṇa on the ear with a broad arrow.*

In the next line Bhīma also pierces his chest, which of course is no longer protected by the divine and invulnerable cuirass which

Indra had taken. This same phrase where the triple play on ear is made had also occurred sixty lines earlier on in the chapter, when someone else attacks Karṇa. So twice the audience is signalled this new mortality of the hero by the poet's repetition of the symbolic locus of that mortality.

Similarly, just a few lines before the wheel of Karṇa's chariot sticks in the earth in book eight, there is again such a signal (VIII,66,42). The audience has heard prophesied several times that the grounded wheel will be a sign for Karṇa's death. A few lines prior to this, Karṇa, of course, has his ear-rings—presumably a new and 'mortal' set—and his crown, struck off by an arrow of Arjuna. Again, we observe the same pattern appearing: ear-rings or the absence of ear-rings and death.

Bhīma's demon son, the *rākṣasa* Ghaṭotkaca, who wears 'brilliant ear-rings', *dīptakuṇḍalam,* then goes into the attack. This initial duel between Karṇa and the demon continues over many lines (VII,150,4-103). It is because Ghaṭotkaca is destroying the Kuru forces in book seven that they beg Karṇa to save them (VII,154,48ff.). Just as Karṇa generously and impersonally relinquished his ear-rings, so he relinquishes the missile; he does not hesitate to save his companions. He destroys Ghaṭotkaca by using this final supernatural resource, the special spear, the *śakti* which was guaranteed to always find its target and which he had previously reserved for Arjuna.

VII,154,54: *A meteor, like the blazing sister of Death.*

By the time the final duel with Arjuna happens, Karṇa no longer has either the protection nor the weaponry to triumph: which of course means death.

This stratagem to weaken and defeat Karṇa had been engineered by the super-subtle deity Kṛṣṇa, who danced with delight and became *atiharṣam,* 'overjoyed' (VII,155,11) when Karṇa was no more invincible to Arjuna. He says,

VII,155,13: *What man is there in the world who could withstand Karṇa with the spear in hand?*

Complete with ear-rings and spear Karṇa was invincible in the three worlds; neither Indra nor Varuṇa nor Yama himself could defeat him (VII,155,15ff.), even Kṛṣṇa was powerless. Kṛṣṇa adds that Karṇa had now attained 'human status', *so'dya mānuṣatām prāptaḥ* (VII,155,27) that is, he could be killed. It should be mentioned that previously in the poem, in book one in fact, we heard that Ghaṭotkaca was 'created by Indra himself' especially for the destruction of Karṇa, *saa sṛṣṭo maghavatā ... karṇasya ... vināśāya,* (I,143,38).

What is important here therefore, is firstly, how these divine ear-rings are really objects which denote great power and a certain non-mortality and which Karṇa is prepared to exchange in return for extraordinary fame and a spear. Secondly, when he does give up his invincibility even more, by using that special missile to finish off Ghaṭotkaca, he is again behaving in a fashion that will secure him fame and in conditions marked by the presence of these *kuṇḍale,* ear-rings.

In return for this second act of bestowal we hear,

VII,154,63: *Then Karṇa was being honoured by the Kurus,*
as Indra by the Maruts after the destruction of Vṛtra.

That is, Karṇa is being praised as if he were the chief of the immortals himself. There is a circulation here of fame, and the two exchanges are marked by the unusual presence of ear-rings. In French one would say that, 'Pompidou a cassé sa pipe', or in English, 'George has kicked the bucket'. It is as if the idiom here is that 'Karṇa has lost his ear-rings'. This is perhaps pushing the model a bit far, but the import is carried through.

As a corollary to the above, when Arjuna eventually slays Karṇa—and we have been hearing this refrain about his imminent death right from the beginning of the poem when the blind old king Dhṛtarāṣṭra mentions him in his lament (I,1,139)—Arjuna is again and again likened to Indra slaying the demon Vṛtra. That is, Karṇa is again and again put in the position of Vṛtra.

VIII,63,16: *They appeared ... like Indra and Vṛtra.*

We hear of this particular myth many times in the Ṛgveda, it could almost be said to be the 'charter myth' of Vedic culture or poetry. It is a myth associated with the primary cosmogonic act whereby the three worlds are made viable for human life. At this point where Vṛtra perishes, the 'waters' of creativity are released. Thus the death of Karṇa is by analogy being signalled to an audience as a moment of extreme fecundity or fruition. The life which has won for him, by his own account, such fame, is in its conclusion seen as a metaphor for that victory whereby the chief of the deities established order and feasibility in the world. The ear-rings are the primary metonym of this death.

Secondly, as well as signifying 'ear', the word Karṇa also means helm or rudder. The metaphor of steering a boat is a figure of speech that we shall see is also dear to the *Mahābhārata* poets. It is possible to show that certain metaphors, like this one, do not exist alone, that there is a field or network which they amplify anaphorically.[12]

One such figure of speech that we repeatedly hear of in the epic is that of a 'vessel' or 'raft', *plava,* that is at risk in the sea, or is being submerged. This often refers to the Kaurava cause. Sometimes the metaphor is extended, and battle itself is the referent for sea.[13] Dhṛtarāṣṭra in book seven describes his army as a 'great sea', *mahodadhi,* and says that Karṇa is 'the full and risen moon' to this, *karṇacandrodayoddhitam* (VII,89,14). Heroes are often the *plava* that will cross the dangerous ocean, the threat usually coming from battle. Karṇa receives many such mentions and his name connects him more closely to this metaphor than other heroes.

We should remember at this point that when Karṇa was born he was exposed to the river Gaṅgā: he is *gāṅgeya,* a metronym for one born of the Ganges. Thus implicit in his very person and title is that primary fluid image.

Also we have Duryodhana making the interesting comment in book one that,

I,127,11: *The origins of heroes and rivers are indeed difficult to understand.*

In fact one of the very constant metaphors of battle in the poem is that of a *nadī*, 'river': with the dead elephants being islands, wrecked chariots being sand-banks, the fallen warriors being like the trunks of trees floating, with vultures and dogs being like predatory sea-creatures. It is the one metaphor of battle that an audience hears more than any other.

Returning to the theme of the ship, in book seven, before Karṇa has been proclaimed commander of the Kaurava forces, Duryodhana refers to his army as being, 'like a boat overwhelmed or submerged in the sea', *majjatīm nāvam ivārṇave* (VII,2,3).

In book five, Karṇa is talking with his mother, Kuntī, who has come to speak with him for the first time ever. She pleads for his mercy so that he will not kill all her other sons, the five Pāṇḍavas, who are in fact his younger brothers. He rejects her plea on the grounds that he had given his word to king Duryodhana, his patron, and in whose fealty he now stands, and who is the cousin and rival of those brothers. Karṇa says that he can never change anything once he has spoken it. Correct and undeviating speech is vital for both kṣatriyas and brahmins and is something to which Karṇa adheres absolutely. This statement about the irrefrangibility of his words is typical.

He then says to his mother,

> V,144,14: *With me as boat they desire to cross the unfathomable battle.*[14]

The boat here is the *plava*, and 'they' are the Kauravas. This is a metaphor that recurs many times in the poem, either spoken by Karṇa or by someone else and which he is often the referent of. In a similar vein, Yudhiṣṭhira, instructing his herald, Saṃjaya, asks,

> V,26,20: *Why was Karṇa not an isle for them?*

Equally, the old blind king, says,

> VIII,5,23: *Having heard that Karṇa was slain in a duel by Arjuna*
> *I am plunged in a sea of grief, like one, boatless in an ocean.*

The interesting cornerstone to all this however comes after the fatal wounding of the most senior hero, Bhīṣma. King Duryodhana approaches Karṇa and asks him who he considers should be the next commander. Karṇa had refused to participate in the fighting right from the first day, after being insulted by Bhīṣma, the most distinguished of the kṣatriyas. Rather like Achilles, Karṇa had withdrawn from combat.[15]

Duryodhana says to Karṇa,

> VII,5,8: *Without a guide, the army does not stand even a moment in battle, O best in battle! Like a boat in water without a governor.*

He continues in the next line, by making a comparison, using the form of *śleṣa* or 'pun'.

> VII,5,9: *As a boat without a helmsman and a chariot without driver.*

This is a very subtle way of saying to Karṇa that the army is *akarṇa,* without a helm, and who does he think should be appointed to be the next marshal?[16] Again, the *Mahābhārata* poets are giving their audience an ironic message that is not actually taken up within the poem itself but is directed outside of the narrative.

Finally, to take a step back to the beginning of the poem, where Śaunaka is requesting that Ugraśravas recite the great tale of the Bhāratas to him, he refers to this *kathā* as *manaḥsāgarasaṃbhūtām maharṣeḥ,* 'born of the oceanic mind of the *ṛṣi* Vyāsa' (I,53,34), which in terms of narrative would denote the primary sea.

As a rider to the above we have in book two of Ṛgveda, in a hymn to Indra, the deity who has a strongly genetic importance for heroes. The poet says,

> II,16,7: *I advance towards you in the festival a song [like] a boat.*

The metaphor of a hymn being a vehicle is commonplace in the Ṛgveda. The epic poets extend that image to the valour of a hero, which, as we know, only exists *in* the song. Epic poetry and its primary metaphor of marine imagery thus fuse on many levels, and Karṇa, by virtue of his name as 'helmsman', is profoundly part of this order.

* * *

Six Speeches

There are six major dialogues in which Karṇa participates, excluding those exchanges that he makes with Duryodhana, Arjuna, and Bhīṣma. . . They all fall into a general pattern of projecting kṣatriya dharma, with the exception of the conversation which Karṇa has with Kṛṣṇa.[17] This particular dialogue reflects certain unique aspects of Karṇa's persona which we hear of nowhere else. Five of these speeches are private, that is, only the speakers hear what is said. The exchange with Kṛpa is public and although all of the speeches are to some extent 'performative', this particular speech functions as a commentary on the manner in which heroes, and especially Karṇa, address each other [. . .]

Kṛṣṇa

This dialogue and the one immediately subsequent, when Karṇa speaks with his mother, are called, in the *parvasaṃgraha, vivādaparvan,* 'the narrative of dispute' (I,2,52).[18]

What occurs in this exchange is unlike anything else in the poem as it relates to Karṇa. In a way this conversation is a reflection of the speeches in the Gītā. Here we see the hero and his driver on a chariot, or the hero and a deity. Kṛṣṇa, as we have already noted, behaves more like a hero in the course of the epic than like a deity, except that, only nine chapters previously, he had revealed his divine nature before the assembled *sabhā*.[19] In this account, what Karṇa says is unlike anything else he ever speaks: it is almost as if he is in the place of the theophanist himself, relating all as it will be, but in divine and atemporal terms.

Kṛṣṇa begins by first complimenting the other on his knowledge of the Vedas and the subtlety of *dharmaśāstra*; Karṇa, he says, is *pariniṣṭhita,* 'accomplished' in these skills (V,138,7). This is something that the audience has never heard about Karṇa before, for usually one only hears of how great an exemplar of kṣatriya virtue he is, in a physical sense, rather than what habitually comes under the rubric of a brahmin. Right from the beginning of this scene then, something very different is being signalled: in this conversation, the audience is to hear what is a unique discourse.

Kṛṣṇa then tells him that by law he should be considered as the eldest born of Pāṇḍu's sons and that, 'you will be king' *rājā bhaviṣyasi* (V,138,9).[20] Also, through his mother, he is related to the Vṛṣṇis, the clan of Kṛṣṇa himself: in fact, Kṛṣṇa is his cousin.[21] He tells Karṇa that all the Pāṇḍava allies, the kings and kṣatriyas and their sons, shall be tributary to him, *pādau tava grahīṣyanti*, 'they will touch your feet' (V,138,12); and that in time he will sleep with Draupadī.

> V,138,15: *In the sixth place, Draupadī will, in time, approach you [sexually].*

That is, he will join the five brothers in sharing her as a wife.[22] He will be anointed as king and Yudhiṣṭhira will stand behind him holding the 'fan', *vyajana,* as the 'crown prince', *yuvarāja.* Bhīma will hold his 'great white umbrella', *chatram ... mahac chvetam.* Kṛṣṇa gives a long list of the pageant which will follow in Karṇa's train and the tributes that other kings will bring.

> V,138,26-27: *Let the Pāṇḍavas sound out the triumph of Karṇa! You, surrounded by the princes, as the moon by its stations.*

Finally, he admonishes 'brotherhood', *saubhrātram* with the Pāṇḍavas (V,138,28).

How does Karṇa respond to being offered lordship of the world?[23] This is of course what Duryodhana is struggling for. He replies formally and eloquently, dealing with Kṛṣṇa's points. One thing about Karṇa is that when he is not boasting, he always speaks with dignity and great art: he truly is *vadatām vara,* 'best of speakers'.

He admits to knowing of his divine father and his mother's subsequent exposure of him at birth as if he had been 'inauspicious', *yathā na kuśalam* (V,139,3-4). It was Rādhā who gave him succour though, the wife of a *sūta.* 'From affection', *sauhārdāt,* and not just from scriptural injunction, he knows Adhiratha, the *sūta,* as a father. It was Adhiratha who had rites performed for him, *putraprītyā,* 'with love for a son', and had him named Vasuṣena by brahmins; who found him wives with whom he got sons, who then gave him grandsons (V,139,9-11).[24] With them, 'bonds of love were born', *kāmabandhanam saṃjātam.*[25]

His next loyalty goes to his patron and king, Duryodhana, with whom he has been in allegiance for thirteen years and whom he cannot betray:

V,139,12: *Not from joy nor fear, Kṛṣṇa, am I able to speak untruth.*

During that time, he had performed all the appropriate rites and sacrifices and marriage rituals with *sūtas,* that is, with those appropriate to his station—he had kept to his caste (V,139,14). Duryodhana had 'depended' on him, he says, *samāśritya,* and selected him to fight against Arjuna in battle, *dvairathe,* 'in a duel'. Karṇa cannot breach that trust by not accepting the duel.

V,139,18: *If I would not go to the duel with Arjuna,*
O Kṛṣṇa, infamy would belong to both me and Arjuna.

For Karṇa, allegiance is something derived from emotion and verbal commitment. It does not depend on blood ties nor upon any organic relation. Such an approach to kinship would appear contrary to the usual *varṇa* formations, and is certainly contrary to what Kṛṣṇa himself speaks of in the Gītā, where any kind of miscellany is decried.

As with Bhīṣma, when he had given his word and vowed to remain celibate, there is no possible revocation of such verbal commitment. Truth for kṣatriyas, especially the heroes, is something existing within spoken language. For brahmins, truth is much more textual or canonical, it is more 'external'. In book one, Bhīṣma says, *parityajeyaṃ trailokyaṃ rājyaṃ deveṣu va … na tu satyaṃ kathaṃcana,* 'I would abandon the three worlds or kingdom among the deities … I would in no way abandon truth'; his oath is so vital (I,97,15). He gives three *ślokas* of similes detailing the intensity of such commitment, concluding with,

I,97,18: *So may I in no way resolve to abandon truth.*

The situation is like that now facing Karṇa.[26]

Immediately prior to the opening of battle at Kurukṣetra, Kṛṣṇa goes over to Karṇa, admitting that he had heard of Karṇa's announcement not to fight until Bhīṣma falls. Kṛṣṇa again asks Karṇa to forsake the Kauravas, *asmān varaya rādheya,* 'choose us, Karṇa' (VI,41,85), so long as Bhīṣma remains unslain. Karṇa again refuses, *na vipriyam kariṣyāmi dhārtarāṣṭrasya,* 'I shall do nothing offensive to Duryodhana'.

VI,41,87: *Know me as one who has abandoned his life wishing the good of Duryodhana!*

To return to the earlier scene, Karṇa then says something slightly ominous or *unheimlich,* strangely out of character.

V,139,20: *O best of men, you should hold back this speech.*

Karṇa advises Kṛṣṇa not to tell Yudhiṣṭhira of what is Karṇa's true position, namely, that he is a brother. Yudhiṣṭhira then 'will not uphold the kingdom', *na sa rājyam grahīṣyati,* if he thought that he was not, in terms of dharma, the true heir to it (V,139,21).[27]

V,139,23: *Let Yudhiṣṭhira, the dharma-souled one, be perpetual king!*

Karṇa says that if he himself 'obtained the great rich kingdom, he would give it to Duryodhana', *prāpya ... mahad rājyam ... sphītaṃ duryodhanāya ... saṃpradadyām* (V,139,22). This is completely contrary to what he and Śakuni and Duḥśāsana have been dubiously propounding for the sake of Duryodhana. All their schemes have been to secure the throne, and now Karṇa is rejecting the offer. The audience suddenly hears of a unique side to Karṇa that never appears again outside of this exchange. His role as a hero thus needs some modification.

He next describes,

V,139,28: *Kṛṣṇa, this great assembly of kṣatriyas has been effected.*

Karṇa then relates *in extenso* the metaphor of war as a sacrifice, *śastrayajño* (V,139,29-44), an image first given by Duryodhana above.[28] The sacrifice is to be performed by Duryodhana.

V,139,29: *Kṛṣṇa, there will be a sacrifice of weapons of Duryodhana, you will be the witness of this sacrifice, Kṛṣṇa.*

Arjuna is the *hotṛ,* whose bow will be the ladle and Kṛṣṇa will be the officiating *adhvaryu.* Karṇa lists all the roles of the ritual as the Pāṇḍavas will play them.[29]

Karṇa then describes the imminent death of his fellow warriors and himself and Duryodhana and the ritual laments of the women that will follow this. The metaphor for his own death also participates in this general metaphor of the sacrificial rite: this is the *punaścitiḥ,* 'repiling' of the fire altar (V,139,46). It is what occurs after the main action of the sacrifice is completely done, and is a preparation for another ritual occasion. Is Karṇa thus saying, metaphorically, that his death will be a preparation for what is to succeed, that is, the subsequent *yuga?*

Karṇa is speaking out of character in describing not only his own death but the total defeat of the Kauravas and death of Duryodhana. Not only is he doing that, but he is perverting his king's own metaphor, that of the *śastrayajña,* 'sacrifice of weapons'; and this is when he has only just been describing how his loyalty to Duryodhana was superior to any other relation in his life! This speech is contrary to every other speech that Karṇa has given or will give in the poem. He has rejected the absolute sovereignty that Kṛṣṇa has offered and instead presents his unique vision of what the consequences of all this conflict will be. If one ignores the question of textual emendation here, such a pronouncement, being so adverse to every other statement of Karṇa's in the epic, puts him in an even more isolated position than Achilles with his desire for *kléos* above all else. It is a strange and haunting moment whose open-endedness and irresolution only makes for an even greater effect, at least in terms of the ominous. It is as if this moment represents Karṇa at his most stable, most truthful, because it is his most unearthly speech; at this point he possesses no preoccupations nor attachments.

He concludes by asking Kṛṣṇa to do what pleases him, *vidhatsva yad abhīpsitam,* 'dispose whatever you wish!'

V,139,53: *May the accomplished ring of kṣatriyas go to a destruction by weaponry at Kurukṣetra ...*

To this, he adds,

V,139,54: *So that, Kṛṣṇa, the kṣatriya order may obtain heaven entirely.*

Returning to fame again, he finally says,

V,139,55: *Kṛṣṇa, as long as mountains and rivers will stand, so long will this perpetual sound that arises from fame exist.*

Karṇa adds that Kṛṣṇa should keep this exchange private, *mantrasaṃvaraṃ kurvan nityam*, 'always making a concealment of [this] speech', echoing what he had similarly adjured at 139,20, and giving closure to the speech.

What the audience has just heard is in fact a reversal of the norm, where the (divine) charioteer informs his warrior-hero about the future events of a battle: using his supernatural vision the *sūta* usually relates to the hero the course of events and victory. Here the *sūta*, Karṇa, is the one who is telling Kṛṣṇa about what is going to happen, which is the opposite of what occurs in the Gītā, where it is Kṛṣṇa who reveals in his speech the hypostatic nature of what is about to occur. Also, as a second reversal, Karṇa quite joyously describes his and his side's monumental if not cosmic defeat. All that he had spoken about loyalty and integrity is suddenly irrelevant. Karṇa is placing himself, or the poets are placing Karṇa, in a position within the poem that is superior to that of any other character: the usual distinction of life and death has collapsed. Or, Karṇa is suddenly out of the causal sequence of narration. Even Vyāsa himself never speaks with such visionary forecast. The fact that Karṇa also embraces his own annihilation as part of this only accents his clarity and unearthly view. Certainly, Arjuna is never party to such selfless lucidity.

Kṛṣṇa is pleased and laughs and repeats his offer of the earth as a gift.

V,140,2: *Would the taking of the kingdom not burn you, Karṇa? For, you do not wish to rule the earth given by me?*

The metre then reverts to *triṣṭubh* form for three stanzas: these are sung by Kṛṣṇa. They are in praise of the 'victorious flag' of Arjuna, *jayadhvaja,* and seem curiously disjunctive—these stanzas seem to having nothing to do with the flow of exchange. He also says that victory is now certain for the Pāṇḍavas, echoing what Karṇa had just said (V,140,3). The audience then hears Kṛṣṇa, referring to himself in the third person (V,140,6), giving a description of how the *dvāpara yuga* will end, although he makes no mention of the *kali yuga,* which seems curious.[30] He finally gives Karṇa specific instructions as to when battle should commence, qualifying this with an account of how appropriate the present moment is. Here, Kṛṣṇa displays astronomical knowledge that is more typical of brahmins than of kṣatriyas. He concludes by saying that the kṣatriyas who die then,

V,140,20: *Having obtained destruction by weapons, they will obtain the highest end.*

Karṇa inquires as to why Kṛṣṇa attempted to delude him if he knew that the world was about to come to an end (V,141,1-2). Then he confesses that 'the destruction of the entire earth', *pṛthivyāḥ kārtsnyena vināśaḥ,* was due to the gang of four: Śakuni, himself, Duḥśāsana, and Duryodhana (V,141,2). All who follow Duryodhana 'will proceed to the dwelling of Yama', *prāpsyanti yamasādanam.* He proceeds to give a highly accurate astrological account of why battle would be immediately appropriate and why the Pāṇḍavas will triumph (V,141,5,ff.)[31] Again, such detailed technical knowledge sounds unusual for the character of Karṇa, but so much of this speech is of that nature. This description of signs and portents continues for a long twenty *ślokas.*

The meeting is terminated by Karṇa describing an apocalyptic dream of a 'vast white palace', *sahasrapādaṃ prāsādam,* in which he viewed the Pāṇḍavas, dressed in white and triumphant, and the earth full of bones and blood (V,141,27-42). He makes the very *vaiṣṇava* statement that, *yato dharmas tato jayaḥ,* 'wherever there is dharma, *there* is victory' (V,141,33). He closes the vision by saying that he and the other kings will soon enter the dwelling of Death, and,

> V,141,42: *I and the other kings and the whole ring of kṣatriyas*
> *will enter the fire of the Gāṇḍiva bow ...*

The unique, to Karṇa, statements made in this dialogue lead the reader to wonder if they are not 'later additions' to an earlier form of this part of the poem. The above phrase is particularly associated with *vaiṣṇava* devotion to Kṛṣṇa as a deity, as related in the Gītā:

> VI,41,55: *Where there is dharma there is Kṛṣṇa.*
> *Wherever Kṛṣṇa, there is victory.*

How is one to explain why Karṇa speaks so paraleptically and in such an out-of-character manner during the passage? If it is not the case that this passage is a later addition, there is something extraordinarily peculiar about the speech: the prophecy about the sacrifice of war and Karṇa's own death, as well as the vision of the apocalypse. It could be argued that the Bhārgava editors of the poem only touched this one moment in the story of Karṇa and considered that sufficient for their patently ideological purposes; it is a moot point which cannot be resolved. One can only understand how the infinitely innovative flexibility of an oral tradition makes this possible and that the poets were performing in constant adjustment or reciprocity with their audience.

Kṛṣṇa reiterates that the end of the world is imminent. Karṇa's last word to the other is that they might both escape *vīrakṣayavināśanāt,* 'from the annihilation and ruin of warriors', and meet *svarge,* 'in heaven'. Again, both eschatological considerations fit more with the world expounded in the Gītā than with the views expressed in Karṇa's other speeches throughout the poem. It is as if there had been a switch in genre, from the strictly heroic to the more sectarian. They separate, 'having embraced closely', *pariṣvajya pīḍitam.*

It should be recalled that Kṛṣṇa is the one character who later does his utmost to engineer the death of Karṇa by arranging that Ghaṭotkaca enter the fray (VII,148,35), and then by encouraging Arjuna to strike at Karṇa when the latter is pleading for mercy after his chariot wheel sticks in the earth, reminding him of all that Karṇa did and said to Draupadī in the *sabhā* (VIII,67,1ff.) [. . .]

Notes

1. This extended metaphor is repeated by Yudhiṣṭhira at V,29,46ff. It is indicative of the poetics which are at work in the epic, that the same lines can be spoken by different voices at different times. There are four major metaphors, related to the hero, that are at work in the *Mahābhārata*: those of trees, of water, of fire, and of mountains. These four images generate, via metonymy, many other images that oscillate, as it were, from the initial key icon. Other metaphors that are typical but not so extensively repeated and which do not generate metonyms with such freqnency are snakes and astronomical imagery. Another way of looking at how metaphor works in the poem would be to conceive of it as a fabric, with the warp being supplied by metaphor and the weft by metonymy. Thus an extraordinary reticulation can be developed by the poets, amplifying just a single theme. For example, from the metaphor of boat, one can proceed to metonyms of oars, rough seas, tillers, and so on, extending that original first image throughout the text. From the point of view of an audience, this kind of poetic is able to address areas of particular familiarity with extraordinary range or magnitude. I am grateful to Gregory Nagy for introducing me to this idea of a fabric of meaning. See Jakobson, 1980, p.129ff. on metonymy and metaphor.
2. It should be noted that representations of the Buddha were at first aniconic—except for the Jātaka scenes—and were often made in the form of a tree, the *bodhidruma*. In fact the image of the 'sacred tree', *caitya vṛkṣa*, goes back to Indus Valley times: see Parpola, 1994, fig.13.8, p.229.
3. Similarly, the first of the battle books, the Bhīṣma *parvan*, commences, just prior to the opening lines of the Gītā, with Saṃjaya declaring that Bhīṣma had been struck down (VI,14,3). Then, the poet is asked *how* this occurred, and the audience hears about the ten days leading up to the moment. This kind of narrative recapitulation is the norm for the *Mahābhārata*, with the poet announcing the death of a hero and the interlocutor requesting an account of such—'how did it happen?'
4. I use the convention throughout of 'sing' for epic declamation. Certainly, melody is not in question here, but sonority is not to be excluded. See Nagy, 1991, Ch.1. Any modern verbal rendering of *Mahābhārata* supports

this view. Hopkins, 1888, p.323, "The verses are sung by the musician to a musical accompaniment in honor of the king and his ancestors ... We find, not one, but a band (*gaṇa*) of musicians singing the deeds of old heroes, and accompanying themselves on the lyre (*vīṇā*), and called *vīṇāgāthin* (lyre-singer)." Also, there is the obvious reference to what is 'sung', *gītā*, by Kṛṣṇa.

5. I propose to translate the word *vīra* by 'warrior', and the word *śūra* by 'hero'. Hopkins, 1888, p.99, comments on a verse in the Rāmāyaṇa (whose placement he cannot recall), "that defines the *çūra*, or knight, as ... *pauruṣeṇa hi yo yuktaḥ sa çūra iti saṃjñitaḥ*. That is, a man of might is the real knight. But *çūra* means more than this, and, associated as it almost always is with *satkulīna* 'well-born', means a noble, technically speaking—a man of the upper class at court and in the field. *Kulaja* (well-born), as epithet of a warrior, is indicative of power ..." It does seem appropriate that when Karṇa's mother submits to the attentions of Sūrya she makes him formally promise that her son would be a *śūra* (III,291,17), for he is going to become the best of the Kurus. A glance at the *pratīka* Index will reveal that *śūra* occurs fifty per-cent plus more times in the second five books of the poem than in the first five books.

6. The conception and events leading up to it, the birth, and then the encounter with Indra, are all given in compressed form, an account amounting to only twenty-one *ślokas*. Such versatility on the part of the poets is typical of preliterate technique.

7. Karṇa. It is entirely fitting that, for a hero who is intensely pre-occupied with fame, 'that which is heard', that his very name be connected with such 'hearing'. He is also sometimes, although not very often, referred to as *vṛṣan*, 'bull', or 'best', or simply, 'male'. Śiva, Indra, as well as Kṛṣṇa, are also referred to by this name, and it thus takes on something of the quality of an epithet.

8. Note that Karṇa is referred to as *śūra*, and not *vīra*: 'hero'. Skanda, the divine son of Agni and Svāhā, is really the only other significantly ear-ringed hero in the poem who is in any way like Karṇa. *tam varadaṃ śūraṃ yuvānaṃ mṛṣṭakuṇḍalam*, 'That beneficent young hero who possessed shining ear-rings' (III,218,3). He is in fact more of a deity than a hero although Indra on meeting him addresses him as *vīra* (III,218,15), just before he is anointed as commander of the divine army that is to attack the *dānavas*. This he does victoriously and Indra acclaims him, *triṣu lokeṣu kīrtiś ca tava akṣayyā bhaviṣyati*, 'And your fame will be imperishable among the three worlds' (III,221,76). Thereafter Skanda plays no important role in the *Mahābhārata* narrative.

9. Throughout the course of the poem, the most common occasion for ear-rings to be noted by the poets is when they describe a decapitated head

lying on the ground embellished by such ornaments. (VI,66,7; VII,15,37; VIII,19,28; IX,13,15). Thus the most typical instancing of ear-rings in the epic is intimately associated with death. In book six, for example, of the twelve occasions for *kuṇḍala* being mentioned, ten concern decapitated heads. (In book six, the usual formula is *śirobhiś ca sakuṇḍalaiḥ*; in book seven the elements of the typical formula are *śiraḥ kāyāt sakuṇḍalam.*) The final reference to ear-rings in the poem comes when all the dead heroes rise out of the Gaṅgā and meet one last time with the remaining Kurus. All these dead are described as 'possessing radiant ear-rings', *sarve bhrājiṣṇukuṇḍalāḥ* (XV,40,15).

10. His henchman, Koṭikāśya, with whom he attempts to kidnap Draupadī in the forest, is similarly described as *kuṇḍalī*, 'ear-ringed' (III,248,17). Like Saṃjaya, Koṭikāśya functions as a *sūta*, a 'charioteer'. It would thus seem that *kuṇḍalin* is a signifier for this class of individual; Karṇa of course, belongs to the *sūta* class. In the Virāṭa *parvan* ear-rings appear with a much greater frequency than any other book in the *Mahābhārata*: for some reason they are far more commonplace in this section of the poem.
11. The reason he does not use this to destroy his main enemy, Arjuna, is given in VII,157,37, where Kṛṣṇa says, *aham eva tu rādheyaṃ mohayāmi yudhāṃ vara / yato nāvasṛjac chaktiṃ pāṇḍave śvetavāhane*, 'So I delude[d] the son of Rādhā, best of warriors. Hence he did not discharge the weapon at the son of Pāṇḍu, him of the white horses'.
12. For instance, at the outset of the Karṇa *parvan*, the formation of the army at the moment of Karṇa's first entry onto the field, is that of a *makara*, 'sea-monster' (VIII,7,14). Perhaps there is an even larger field of reference here, as, for instance: ... *lokā hy āpsu pratiṣṭhitāḥ / āpomayāḥ sarvarasāḥ sarvaṃ āpomayam jagat*, ' ... the worlds stand in water, every taste is made of water, all the world is made of water' (I,171,17-18). To take the metaphor even further, *saṃnimajjaj jagad idaṃ gambhīre kālasāgare / jarāmṛtyurmahāgrāhe na kaścid avabudhyate*, 'No one perceives this world sinking in a deep sea of time [where there are] sharks of death and age' (XII,28,43).
13. A study of the imagery connected with water in the *Mahābhārata* would produce fascinating results. The sea, rivers, rain, the primal 'waters', and all the associated metaphors and metonyms, fishes &c., supply an enormous range of visual information. Water and its counterpoint, fire, are the two key images of the poem, and the poets constantly make these references with degrees of extraordinary complexity.
14. Arjuna, uttering *kathā* to Kṛṣṇa, as they ride together in a chariot in the Aśvamedhika *parvan*, says something very similar. *pāṇḍava ... bhavantaṃ plavaṃ āsādya tīrṇāḥ sma kurusāgaram*, 'The Pāṇḍavas crossed the Kuru-sea having used you as a boat' (XIV,51,7).

15. Tod, 1929, vol. II, p.637, depicts Karṇa as "the Hindu Apollo", because of his radiance. This is similarly an aspect of Achilles.
16. Karṇa, of course, despite the fact that the army have been clamoring for him, decorously proposes that Droṇa be appointed as commander. This is not an occasion for boasting and self-promotion, the conditions are not present for such (VII,5,12ff.) Karṇa is always correct in protocol; even the bragging occurs only when it is appropriate that such a performance should take place. Despite the joy of the army that the best hero is now with them and despite Duryodhana's mute offer, Karṇa only does what is fitting.
17. Niles, 1999, p.8, comments on epic as being "a form of ritualized discourse through which powerful people enhanced their prestige and self-esteem and articulated a system of values that was meant to benefit society as a whole."
18. This narrative is also referred to in its colophon at V,148 as the *upanivāda parvan*, 'book of flattery or secret cajolery'. It is pertinent that this section of the poem is related by Saṃjaya, who makes use of his divine poetic insight in order to describe to Dhṛtarāṣṭra what happened on the chariot between Kṛṣṇa and Karṇa. This kind of narration is usually only specific to the four battle books.
19. When Kṛṣṇa first makes his entry into the poem he is described as *yadupravīraḥ*, 'champion of the Yadus' (I,179,9). Yudhiṣṭhira calls him *no gatiḥ ... nātho ... guruḥ*, 'our path, protector, guru' (V,145,12).
20. He is echoing what Pāṇḍu told Kuntī in I,111,27 concerning the *ṣaṭ purtā*, 'six forms of son', when he, cursed with celibacy by a copulating buck, was encouraging his wife to become pregnant by a brahmin.
21. Kuntī is the sister of Kṛṣṇa's father, Vasudeva.
22. In the popular version of the epic related in Hiltebeitel, 1988, p.316, "Draupadī reveals her longings for Karṇa." She has "unrealisable sexual longings" for him.
23. Shulman, 1985, p. 399, notes that Karṇa cannot accept this and become king for "he is wholly identified with the ethos of the hero, with the hero's ... path to fame ... His world is closed, relatively static, locked into meaning." Kingship in this instance is more concerned with the shifting and subtle dynamics of dharma, with balances. King and hero here occupy two very different semantic fields.
24. The only occasion for the audience to hear of a wife of Karṇa occurs during the Strī *parvan*, when Gāndhārī sings of the dead and lamenting after the battle is over. *paśya karṇasya patnīm*, 'Look, there is Karṇa's wife' (XI,21,10). This woman is also, incidentally, the mother of Vṛṣasena and of Suṣeṇa, his favoured sons.
25. Sjoestedt, 1949, p.61, remarking on the very common tradition of

fostering in the cognate Irish epic tradition, comments that, "The bond created by ... fosterage was regarded as more sacred than the natural bond."

26. Note that Karṇa speaks of *anṛta* whereas Bhīṣma uses the word *satya*.
27. When Yudhiṣṭhira discovers that Kuntī knew about Karṇa's identity and did not inform any of the Pāṇḍavas, especially himself, he curses her: *śaśāpa ca mahātejāḥ sarvalokeṣu ca striyaḥ*, 'and the austere king cursed women throughout all the worlds' (XII,6,10).
28. Shulman, 1985, p.386 goes so far as to say that "the true hero, like Karṇa himself, is a sacrificer, an archetypal Vedic *yajamāna*."
29. Although the metaphor is the same as employed by Duryodhana at V,57,12ff., the import is totally different. In Duryodhana's model, he and Karṇa were participants in the ritual. Here, it is the case that Duryodhana is a *yajamāna*, the one to commission the rite. In the former case, Yudhiṣṭhira was in the place of the 'victim', *paśum*, whereas now, *yudhiṣṭhiraḥ / japair homaiś ca saṃyukto brahmatvaṃ kārayiṣyati*, 'Yudhiṣṭhira will act as a brahman, conjoined with prayers and libations' (V,139,34). Karṇa's death is part of the latter model, whereas in the former instance he was a sacrifier. On the idea of war being associated with the sacrifice, see Oguibénine, 1985, p.97, "le sacrifice comporte une compétition entre poètes et secrète la guerre qu'on fait aux adversaires du sacrifice exclus de l'univers sacrificiel".
30. As there are no long-term survivors of Kurukṣetra, could one then infer that heroes probably only obtain in the former period? Is Parikṣit to be considered heroic therefore, or just a great king? In book one of the text, in the minor narrative of Āstīka, where the story of Parikṣit's death is related at length, he is nowhere described as a hero, but only as a king. In the Āśvamedhika *parvan* however, the fourteenth book of the poem, the descendents of those fallen at Kurukṣetra remain to fight with Arjuna as he follows the horse. It is a curious *coda* to the heroic accounts of what occurred at Kurukṣetra, and reads like a studied imitation.
31. The battle of Kurukṣetra occurs around the time of the autumnal equinox and Bhīṣma dies after the winter solstice.

Arguments of a Queen
Draupadī's views on Kingship

Angelika Malinar

The dialogue between Draupadī and Yudhiṣṭhira in the *Āraṇyakaparvan* is one of many debates in the *Mahābhārata* to feature a female character accusing a male character of not doing his duty, and demanding him to act properly.[1] The depiction of women as self-confident, critical of their male relatives and rhetorically skilled, stands in contrast to the role usually accorded them in the law books and elsewhere in the epic. As is well known, women are regarded as being subordinate, weak and dependent, and it is commonly held that they should be kept in this position. Stephanie Jamison has put this contradiction as follows: 'These fearsomely able women and the women who "don't deserve independence" do not seem to inhabit the same conceptual planet. What is the source of the narrative pattern that contradicts the explicit doctrine of female weakness?' For her this pattern is an 'almost accidental byproduct of . . . conflicting (male) religious goals' (Jamison 1996: 15-16).[2] While such conflicts are certainly influential, I propose to understand what seems to be an ambiguity, or even a contradiction, as the interplay—and sometimes also clash—of different levels of a gender relationship that is construed as one of mutual dependence. In analysing this interdependence one needs to employ a relational notion of gender, since men and women are defined in relation to each other and in relation to the social role they must fulfil. Thus, we are dealing here not with a binary opposition based on fixed attributes or intrinsic, essential properties ascribed to each sex, but with a hierarchical structure in which attributes depend on the relationships between the different actors, and this means that they can change according to context and situation.

In the following, the arguments that are exchanged between a man and a woman—here Yudhiṣṭhira and Draupadī—will be analysed against the background of the mutual dependence implied in their social relationship. It will be shown that the debate serves to negotiate a relationship that has become problematic because the partners have been deprived of the chance to perform their inherited social roles. This seems to be especially critical when the husband and wife are a king and a queen. The reason for the special quality of this relationship lies in the fact that, in the social structure depicted in the *Mahābhārata,* gender relationships are defined by marriage or other kinship ties, which in turn reflect the status of the partners in the social hierarchy. Moreover, this status has to be represented and performed, since it is observed and commented upon by others, be they those who appear in the epic as characters, bards or 'the people' *(jana),* or the audience of epic text when it is recited, read or otherwise published.[3] The task of 'representation' was a particular challenge for the aristocracy, as they were charged with representing society not only as an ordered whole, but also as legitimate, beneficial and—not to be neglected—aesthetically satisfying. When I use the term 'representation', I do not understand it primarily in the more modern sense of 'political representation' as it is the case, for instance, in the *pars pro toto* structure of democratic systems. Rather, I refer to a pre-modern sense in which the upper strata of a hierarchically organized society represent the values and powers that guarantee the functioning of society.[4] In this case representation is located on two interrelated levels: firstly—and this is well studied—the king must be able to exercise his power and maintain social order; secondly—and less studied—he should represent the orderliness, appropriateness and legitimacy of this social order by living up to its values, in brief by incorporating them as the king. However, this incorporation is only complete with a queen at his side. It is the very corporeal dimension of representation, its visibility and material character, that constitutes its attraction in the eyes of the others, be they family members, other kings, gods and goddesses or—not to be forgotten—the other social strata. I am going to argue that this 'representational' quality of kingship is an important feature of the discourse between exiled Draupadī and Yudhiṣṭhira in the *Āraṇyakaparvan.*[5] It is a feature closely connected to the implications of the socially accorded roles of husband and wife. The discourse is a negotiation of a crisis in their relationship, because Yudhiṣṭhira is no longer the royal husband Draupadī once married. In losing everything during the dice game, he has lost their status; therefore she demands him to take action. Seen from the perspective of the aforementioned construction of gender relationships, the crisis emerges because their customary roles as each other's husband and wife are no longer in harmony with their royal status. This causes grief, complaints and controversies. The question then is: how does one represent one's status when one has lost it? Or, to address the issue of the debate in the *Āraṇyakaparvan,* how can one be Yudhiṣṭhira's wife without being a queen, and, conversely, how can one be Draupadī's husband and not be a king?

These questions indicate that the situation both partners find themselves in does not at all facilitate the ideal relationship between a king and his queen (representing his *śrī*) because royal status has been lost and its representation has become a problem.[6] Let's see how this problem unfolds in the exchange of arguments in 3.28-33. For the sake of orientation, I will first provide an overview of the main points of the debate.

The discussion between Draupadī and Yudhiṣṭhira is transmitted as a part of the *Āraṇyakaparvan,* and is said to have occurred after one year of exile. It is a debate on the pros and cons of putting up with the miserable situation of exile and refraining from immediate retaliation for Duryodhana's transgressions which made him king.[7] Before going into some of the arguments more closely, a survey of chapters 3.28-37 will be given. Chapters 28-33 contain the dialogue between Draupadī and Yudhiṣṭhira, while in 3.34 Bhīma puts forward his point of view and Yudhiṣṭhira continues arguing with him.

Chapter 3.28 starts with a very brief description of the dialogue situation. One evening the five brothers and Draupadī are sitting together in their forest abode, absorbed by pain and grief. Then Draupadī turns to Yudhiṣṭhira and begins to complain about Duryodhana's lack of pity and remorse. She vividly reminds Yudhiṣṭhira of what he and his brothers have lost, and wonders where his enthusiasm for self-assertion (*manyu*) has gone. The chapter ends with the unexpected statement that forgiveness (*kṣamā*) is sometimes called for. The word *kṣamā,* mentioned in the last verse of 3.28, gives Draupadī the opportunity to report a conversation between the former kings Prahlāda and Bali Vairocana. Bali asks Prahlāda whether forgiveness (*kṣamā*) or the demonstration of power (*tejas*) is better. The diplomatic answer is that there is a time and a place for both. Draupadī concludes that the time has come for taking action against Duryodhana. In 3.30 Yudhiṣṭhira replies that uncontrolled demonstrations of power will result in nothing but destruction. In 3.31 Draupadī accuses Yudhiṣṭhira of delusion (*moha*). Instead of following the heroic path of his ancestors, he subjects himself to some dubious 'distributor' (*vidhātṛ*) of the fruits of action. She points out that this 'distributor' does not care for appropriate retribution.

Yudhiṣṭhira, in turn, accuses Draupadī of being an 'unbeliever' (*nāstika*) and asks her to stop (3.32). Although Draupadī complies, she continues arguing her cause, and ends with a final demand for action (3.33). There is no reply from Yudhiṣṭhira at this point; rather, at the beginning of 3.34 Bhīma is made to speak up against his brother, fighting for Draupadī's cause—as always—but with a different set of arguments. The dialogue between Bhīma and Yudhiṣṭhira gets stuck in 3.37 and ends in mutual embarrassment when Bhīma finds no answer to Yudhiṣṭhira's confession of weakness. This situation is only solved by the appearance of Kṛṣṇa Dvaipāyana Vyāsa, the epic's composer, who announces the Pāṇḍavas' future victory and teaches Yudhiṣṭhira a *vidyā,* a magic means for consecrating weapons. A remarkable feature of this sequence of arguments is that there is no clear solution to the conflict addressed in the debate between king and queen. Rather, if one takes Vyāsa's word as final, both of their positions are partially accepted: one should put up with the situation, but meanwhile get ready to fight.

This outline shows that chapters 3.28-37 form a unity in the sense that Vyāsa's appearance is necessary to bring the awkward situation to an end. This does not mean that all these chapters have been incorporated into the *Mahābhārata* at the same time (3.29 especially raises questions). However, my analysis will consider the extant text, and concentrate on the dialogue between Draupadī and Yudhiṣṭhira, since this part of the passage invites an analysis of gender relationships. In the present context this cannot include all the twists and turns of the argument. Rather, I will deal with the main topics of the debate, and closely analyse some of the themes related to the problem of representation and the crisis in the relationship between king and queen.

Duryodhana the winner versus Yudhiṣṭhira the loser

Draupadī, described by the four attributes *priyā, darśanīyā, paṇḍitā* and *pativratā*,[8] begins her speech by complaining about Duryodhana. She does not, as in other speeches, refer to Duryodhana's misbehaviour against herself, but rather blames him for his lack of sympathy for Yudhiṣṭhira's misery. Having a heart made of iron (*āyasa hṛdaya*), a typical epithet for a merciless person (see also 5.133.1), he did not show any sympathy when Yudhiṣṭhira was sent into exile clad in antelope skin (3.28.3-7). Draupadī bitterly contrasts the past and the present by recalling the visible requisites of royalty and their former conjugal happiness. Thus, she starts by recalling the matrimonial bed: 'I see your bed before my eyes, the one of old, and I pity you, who deserves to be happy, not to suffer' (3.28.10).[9] She then conjures up the throne: 'When I see your throne before my eyes, made of ivory, in the middle of the audience hall, adorned with jewels, covered with a cushion made of *kuśa* grass, grief tears me apart' (3.28.11).[10] By putting the bed first, she reminds Yudhiṣṭhira that their marriage has been the precondition for his accession to the throne and, *vice versa,* that losing the throne has deprived them of this 'old' (*purātana*) bed and thereby of their appropriate conjugal life. She continues the list of losses with the *sabhā* and the assembly of allied kings. Then she contrasts his being anointed with sandal paste with his now being covered with mud, his silk dress with the rags he is now wearing,[11] and his feeding of brahmins and renouncers with their present forest diet. In the last seventeen verses of the chapter she describes the poor condition of his brothers, who are condemned to brooding in inactivity. Her lament turns into a complaint, which is orchestrated by the following question repeated eight times: 'Why doesn't your anger (*manyu*) grow?'[12]

The key word of this refrain is *manyu* (anger, wrath). As Malamoud has shown in his study of Vedic texts, *manyu* is not just another word for *krodha* or *kopa,* that is, anger as a passion or transient emotion. Rather, *manyu* is regarded as an essential quality and capacity of (royal) gods like Indra or Varuṇa, which allows them to maintain their status and enact their power. According to Malamoud the '*manyu* of a god is that vigour which brings him to accomplish those deeds through which his divinity is affirmed' (1989: 186, my translation).[13] In this sense it can also be applied to warriors. Draupadī's demand for Yudhiṣṭhira's *manyu* seems to draw on this dimension, because she regards the lack of this capacity in her husband to be the cause of their situation. She states in 3.28.34: 'There is no *kṣatriya* without *manyu*—this saying is well known in the world. In you, however, I now see a *kṣatriya* who is (acts) like the opposite.'[14] For Draupadī, *manyu* is positive because it is a necessary quality of a warrior and thus a quality which she, as the daughter of a king (*rājaputrī,* 3.32.2), must expect from her husband. This positive evaluation of *manyu* is not only in accordance with the Vedic meaning of *manyu,* but also with other passages in the epic, in which it is attributed to or demanded from a hero (e.g. 5.131.2, 5).

In her speech Draupadī places their misery[15] in its visible context and thereby touches upon the very problem of representation pointed out above. She does not draw on the symbolism certainly implied in the paraphernalia listed, but uses them to confront Yudhiṣṭhira with the obvious, that is, with those things whose absence could be noticed by anyone. It is the visibility of the loss which makes the situation so painful and intolerable;

and this pain increases when this loss is contrasted with Duryodhana's happiness. For Draupadī's status as the wife and queen of Yudhiṣṭhira, it is this referential framework which counts. She does not hesitate to have a closer look[16] and point out that a king who no longer represents (that is, enacts and incorporates) kingship is no longer a king, even if he claims to be the virtual, rightful or appropriate king. For Draupadī, this is a situation a warrior and king should not tolerate, if he still claims the title 'king' and wants to be regarded as one.[17] Yudhiṣṭhira has turned into a husband who no longer lives up to his social position; he is, as we have heard, a husband who does not even own a proper bed. All this threatens the desirable symmetry of the relationship, as Draupadī has to deal with a weakness she has not learned to tolerate—although she has certainly been brought up to be a wife, that is, simply to put up with her husband's decisions.[18] Her argument points to a conflict of role models and social values that has been caused by the situation of exile. However, at the very end of the chapter, in the last *śloka* (3.28.37), Draupadī's complaint is suspended by the authors, or later redactors,[19] by her statement that sometimes forgiveness (*kṣamā*) is called for.

Self-assertion versus forgiveness in 3.29-30

With this we turn to the next main theme of the debate, the question of which norm should be followed in this situation: striving for retaliation, thus displaying *tejas* and *manyu,* or *kṣamā,* putting up with it? This is the topic of Draupadī's speech in 3.29 and Yudhiṣṭhira's reply in 3.30. I will only give the gist of the argument that is put forward in 3.29 by means of a report of a conversation between Bali Vairocana and Prahlāda. According to Prahlāda there is a time for both, and thus one has to decide according to the situation. The referential framework of this interpretation is not symbolic or philosophical, but consists of a discussion of various concrete situations in which a king or a superior might find himself. We are thus given a casuistic, situational interpretation of the criteria for displaying one faculty or the other. In consequence, Draupadī draws the conclusion that their present situation meets the criteria for displaying *tejas* and not *kṣamā*.

In his reply in 3.30 Yudhiṣṭhira disagrees and, in doing so, shifts the level of argument. First of all, he does not address the issue of *manyu* as a capacity, but the problem of *krodha*.[20] 'Wrath' is thereby no longer regarded as an essential quality, but as a passion that must be controlled. This is a favourite strategy for turning down demands, whereby capacities or powers regarded by the other as desirable for asserting one's social position are re-interpreted as problematic emotions or undesirable passions that need to be controlled (see for example 1.37; 5.133-4). It is denied that *krodha* is a capacity, rather it is condemned as a lower, destructive passion that has to be controlled and erased; at best it can be used as an opportunity for developing forgiveness, *kṣamā*. Rather than viewing both *kṣamā* and *manyu* (or *tejas*) as capacities to be used according to the situation, as suggested by Draupadī on the authority of Prahlāda,[21] Yudhiṣṭhira builds up a binary opposition between them, and asserts that *kṣamā* is always better.[22] He employs a strategy that favours and enforces binary oppositions, instead of situational, casuistic considerations which take the ambiguity of values and attitudes into account. Such ambiguity leaves one with the difficult task of making decisions in various situations and not with a general principle that can be applied at all times.

Thus Yudhiṣṭhira's line of argument changes not only the vocabulary, but also the referential framework. Although concrete situations were adduced in the discourse of Prahlāda in order to explain the different contexts that demand from the king a display of either anger or endurance, Yudhiṣṭhira interprets both as matters of principle, and assesses their metaphysical or even ontological value without applying it to any of those concrete situations. Only twice does he address aspects of the issue put forward by Draupadī. In the first instance, he states that a weaker person, who lacks strength and power, should not show his anger against a stronger one (3.30.10-11). He thereby indicates, again on a rather abstract level, that he may not be strong enough to face Duryodhana in battle. (As mentioned above, the open concession of the Pāṇḍavas' actual weakness in front of Bhīma will close the whole debate and invite Vyāsa's entrance.) In the second instance, he compares himself to Duryodhana by taking *kṣamā* as the point of comparison (3.30.49). Yudhiṣṭhira praises himself as superior to merciless, intransigent Duryodhana by declaring: '*Kṣamā* has found me because I am worthy of it' (3.30.49).[23] What is remarkable about this expression is the active role ascribed to *kṣamā*. This is reminiscent of the goddess Śrī, who finds and chooses as king that man who has the right qualities and is therefore worthy of her. If one pursues this association one might say that, instead of the royal virtues symbolized by Śrī and incorporated by Draupadī as the queen, *kṣamā* seems now to have become Yudhiṣṭhira's essential quality and thus the functional equivalent of Śrī. *Kṣamā* is the virtue that now, in times of crisis, guarantees his future well-being and prosperity. In saying this, he claims that a virtue which later in the text is identified as belonging to the earth is the basis and object of kingship. Yudhiṣṭhira seems to hint at an inversion of his role as king, the protector of the earth, when he compares those who possess *kṣamā*—that is, people like him—with the earth (3.30.25b, 31b: *kṣaminaḥ pṛthivīsamāḥ*). In shifting the level of the argument, Yudhiṣṭhira avoids facing the misery by refusing to mirror his situation in Draupadī's arguments. He identifies himself with the earth by claiming one of the goddess's characteristics, endurance. It seems that the ideal symmetry of king and queen with regard to royal virtues has been broken off, and other values prevail.

However, as this is a position taken by her husband, Draupadī, in her role as *pativratā*, the dedicated wife, should now give in and be silent. To put it pointedly, she should practise wifely *kṣamā* with regard to her suffering from her husband's inactivity. However, should she? Not necessarily. According to the very logic of her position in the gender relationship, as a *pativratā* it is not only her duty to support and propel her husband,[24] but she also has to take care that her man does not go astray or fail to live up to social standards. Ideally, as part of her role as queen, she 'guarantees the social construction of a man in accordance with the aristocratic standards' (Wenzel 2003: 24, my translation).[25] Once already Draupadī has cleared up the mess created by her husband's dicing and rescued them all from enslavement. Seen from Draupadī's perspective, her husband is now endangered by another cherished idea turned into an obsession. His clinging to *kṣamā* seems to drive him away from her again, without his thinking about the consequences for his wife and queen. He claims the metaphysical superiority of *kṣamā,* but disregards the contexts in which it is recommended by the 'learned'. These contexts are royal power, as we have seen in the teaching of Prahlāda, and asceticism and female suffering, as Hara has shown.[26] At present, Yudhiṣṭhira cannot claim any of these contexts for himself. As if it were not enough that he cannot use *kṣamā* from a position of strength, he also mixes up the two other contexts, asceticism and female suffering. Yudhiṣṭhira wants to have it both ways: while he is currently comparable to a *tapasvinī,* a woman who suffers from an intolerable situation but cannot do anything against it, he claims to behave like an ascetic, whose strength lies in his capacity to control anger through *kṣamā* and who therefore does not lose his *tapas,* ascetic power. It comes as no surprise that this invites critique because Yudhiṣṭhira is neither a woman, a *tapasvinī* for whom *kṣamā* would be a respectable thing, nor really an ascetic, because he has not renounced his social life, but lost it unintentionally. However, Yudhiṣṭhira interprets what Draupadī regards as weakness as a test case for his strength as a *siddha,* a successful ascetic, and this allows him to ignore her arguments about their royal status. According to Draupadī, this is only *moha,* delusion.

Yudhiṣṭhira makes it clear that restoring *śrī* and freeing Draupadī from her grief are currently not on his agenda. In consequence, he never actually faces Draupadī's words, appearance and emotions. He deflects and escapes her arguments by shifting to a different context. This does not necessarily point to his weakness, but rather confirms what I propose to regard as the structure of mutual dependence which determines the representation of status and gender roles in the epic. Social relationships are in general construed as mirror situations of looking and looking back, that is, as being based on the capacity to face each other. This becomes increasingly difficult during a conflict or in a situation where the image that usually attracts its reflection is distorted (Malinar 2005; Tschannerl 1992: 101-26). Thus, to accept Draupadī's point of view Yudhiṣṭhira would need to take a look at himself, but this is not desirable when the gaze of the queen, which serves to define him according to the norms of their social position, is unfavourable. Yudhiṣṭhira is not only intensively looked at by Draupadī, but also looked up and down, as we have seen in her vivid depiction of his appearance.[27] He, in turn, does not deal directly with her line of thought. Instead, he re-frames her whole argument.

What about retribution?

It seems that Draupadī has very well understood the message whereby their miserable situation is reinterpreted as a test case for a superior value. At the beginning of 3.31 Draupadī again goes on the offensive and in her own way re-establishes a symmetry between the two of them, by also stepping out of *her* roles of obedient, enduring wife and respectable queen. Without hesitation she rejects her husband's praise of himself as better than Duryodhana because *kṣamā* has become his *dharma*. For her this is just a delusion (*moha*): 'Praise to both the "arranger" and the "distributor" who have deluded you! Although you should carry on in the way of your fathers and grandfathers, you have a different outlook (*mati*)' (3.31.1).[28] Now it is her turn to re-frame Yudhiṣṭhira's argument by declaring that regaining *śrī* should be the primary aim of all his activities and that *dharma* defined as *kṣamā* does not serve this purpose.[29] Draupadī points out that their suffering seems to leave Yudhiṣṭhira comparatively cold, because his heart beats more for *dharma* than for his life (and thus for her or his brothers).[30]

In contrast with the rather abstract level of Yudhiṣṭhira's argument, Draupadī comes back to the actual situation and again takes a look at her husband. This time the emphasis is not on his physical appearance and the requisites of kingship. Rather, the outcome of his pious observance of dharmic duties comes under scrutiny. Draupadī's evaluation is guided by the following definition of the working of *dharma*: 'The Law, when well protected, protects the king who guards the Law, so I hear from the noble ones, but I find it does not protect *you*' (3.31.7, tr. van Buitenen).[31] Here she defines *dharma* as a principle of just retribution and almost equates it with *karma*. She takes her husband as the test case for the truth of this definition, and she shows that there is something wrong with it since the observance of *dharma* is not only inefficient and fruitless, but even counter-productive in that it yields the wrong fruits and thus produces injustice (*viṣama*). Although Yudhiṣṭhira has meticulously followed all the prescriptions, he has met misery. Again she vividly describes his former dharmic activities such as sponsoring sacrifices and feeding brahmins, guests and ascetics (3.31.9-16). In spite of this, she observes, everything went wrong during the dice game. This seems to suggest that this was a situation in which *dharma* should have protected Yudhiṣṭhira, because he had protected *dharma* before, but it did not. What does this tell about the efficacy of human efforts and the justice of dharmic retribution? At this point in her argument Draupadī goes into matters of principle too, and inquires who or what is in charge of the business of retribution. This brings her to the *dhātṛ* (arranger) and the *vidhātṛ* (distributor), the *īśvaras*, the lords who rule over the fruits of one's efforts.

Once again she cites ancient lore (*itihāsa purātana*, 3.31.20) on the unpredictable decisions of the lord (*īśvara*), who distributes happiness and suffering amongst the creatures according to his will. Living beings are not free in what they do, and what they achieve is not in their own hands, but in those of this hidden 'arranger', whom Draupadī compares to a puppet-player. He moves his dolls in this or that direction according to a script as secret as he himself:

> This blessed God, the self-existent great-grandfather, hurts creatures with creatures, hiding behind a guise, Yudhiṣṭhira. Joining and unjoining them, the capricious blessed Lord plays with the creatures like a child with its toys. The arranger does not act towards his creatures like a father or mother, he seems to act out of fury, like every other person.
>
> (3.31.35-7, tr. van Buitenen, slightly changed)[32]

In order to demonstrate the fundamental injustice implied in the distribution of fruits, Draupadī again contrasts the pleasures Duryodhana enjoys, because 'the arranger has given him *śrī*, royal prosperity' (3.31.40),[33] with the misery of noble Yudhiṣṭhira. Far from putting up with this by drawing on 'superior values', she draws her own conclusions about the nature of power. She complains about this injustice (*viṣama*) and in the end condemns this 'arranger' who does nothing against it (*dhātāraṃ garhaye,* 3.31.39). Diagnosing that the law of *karma,* the law of just rewards, does not work and seems to be suspended in their case, she ends her speech as follows: 'If the evil that has been done does not pursue its doer, then mere power is the cause of everything, and I bemoan powerless folk!' (3.31.42, tr. van Buitenen).[34] With this statement Draupadī has reached the very end of her argument, which brings her back to the *abala,* the powerless, that is, folk like Yudhiṣṭhira and herself. She has now made explicit what has remained only hinted at throughout this discourse, that is, that the Pāṇḍavas lack the strength to fight, a situation warriors had better not find themselves in. Her argument is double edged. On the one hand, it establishes a symmetry between Yudhiṣṭhira and Draupadī, in that they are now equally in a situation of weakness. On the other hand, in order to keep the ideal symmetry necessary for representing their status as the royal couple, Yudhiṣṭhira should not be weak, as he then would not deserve his wife and queen as the representative of *śrī.* Draupadī has touched a sore point: her metaphysical interpretation of their fate cannot easily be rejected, but nonetheless Yudhiṣṭhira cannot concede. It is only at the end of the whole exchange of arguments, and after Bhīma has entered the discussion, that Yudhiṣṭhira concedes this central point and indirectly (that is, not addressing Draupadī) agrees with his wife that *kṣamā* may not be enough. This is why he so readily accepts Vyāsa's special *vidyā* (3.37.25ff.). In his exchange with Draupadī, however, he rejects this reasoning.

Draupadī the heretic

This rejection essentially consists in an attempt to call Draupadī to order. After having politely praised Draupadī's rhetoric (3.32.1ab), Yudhiṣṭhira puts the brakes on her and accuses her of propagating *nāstikya*, 'heresy' and 'unbelief' (3.32.1cd). In his view she is guilty of a serious transgression, because she doubts the inner or ultimate orderliness of the created world and that things are, in general, right and good as they are. His reply is basically an argument *ex negativo* (a *prasaṅga*), because he points to the undesirable consequences of her thought. However, if one considers the dialogue as a re-negotiation of the relationship between the king and the queen in a situation of crisis, Yudhiṣṭhira's reply succeeds in re-establishing a symmetry between the two. Draupadī has suggested that Yudhiṣṭhira's view (*mati*) has proved unsuccessful and brought him into a situation whereby he no longer represents and embodies kingship and thus has stepped out of his role. This is balanced by Draupadī, the queen, expressing her deepest suspicions about that very order, the very *dharma* she otherwise (that is, officially and *per officium*) represents and enacts. A *nāstika* queen on the throne is as scandalous as a king turned into a deplorable weakling. By depicting her crossing the line and falling out of her role too, the authors re-establish the symmetry of the relationship between the dialogue partners. As Wenzel notes with regard to the construction of gender in the medieval epic *Erec et Enide*: 'When the man steps out of his socially codified role, then the woman also steps out of her social role; in this way, the symmetry of the relationship . . . is still kept' (Wenzel 2003: 265, my translation).

Draupadī's view is therefore denounced as a transgression throughout Yudhiṣṭhira's reply. This can be seen by the many occurrences of the prefix '*ati-*' signifying an excessive or deviant performance of the activity denoted by the verb. Thus, Draupadī is said to 'doubt too much' (*ati+śaṅk*, 32.6—twice; 32.7, 9, 15, 17, 21), to 'argue too much' (*ati+vad*, 32.6), to 'transgress' (*ati+gam*, 32.9, 20) and to 'violate' (*ati+vṛt*, 32.18) norms. The checking of Draupadī's deviant reasoning is substantiated by the depiction of a Yudhiṣṭhira who does not sway under Draupadī's attack but is a husband in control. Being absolutely determined, he tells the king's daughter' (*rājaputrī*, 3.32.2) that he does not pine for the fruits of *dharma* (*nāhaṃ dharmaphalānveṣī,* 3.32.2). Reminding her of teachings about 'disinterested action' (*niṣkāma karman*) and the fulfilment of one's social obligations as *l'art pour l'art,* Yudhiṣṭhira claims that his belief in *dharma* is not based on retribution. However, this is not the whole truth, since Yudhiṣṭhira does not exactly relinquish the fruits, but rather employs a different time-perspective so that he can tolerate a postponement of retribution. In contrast to Draupadī's insistence on immediate justice and retribution, he opts for the long-term growth of his dharmic capital. Being a true believer in '*āstikya*', he trusts in the proper functioning of the economy of *dharma.* He is therefore convinced that in the end the fruit will come, even if this might only happen in some after-world or through the attainment of salvation. *Dharma* never fails to produce fruit, and this is confirmed by the fact that all the wise and respected persons fulfil their dharmic duties (3.32.29, 31, 37). They never doubt the orderliness of order, of *dharma,* whatever its outer appearance may be. Thus *āstikya,* belief and confidence, is in any case better than *nāstikya,* unbelief, as this will certainly lead nowhere, or to degradation. In consequence, Yudhiṣṭhira reminds Draupadī that she might easily find herself reborn as an animal (3.32.6) if she does not control her passion for logical reasoning—a passion which only results in establishing herself as the means of proof (*pramāṇa*) instead of the elderly, male experts (3.32.15).

However, it is not only wrong to cast doubt on the integrity of *dharma* and the divine administrative forces behind it, but also inappropriate and embarrassing. Yudhiṣṭhira suggests that Draupadī is inquisitive and seems to have lost her sense of modesty, because she speculates about what the gods are doing behind the scenes (3.32.33-6). It is not only that Draupadī speaks as if she might know better than the gods what should be done, but also that she has missed the crucial point about lords of all kinds: they are not only hidden, they also hide. Gods live by their secrets and it is up to them alone to keep or disclose them. The distribution of the fruits of one's deeds is a 'secret of the gods' (*devaguhya,* 3.32.33). Thus, to be a believer means to accept that the miraculous power of the gods is hidden (*gūḍhamāyā hi devatāḥ,* 3.32.34).

This secrecy cannot be overcome by human beings, and this indicates the fundamental divide between the human and the divine: while human beings can be stripped of everything, the curtain between gods and men can never be torn down, but only lifted up. Yudhiṣṭhira is sure that the ultimate outcome will be a happy one and that, by the grace of the hidden lords, they will reach immortality. Consequently, at the end of his reply he warns Draupadī about doubting and arguing too much.

While this does not leave Draupadī unimpressed, she does not withdraw completely. Her final reply in 3.33 moves on two levels. On the one hand, she obeys Yudhiṣṭhira's admonition and stops expressing her suspicions. She moves back to her accorded role in which she represents an order, the *dharma* she actually believes in. On the other hand, her retreat is turned into another discourse about the different causes of success.[35] Thereby she not only proves her qualification as a *paṇḍitā,* a learned woman, but also manages to substantiate her primary argument, and can in the end demand again that something be done.

Conclusion

What does this tell us about the gendered presentation and articulation of values and ideas in the *Mahābhārata*? Throughout the epic speech and argument are based on the relationship between the speakers, that is, first of all, on their position in the social hierarchy. Arguments serve not only to put forward philosophical doctrines, but also to define and negotiate social relationships. This seems to be especially true of arguments that are exchanged between husbands and wives, which in the epic usually means between kings and queens. Their relationship is characterized by a complementary structure. However, this structure operates in two directions: on the one hand, it is construed vertically according to the normative gender hierarchy, and thus implies an asymmetry in the sense that the wife depends on the husband and is not free in her decisions; on the other hand, there is the horizontal dimension in which both partners move on the same level in order to represent their social status. Here we find a symmetry in that a husband has to maintain the status of his wife in order to keep his own, and the wife has to ensure that her husband lives up to the standards of their class. The specific characteristic of the gender relationships in the epic is that they combine the symmetry of representation with the asymmetry of female subordination.

Therefore the question of the appropriate 'representation' of social status, especially royal status, is an important referential framework which determines the structure not only of gender relationships, but also of gender-related discourses about kingship. Draupadī's verbal attacks on Yudhiṣṭhira are directed at his being displaced from the social context of 'status representation'. Through this displacement a certain asymmetry has set in between the two, as he has lost his position. The dialogue can be regarded as compensating for this asymmetry, as Draupadī is shown to cross the line too. For a moment she stops being the obedient wife and respectable queen, as she doubts the very order she must otherwise represent. In this way the symmetry between king and queen is re-established: Yudhiṣṭhira asserts his position and depicts himself as the one who, as a stout believer in the ultimate efficacy of *dharma,* continues to represent social order even in the moment of crisis and exile. Different arguments can be put forward in order to sustain or re-establish this complementarity, and no typical 'female' argument can easily be identified. Thus, although the idea of fate can also be expressed by a male voice, its use, and thus its quality, is determined by the social identity (which includes gender) of those who are communicating in debate. This does not imply that the relationship between the dialogue partners is negotiated in every debate. In situations where a king is counselled (as for instance King Dhṛtarāṣṭra by Vidura), or where we have a didactic discourse, the very basis of the whole relationship is not necessarily at stake. But in many of the verbal encounters between men and women in the epic, the foundation of their interdependence is the central topic. This is true for the dialogue between Draupadī and Yudhiṣṭhira, as it is, for instance, for that between Śakuntalā and Duḥṣanta (1.68-9). However, given the structure of the relationship that combines the symmetry of representation with the asymmetry of female subordination, the relationship is never broken up by the woman.[36]

These gendered verbal encounters thus have to be distinguished from the construction and usage of gender in normative and even philosophical texts, where gender relationships are used to exemplify the principles of existence (as is the case in Sāṃkhya philosophy),[37] or the duties of men and women are defined on the basis of a certain cultural construction of their 'way of being' (*svabhāva*).[38] However, what seems to be a current topic in those speeches in which women (usually Draupadī) demand their men to act, is that they are not willing to put up with a man who puts up with whatever happens to him, who suffers degradation and defeat without fighting back and who, on top of everything, finds reasons to feel good about it. Faced with passive, suffering men, women, especially aristocratic ones, seem to lose their belief in the sense and value of putting up with the very passivity and suffering they are destined to tolerate in order to gain their merits (cf. Mallison 1979). Their status can only be kept when their husband acts as a *kṣatriya.* As Draupadī states, if it is only power and strength that count, then one should pity those who are powerless. Thus, better to have power. It comes as no surprise that this line of thought has to be dismissed vehemently when proposed by a woman, especially if this woman is one's wife. To doubt that things are fine and right as they are is dangerous, and transgresses the very order that the royal couple has to sustain and to represent, that is, to embody. Doubt is harmful and, as we have seen, Draupadī yields to her husband's admonition. However, at the very end of her speech she nevertheless manages to argue for self-assertion in the realm of politics and sovereignty. As she ends her speech she resorts to yet another method by recalling her experiences in the house of her father, King Drupada (3.33.56-8). When a visiting teacher gave learned discourses, she stresses, she was sitting next to her father. This is the final image and the final message that her husband has to deal with. Yudhiṣṭhira has to legitimize his view not only against his wife, but also against his father-in-law. However, by returning to the court of her father, she signals that she has come back from what Yudhiṣṭhira regards as a verbal, intellectual and emotional excess.

It is significant that the authors refrain from putting a reply in Yudhiṣṭhira's mouth, so neither Draupadī nor Yudhiṣṭhira is made to lose face. Rather, Bhīma takes over and argues Draupadī's case from his own understanding of the situation. The whole debate gets stuck when Bhīma cannot offer a reply to Yudhiṣṭhira's analysis of their weakness, that is, their lack of weapons. This cannot be compensated for by any dharmic behaviour or merely by strong belief, but only by acquiring them. It very well suits the inner logic of the discourse that in this moment of silence the epic's composer Vyāsa appears in order to announce that Yudhiṣṭhira, and with him faith in victory, will prevail. His message is as much a narrative link motivating the further course of events during the exile, as it is a comment on the previous debate. Vyāsa supports Yudhiṣṭhira's position when he indirectly confirms that *kṣamā* is the choice of the moment since there is no other left; however, he also sides with Draupadī by emphasizing that one must actively secure final victory (and thus dharmic retribution), and he therefore offers Yudhiṣṭhira a (magic) means, a *vidyā* that allows the Pāṇḍavas to acquire superior weapons.[39] Yudhiṣṭhira is in no way disinclined to accept this offer. Thus, after the often rather twisted and sophisticated exchange of arguments, the epic authors manage to establish the symmetry of the relationship between the two protagonists: Yudhiṣṭhira and Draupadī not only keep face, but both get their due.

Notes

1. Other instances are 4.16-20; 5.80; 5.131-4; 12.14; 12.18.
2. See also Falk (1977: 91-2), who discusses the view that the strong portrayals of female characters belong to older parts of the epic, and that the contradictions in the depiction of female characters result from the coexistence of different textual layers in the extant epic. She points out that later redactors could not have recast Draupadī 'without destroying their work. Her words are too important to the epic, too crucial to the delineation of its central problem' (ibid.: 92). While this certainly goes

too far and does not pay enough attention to the absence of Draupadī's voice during much of the epic, I would also not completely subscribe to Mary Brockington's view that Draupadī ... in fact has hardly any influence on the plot, and is not a person in her own right' (2001: 257). According to Brockington, her role as a minor character in the epic can be equated with that of the younger brothers in that their function is to stress the accuracy of Yudhiṣṭhira's view and therefore they have to be 'automatically wrong' (ibid.: 256). While I follow Brockington when she points out that the narrative techniques implied in the presentation of minor characters must be taken into consideration, I would allow for the possibility that they are not always totally wrong. In the dialogue under discussion in this chapter, the crucial point is not primarily to teach the audience about right and wrong, but to negotiate the relationship between the characters.

3. On the 'implied audience', see Mangels 1995; on the importance of 'seeing' and 'observing' as a form of social communication, see Malinar 1996: 97-114; 2005; Tschannerl 1992.
4. This has been labelled the '*caput*' or head-form of representation typical, for instance, for monarchic organizations. On the concept of 'representation' with regard to pre-modern societies, see Wenzel 1990, Hofmann 1974, Kantorowicz 1957 and, in contrast with the functional differentiation in sub-systems in modern societies, Luhmann 1998.
5. The importance of this dimension has also been stressed in my study of the epic context of the *Bhagavadgītā* and the 'political' aspects of the manifestation of Kṛṣṇa as God; see Malinar 1996.
6. Important studies on the symbolic aspects of the construction of sovereignty in the *Mahābhārata* have been made by Hiltebeitel (1976). He especially focuses on Draupadī's connection with the goddess Śrī and thus with the symbolic and mythological background of epic stories. He has shown that as a queen Draupadī represents the goddess whose presence is necessary for making a king prosper. Accordingly, in many epic and Puranic texts we meet a king either united with Śrī, or separated from her—and therefore from his kingdom. These are the two possible relationships between the goddess Śrī and a king, and thus between the divine and the human realm. They demonstrate the two opposite ends of ideal kingship: to be or not to be with Śrī. In the symbolic realm there is no other way. This topic is discussed in some passages in the epic, such as the dialogue between Bali and Indra in the *Śāntiparvan* (12.216-18, 220), and has also led to the depiction of Śrī as 'fickle' and 'unreliable', as she leaves the king who loses his power. As far as I know, Śrī is not met in any situation of crisis where she is attacked, appears helpless or is sent into exile. If such things happen, she seems to have already left the king beforehand (a fact which can then serve as an explanation for the crisis).

In contrast, epic literature is full of princesses and queens who are in exactly such a situation of being separated from their royal husband, but are still wives and queens. My emphasis here is less on divine, dharmic or mythological symbolization, and more on the human or social level and thus on how the relationship between Draupadī and Yudhiṣṭhira is embedded in a framework of social relations.

7. Seen in the larger context of the pre-war books of the *Mahābhārata,* this dialogue of a royal couple is one of several that are to be found in these books. We come across other narratives of royal couples in crisis, for instance Duḥṣanta and Śakuntalā (1.62-9), Nala and Damayantī (3.50-78) and Rāma and Sītā (3.258-75). The situation of Draupadī and the Pāṇḍavas is refracted and recast in these adjacent stories. A different case is the dialogue between a mother and her son in the *Udyogaparvan* (5.131-4), called 'fierce speech of encouragement' (*uddharṣaṇaṃ bhīmam*), in which the son is blamed for his unmanliness. See Malinar 1996: 175ff.

8. This list confirms the representative dimension of Draupadī's status as wife and queen. Four attributes are given that characterize the queen: she is *priyā,* beloved, *darśanīyā,* beautiful, *paṇḍitā,* learned, and *pativratā,* dedicated to her husband. While the last attribute refers to the essential duty of every wife, her subordination to her husband and her responsibility for his well-being, learnedness seems to be a result of her aristocratic upbringing, which is also confirmed at the end of her discourse when she recalls wisdom she imbibed at her father's court (3.33.56-8). This learnedness also extends to her rhetorical knowledge, which Yudhiṣṭhira cannot but praise (3.32.1ab), as she is depicted as a skilful rhetorician. She knows how to raise emotions through vivid images of the past, supports her arguments by citing acknowledged authorities under the heading of ancient lore *(itihāsa purātana)* and what she herself has learned by listening to learned conversations, and, last but not least, she demonstrates her reasoning skills by drawing her own conclusions about *dharma,* however dangerous. Of course she is beautiful; otherwise she could not incorporate Śrī and be the queen. As a consequence, this beauty has to be kept or at least reinstalled at all costs, and this is only possible by being dressed and adorned according to status. See also Hiltebeitel 1980a; 1980-1.

9. *idaṃ ca śayanaṃ dṛṣṭvā yac cāsīt te purātanam / śocāmi tvāṃ mahārāja duḥkhānarhaṃ sukhocitam //* This contrast of actual suffering and deserved happiness is pointed out by means of the repeated expressions *sukhocita aduḥkhārha* and *duḥkhānarha,* 'for whom happiness is appropriate' and 'who does not deserve unhappiness' (see 3.28.6; 28.10; 28.18; 28.20; 28.26). For a study of the topic of suffering, see Bailey 1983a.

10. *dāntaṃ yac ca sabhāmadhye āsanaṃ ratnabhūṣitam / dṛṣṭvā kuśabṛsīṃ cemāṃ*

śoko māṃ rundhayaty ayam // For an analysis of the symbolism of the throne, see Auboyer 1949.

11. 3.28.14. Dress also signifies status in the case of Draupadī, as Hiltebeitel has shown (1980a; 1980-1).
12. *kasmān manyur na vardhate* (3.28.20, 21, 25, 27, 29-32); cf. the variation in 3.28.33 (*tava naivāsti manyur*).
13. 'le manyu d'un dieu est l'élan qui le porte à accomplir des actes par quoi sa divinité s'affirme' (see also p. 182: 'manyu est une qualité permanente, mieux, une faculté essentielle').
14. *na nirmanyuḥ kṣatriyo 'sti loke nirvacanaṃ smṛtam / tad adya tvayi paśyāmi kṣatriye viparītavat* //
15. According to Greg Bailey the cause of Draupadī's suffering is that she finds herself in a situation in which *adharma* overrules *dharma* (1983a: 113-15). This summarizes the whole situation precisely. However, in the dialogue under discussion Draupadī is struggling not only with Duryodhana's adharmic prosperity, but also with Yudhiṣṭhira's interpretation of *dharma*, which seems to make him abandon his dharmic duties as a warrior and king. Hence it is argued that fulfilling dharmic duties does not necessarily yield dharmic results (see p. 87).
16. This passage confirms the importance of 'seeing' as a way of acquiring and expressing knowledge in the epic (see Malinar 1996; 2005), which is corroborated by the numerous occurrences of verbal forms of *paś* and *dṛś*: twenty-three times in 3.28.3-35.
17. To put it pointedly and to give the compound *dharmarāja* a different, rather ironic connotation certainly not in accordance with the dominant interpretation of Yudhiṣṭhira, one could say that he is only a *dharmarāja*, that is, a king only with regard to or according to the law, or morally, but not *de facto*.
18. This education is eloquently displayed in her conversation with Satyabhāmā in *Mahābhārata* 3.222-4.
19. From a text-historical perspective chapter 3.29 could be regarded as an interpolation, because the last verse of the previous chapter (3.28.37) is anti-climactic: it contradicts Draupadī's emphasis in the previous verse, in which *kṣamā* is definitely ruled out. A change in terminology also points in this direction since throughout chapter 3.29 *tejas*, not *manyu*, is regarded as the opposite of *kṣamā*.
20. Consequently, the word *krodha* is primarily used throughout the chapter. There are twenty-one occurrences of the noun and thirteen verbal forms; in addition, the participle of the verbal root '*kup*' (to be angry) appears three times. In contrast, there are only five occurrences of *manyu*, which is used on each occasion directly to reject Draupadī's diagnosis. Firstly, Yudhiṣṭhira explains that perfected men (*siddhas*) are free from anger

and this is why his wrath does not grow (*etad draupadi saṃdhāya na me manyuḥ pravardhate* // 3.30.8); secondly, he argues that a weak and powerless person should suppress *manyu* (*tasmād draupady aśaktasya manyor niyamanaṃ smṛtam* // 3.30.11); thirdly, the wise praise victory over *manyu* (*manyor hi vijayaṃ kṛṣṇe praśaṃsantīha sādhavaḥ* / 3.30.14); fourthly, *manyu* is said to lead to destruction (*tasmān manyur vināśāya prajānām abhavāya ca* // 3.30.30); fifthly, it is claimed that the yonder worlds belong to those who have eliminated *manyu* through *kṣamā* (*yeṣāṃ manyur manuṣyāṇāṃ kṣamayā nihataḥ sadā / teṣāṃ paratare lokās . . .* // 3.30.43).

21. This view, that a king has to know how and when to use both, is also presented by Draupadī at 12.14.17.
22. While *krodha* leads to destruction and non-existence, forgiveness is better, because it secures a pleasant sojourn in the yonder worlds. By also citing an external authority, the '*gāthā*' of Kāśyapa (3.30.36-9), Yudhiṣṭhira praises *kṣamā* as the source of everything.
23. *arhas tasyāham ity eva tasmān māṃ vindate kṣamā* //
24. Jamison calls this 'the Barbara Bush syndrome' (1996: 262 n. 37); cf. Falk 1977: 98.
25. Wenzel is writing on Chrétien de Troyes's medieval epic novel *Erec et Enide*.
26. Hara (1977-8) has dealt with the importance of *kṣamā* for the definition of *tapas* and the *tapasvinī* by arguing that the two rather different meanings of *tapas*, suffering and ascetic heat, are connected in that they both require *kṣamā*: the ascetic practises *kṣamā* in order to prevent his *tapas* being reduced by his giving in to anger; the suffering woman (*tapasvinī*) practises *kṣamā* because she is caught in a hopeless situation, and her *kṣamā* is thus a consequence of weakness and dependence.
27. See n. 16 above.
28. *namo dhātre vidhātre ca yau mohaṃ cakratus tava / pitṛpaitāmahe vṛtte voḍhavye te 'nyathā matiḥ* // It should be noted that the manuscripts of the Southern Recension read *rājye* instead of *vṛtte*.
29. *neha dharmānṛśaṃsyābhyāṃ na kṣāntyā nārjavena ca / puruṣaḥ śriyam āpnoti na ghṛṇitvena karhi cit* // 3.31.2.
30. *nādya bhārata / dharmāt priyataraṃ kiṃ cid api cej jīvitād iha* // 3.31.4 ('There is nothing here on earth which is dearer to you than *dharma*, not even your life'). This also corresponds to Hiltebeitel's observation that the depiction of Draupadī's departure into exile bears 'the connotation of widowhood' (1980-1: 195).
31. *rājānaṃ dharmagoptāraṃ dharmo rakṣati rakṣitaḥ / iti me śrutam āryāṇāṃ tvāṃ tu manye na rakṣati* //
32. *evaṃ sa bhagavān devaḥ svayambhūḥ prapitāmahaḥ / hinasti bhūtair bhūtāni chadma kṛtvā yudhiṣṭhira // saṃprayojya viyojyāyaṃ kāmakārakaraḥ prabhuḥ*

/ *krīḍate bhagavān bhūtair bālaḥ krīḍanakair iva // na mātṛpitṛvad rājan dhātā bhūteṣu vartate / roṣād iva pravṛtto 'yaṃ yathāyam itaro janaḥ //*

33. *dhārtarāṣṭre śriyaṃ dattvā dhātā . . . //*
34. *atha karma kṛtaṃ pāpaṃ na cet kartāram ṛcchati / kāraṇaṃ balam eveha janāñ śocāmi durbalān //*
35. This is a discourse about the different factors that influence the success of one's work, and belongs to the topics of *'daiva'* and *'puruṣakāra'*, which are discussed time and again in the epic. A detailed discussion is not possible within the scope of this chapter. For general discussion of these topics, see Scheftelowitz 1929; Woods 2001.
36. Usually the men turn away, as for instance Nala, who flees from Damayantī (3.59); Duḥṣanta, who leaves Śakuntalā in the hermitage (1.67); Rāma, who rejects Sītā (3.275); and Yudhiṣṭhira, who does not look back when Draupadī falls into the snow during the '*mahāprasthāna*', but blames her affection for Arjuna (17.2). All this underscores women's dharmic dependence and subordination.
37. See for example *Bhagavadgītā* 7.4–10 where Kṛṣṇa describes his relationship to *prakṛti* in terms of procreational activities. Cf. Malinar 1996: 228ff.
38. For later traditions, see Leslie 1986.
39. Vyāsa confers the so-called '*vidyā pratismṛti*' on Yudhiṣṭhira, which allows the magical consecration of weapons; see J.L. Mehta 1990.

Krishna Vasudeva

Iravati Karwe

Krishna enters the story of the Mahabharata at the very end of *Adiparva,* the first part, at the time of the marriage of Draupadi. Before this he is in no way involved with either the Kauravas or the Pandavas. Pandu had married Kunti, Vasudeva's sister (Krishna's aunt). Beyond this one mention, even the house of the Yadavas is not referred to. While the Pandavas were growing up, they survived many attempts on their lives, mainly owing to the ceaseless vigilance of Kunti and Vidura. But during all these hard times Kunti never seems to have sought the help of her parental house, the Yadavas. Gandhari's brother, on the one hand, had established himself firmly at the Kaurava court from the day of his sister's marriage to Dhritarashtra. On the other hand, Kunti's and Madri's people are not even heard of. Perhaps they did attend the weddings but returned immediately as was customary. Once her husband had died and she herself was placed in the lowly position of a dependant at the Kaurava court, Kunti could not expect anyone from her father's home to come and willingly share her own indignity. Certainly, she and her fatherless children would have found a home with the Yadavas, but she feared that their absence from Hastinapura would endanger their claim to the throne. Even today, a wise widow would thus live humbly in her brother-in-law's house so as not to jeopardise her son's right to the ancestral property. Also, the Yadavas themselves were busy during this very period. Krishna had killed Kamsa and as a result made an enemy of the powerful monarch Jarasandha, Kamsa's father-in-law. Jarasandha succeeded in driving the Yadavas out of their home on the banks of the Jamuna. The Yadavas fled south to Gujarat and established the new city of Dvaraka on the seashore and regained their former status. These might have been the various reasons why the Yadavas are not heard of in the story until the time of the Pandavas' marriage. Krishna and Balarama had come there not to win Draupadi but to be present at an important Kshatriya gathering. As soon as Krishna saw Arjuna getting up from among the Brahmans and performing the difficult feat of archery that won the princess, he recognised all the five brothers who, his spies had told him, had not died in the fire at Varanavata. When he saw Dharma leave the assembly, he followed him home, greeted Kunti and went back immediately to Dvaraka, whence he returned with many Yadavas, bearing rich presents for the marriage ceremony. After this first meeting, most of the major successes of the Pandavas were achieved with the help of Krishna. The Pandavas had gained the alliance of the house of Drupada by their marriage. The Yadavas, too, openly acknowledged them as kinsfolk and friends. With two such powerful allies, the Pandavas could not be denied their right to the kingdom of Hastinapura. Dhritarashtra, realising this, made over to them the town of Khandavaprastha and the surrounding forest area. The Pandavas with Krishna's help burnt the forest, brought new land under the plough, enlarged the small town to become their capital, the city of Indraprastha. After settling them there, Krishna went back to Dvaraka. Many people, including learned Brahmans, came to Dharma's new capital and gave him the idea of performing the Rajasuya yajna performed by kings. This sacrifice, if performed succesfully, establishes the superiority of the king over all his contemporaries. In order to accomplish it, a king has to have a core of strong kin-group, personal popularity and some other friendly kings who are willing to agree to his suzerainty. There still remain a few who have to be conquered in battle. The preparations for the sacrifice began by 'conquering expeditions' in all directions, east, west, north and south. As usual Krishna was called for consultations. He showed his knowledge and political acumen by telling Dharma the names of kings on whom he could rely as allies and others whom he would have to defeat. He also recalled the rout of the Yadavas at the hands of Jarasandha, king of Magadha, and convinced Dharma that this powerful monarch would have to be subdued before the Rajasuya could even be thought of. This is one of the few places where we hear from Krishna himself some details of his early life. Apart from this, the Mahabharata says nothing at all of his childhood and boyhood in Vrindavana and Mathura as do, the later Puranas, *Harivamsha* and *Bhagavata*. From the Mahabharata we know that many Yadava clans like Vrishni, Andhaka, Bhoja and others had settled in Dvaraka, apparently under the rule of Balarama, Krishna's eldest half-brother. Many great Yadava warriors are mentioned time and again. We know their clan and parentage, but even if every scrap of information given there is gathered together, it is not possible to construct a connected account and genealogy. It seems from their descriptions that they were rich, strong, quick-tempered, ready to sport their weapons at the smallest provocation, proud, and very skilful charioteers. They possessed enormous riches. There were factions amongst them. One party wanted Krishna to be their king, but he had many opponents too. So, in order to avoid all internal strife, Krishna crowned Balarama, the eldest son of his father, king. There was never any open quarrel between the two, yet they had many differences on important matters. Balarama must have been aware that his position was due mainly to Krishna, and he had to agree to his wishes on some occasions. Arjuna abducted and married Subhadra, their half-sister, with Krishna's knowledge and help. Balarama with the other Yadava heroes were bent on pursuing Arjuna and bringing her back, but Krishna succeeded in convincing them about the desirability of an alliance with the Pandavas. Krishna was especially fond of the Pandavas. Though Balarama wished them well, he was not partial to them as against the Kauravas who, too, were the cousins of the Yadavas. In the war, he remained neutral. When Bhima hit Duryodhana on the thigh with his mace, against the rules, Balarama wanted to kill Bhima for the foul act but once again Krishna stopped him. The internal factions amongst the Yadavas became apparent at the time of the war. Krishna and his supporters were on the Pandavas' side, whereas many other Yadavas went over to the Kauravas. Like all Kshatriyas of his time Krishna had many wives of whom Satyabhama, the daughter of Satrajit, was the eldest and therefore the most important. She always accompanied Krishna on his visits to the Pandavas. Rukmini, who in later books assumes more importance, is mentioned but once or twice. The Krishna shown in the Mahabharata has no resemblance at all to the flute-playing lover of milkmaids, the divine child, or the miracle-worker of later tradition. It is true that he did win many women, as did his friend Arjuna. But this was not a sign of running after women, it was more a symbol of valour. Marriages among the Kshatriyas were contracted more out of political necessity than love. Of the Pandavas, Arjuna was the same age as Krishna. He always bowed to Dharma and Bhima as his elders, and was, in turn, shown respect by the twins, but he always embraced Arjuna as an equal. These two picknicked together, drank together and were intimate friends. At about this time, the Yadavas had not been long in Dvaraka after very troubled times. The Pandavas, too, for the first time in their life, were enjoying independence and safety. Krishna must have seen that for both the houses the alliance would be very profitable. His personal friendship with Arjuna was, however, a matter of pure affection and deep regard. Krishna's relation with the Pandavas cannot be understood without reference to his whole life. Though he says in the Gita that he had no ambition or objective at all, yet he had, in reality, many political and personal goals to attain. Some of these goals concerned his clan, some the whole class of Kshatriyas and some were entirely personal. His reason for killing Kainsa was in part personal, in part it was to liberate his clan from a despot. He had to protect his people from Jarasandha and also, after having given security to them, he had to keep them together, repressing their eternal quarrels. Another of his objectives was to kill Jarasandha. This, too, involved the dual purpose of personal revenge and the good of the Kshatriya class. Jarasandha had imprisoned one hundred reigning kings whom he intended to sacrifice to god. This was totally opposed to the Kshatriya code of those times and had upset the internal order of the class. That is why his destruction was essential for the good of the class. The Mahabharata is very explicit about the structure of the Kshatriya society and the strict code of behaviour of the many clans with respect to one another, who were all related and who ruled over the whole of the Gangetic plain. From west to east, the kingdoms of Sindhu, Saumira, Madra, Gandhara, Matsya, Panchala, Hastinapura, Magadha,

Chedi and Vidarbha, were ruled by hereditary kings for generations. When the Yadavas left their kingdom of Mathura and founded the new capital of Dvaraka, they do not seem to have wrested it from any reigning king. Many battles and conquests are described, but there is not a single mention of any king being deprived by any other of his kingdom. After Dharma won the Mahabharata battle, Vyasa advised him: 'Send messengers to the kingdoms of all those who have died in battle. Assure the widowed queens of personal safety and crown the young heirs and guard them. If a widow be with child give her protection and when an heir is born, make him the king and appoint reliable guardians (regents)' (*Shantiparva* 34.31-33). All this shows that there was a code of war, and conquering each other's kingdom was not a part of it. The advice that Krishna gave to Dharma at the time of the Rajasuya sacrifice brings this out very vividly. When the four brothers conquered many kings, they took from them tribute and their consent to Dharma's suzerainty, invited them to be guests at the sacrifice and returned. Shishupala too had meant this very thing when he told Dharma, in effect, that the Rajasuya was made possible by the consent of all. Krishna again emphasised this while talking about and to Jarasandha. He said, 'It is against the Kshatriya code that you should imprison kings and plan to sacrifice them. We have no quarrel with you if you release them all.' When Jarasandha would not agree to this, he had to be killed. The performer of the Rajasuya had to prove not only his valour but also his adherence to the Kshatriya dharma. According to Krishna, Dharma, the eldest of the Pandavas, fulfilled both these conditions. Though the Rajasuya sacrifice gave the performer the title of *Samrat* (suzerain king) this did not involve upsetting the Kshatriya order in which kings of nearly equal rank and strength ruled neighbouring kingdoms. Jarasandha's defeating and imprisoning other kings had shaken the very foundation of this order.

It is only from Buddhist times onwards that we get descriptions of empires and empire-builders. Kings endeavoured to annex their neighbours' kingdoms to their own. Such empires were built by the king of Kosala, by Chandragupta Maurya, Ashoka, Samudra Gupta, etc. Kalidas, the great Sanskrit poet, who lived about fifteen hundred years after the Mahabharata war, and belonged to the empire-building era, referred nostalgically to the vanished Kshatriya code of olden days. He wrote about the ancient kings of Ayodhya and said, 'King Raghu deprived the king of Kalinga of his glory but not of his land.' Thus, in the Mahabharata times, the so-called 'world-conquest' was a game played according to strict rules. The objective was to gain fame, not territory. Another rule of the game was to collect wealth in the form of tributes from the conquered kings and to spend it in giving gifts at the time of the sacrifice when the invited kings were feasted for days, honoured with suitable gifts and sent back to their kingdoms. This very idea was mentioned by Kalidasa again when he described how Raghu was reduced to poverty after his Rajasuya. Krishna was endeavouring to re-establish this order of the class and for this the destruction of Jarasandha was necessary.

Knowing that it would be difficult to defeat Jarasandha in a full battle, Krishna had Bhima kill him in single combat. After the killing of Jarasandha, the 'world-conquest' was but a formal affair and Dharma could successfully perform the Rajasuya sacrifice.

On the final day of the sacrifice only one duty remained: to honour the assembled Kshatriyas, giving special recognition to the wisest and the best among them. Dharma naturally chose Krishna for this honour after consulting Bhishma. King Shishupala, Krishna's cousin and rival, objected saying that elders like Bhishma or Vidura should receive the honour. Tension in the pavilion rose as Shishupala spoke. He grossly insulted Bhishma and the Pandavas and started to incite the assembled kings to walk out of the pavilion and challenge the Pandavas to a fight. Such a quarrel would have reduced to nothing a year's ceaseless effort to perform the sacrifice. Before such a dreadful thing could happen, Krishna got up and swiftly threw his discus at Shishupala, severing his head. Though shocked, the assembled kings were unable to take any concerted action. They allowed themselves to be pacified and the Rajasuya drew to a triumphant conclusion. This killing of Shishupala was not premeditated and Krishna has been blamed for it. But if one reads the whole episode one can see that he averted a catastrophe by this timely though ruthless deed. Shishupala had come as an invited guest and ally, but he had forfeited his rights by having transgressed the rules and limits of propriety.

All these efforts of Krishna were on behalf of his family, the Yadavas, his friends the Pandavas, and the whole Kshatriya class. He had, however, also a personal ambition. This ambition was to become a *'Vasudeva'*, a position approaching divinity. The Krishna in the Mahabharata is definitely not a god, as depicted in later literature. He was, however, an extraordinary man, and his great personal ambition was to be called Vasudeva.

Exactly what becoming a Vasudeva means is not made clear in the Mahabharata. Ordinarily Vasudeva would be simply a patronymic: the son of Vasudeva. In that sense, as sons of Vasudeva, Krishna and all his brothers were already Vasudevas. All we know from the Mahabharata is that 'Vasudeva' was apparently a title which could be borne by only one man in an age.

The significance of being a Vasudeva can only be understood from Jain sources. The Jains are known as great systematizers. They have divided the wheel of time into twenty-four sections, during twelve of which the world was supposed to be getting better and better. This period was called the *utsarpini* (upgrade). The remaining was one of regression, called *avasarpini* (downgrade). In one epoch of twenty-four divisions, nine Vasudevas were born. Rama and Krishna both were Vasudevas born in a period of regression.

The significance of being a Vasudeva can only be radiance. The *'Baladeva'* was the brother of the Vasudeva, mainly known for his devotion to the Vasudeva. The *'Prati-Vasudeva'* was the main enemy of the Vasudeva. In the last epoch, Krishna was the Vasudeva, his brother Balarama was the Baladeva, and Jarasandha, the Prati-Vasudeva. In one of the previous epochs these were Rama, Laxmana and Ravana.

The Vasudeva was a ruler of great valour, splendour and of the seven most precious things in the world, and the most beautiful woman. Three more things are said of him: he lacked nothing, he found something good in

everything, and he never fought standing on the ground.

The Krishna of the Mahabharata can be said to possess the seven precious things, some of which are mentioned by name in the Mahabharata and all of which are mentioned in the later Puranas. The description of his riches and personal splendour makes it clear that he lacked nothing. He was known as the best charioteer of his times, a warrior who never fought on the ground.

Immediately after the Rajasuya sacrifice, Krishna set out to establish his claim to the title of Vasudeva. He went to Pundra, where the king called himself 'Vasudeva'. Challenging him to combat, Krishna killed him. He came back. He had accomplished everything he wanted for himself, for his friends, his clan, and his class. But to his horror he found that Dharmaraja had lightly gambled away the kingdom which he had won him with such effort.

He did not reprimand Dharma. He only said, 'If I had been here, I would never have allowed this dice game.' While consoling the Pandavas and Draupadi for the loss of the kingdom and their exile in the forest, he promised them that he and the Drupadas would take care of the other queens and the children. In the final year of their exile he went to see them and again reassured them of his friendship, and promised that he would help them regain their kingdom.

A year later, when the Pandavas came out of disguise and declared themselves, their situation was similar to that at the time of Draupadi's swayamvara. Once again, they had just come out of hiding, were without a kingdom, and were arranging a marriage alliance. For, Abhimanyu, the son of Arjuna, was being married to Uttara, the daughter of Virata. Again the friends and allies of the Pandavas assembled: the Yadavas, the Drupadas, and now the Viratas. After a long consultation it was decided to send Krishna to Hastinapura to plead the Pandavas' case. If he could not get Duryodhana to agree to giving back the Pandavas' share of the kingdom, Krishna was empowered to make whatever compromise he thought fit.

Up to the time of the Rajasuya sacrifice, Krishna's main concern was for the political situation of the day. He did, of course, care for his friends, and was an intimate companion of Arjuna. His friendship, however, had been only one part of his many-sided life. But after the Pandavas' exile, he set aside all his other ambitions to devote himself to their cause. The Pandavas were valorous, but they lacked the wisdom to direct their own affairs. Krishna took it upon himself to look after their personal safety, their kingly position, and their reputation as warriors.

He went to Hastinapura and met Duryodhana. Though he tried his utmost to reason with Duryodhana, he could neither bring about a reconciliation nor an honourable compromise. War was inevitable.

Both sides started preparations. To secure allies they visited the neighbouring kings. Duryodhana from Hastinapura and Arjuna from Virata's capital went to Dvaraka to seek the Yadavas' help. Balarama was partial to the Hastinapura house, but he refused to enter the conflict on either side. Kritavarma, from the clan of Hardika, joined the Kauravas. Satyaki and other friends of Krishna, joined the Pandavas. Duryodhana and Arjuna reached Krishna's house at the same time. Krishna was sleeping. Arjuna sat at the foot of the bed, Duryodhana at the head. As soon as Krishna woke, both requested his help. Krishna agreed to help both sides. To one side he would give his famed soldiers, the Narayaniya. On the other side he himself would be present, but would not take up arms. Since on waking he had seen Arjuna first, he gave the choice to him. Arjuna chose Krishna, and Duryodhana, well-satisfied, went away with the army.

Krishna, pleased at Arjuna's confidence and at his request, agreed to be his charioteer. Arjuna had made the right choice. The Pandavas did not lack warriors; what they needed was a dispassionate, determined counsellor. That they found in Krishna.

The very first day of the war, all of Krishna's persuasive power was required to make Arjuna fight. Seeing the Kaurava army filled with his kinsmen and led by his grandfather, and his teacher, Arjuna had no heart to fight. In an impulse of revulsion he threw down his weapons. Krishna remonstrated, reminding Arjuna of his duty as a Kshatriya and warning him that he would be called a coward. Arjuna still refused. Krishna continued his argument: 'What finally are you afraid of? You are afraid of killing these people. But everything that lives must die. Just now as a Kshatriya your duty is to kill these people. You refuse to do what is necessary, thinking thereby that you can avoid doing something bad. But once you are born, you are involved in actions. You cannot choose not to act, nor can you always do as you want. Your whole position in life determines the actions you have to perform. Your action is bad only when you do it for what you will gain from it. Therefore act properly, don't think of what you will gain, don't act for specific ends, and never hope to live without acting.' Krishna continued his arguments, stressing that one cannot run away from life: 'You can realize *Brahman* only by fulfilling the duties of your position on earth. Not ascetic retreat, but dispassionate, considered action is the only way to the Absolute.'

Arjuna at last agreed to fight, but refused to stand against Bhishma. In exasperation Krishna leapt from his chariot, whip in hand, to kill Bhisma himself. Arjuna jumped down, embraced Krishna's feet, and begged him not to break his vow. The next day Arjuna wounded Bhishma, removing him from the battle.

In his philosophic outpouring of the first day, Krishna was Arjuna's teacher and counsellor. But in the events that followed the death of Abhimanyu, Arjuna's son, Krishna revealed the depth of his affection for Arjuna.

When Drona took over command from Bhishma, he sent a diversionary force against Arjuna, and then deployed the rest of his army in an intricate formation called 'the labyrinth'. Arjuna's sixteen-year-old son Abhimanyu was the only one left in the Pandava camp who knew how to penetrate the labyrinth. He managed to go in, but Jayadratha and others immediately closed the entrance again, trapping the boy alone inside. Veteran Kaurava warriors attacked Abhimanyu, killing his horses and his charioteer. He continued to fight bravely on the ground but was finally killed.

That night Arjuna returned to find the entire Pandava camp in lamentation. Weeping and raging he asked his brothers, 'How could my son be killed when you were all there?' He vowed that next day before the sun went down he would kill Jayadratha. Krishna protested, 'What do you mean, you are going to kill him tomorrow? Without even consulting me you have taken a terrible burden on your head. We will be the laughing-stock of the whole world.' Arjuna went on raving, so Krishna said no more. He brought Arjuna back to his camp, gave him his evening meal, and spread fragrant grass on his pallet.

After talking a while with Arjuna, he left him and went to his own camp.

Jayadratha was not a great warrior and killing him was neither important nor difficult. But the next day, the whole of the Kaurava army would be devoted to his protection. If Arjuna failed, he would be bound in honour to commit suicide. Krishna could not bear that. 'I have my wives, my brothers, and my kinsmen,' he told his charioteer. 'None of them is as dear to me as is Arjuna. I could not live for a moment if something happened to him.' He would try his best, he said, to see that Arjuna fulfilled his vow. But if it appeared that Arjuna alone could not accomplish it he himself would take up weapons and fight. 'Keep ready my chariot and all weapons', he said, 'and bring it when you hear my conch. Tomorrow the world will see the test of my friendship with Arjuna.'

When Jayadratha heard of Arjuna's vow, he wanted to leave the war and return to his own kingdom. But the Kauravas persuaded him that he would be safe staying in the rear.

The next day, as Krishna had foreseen, the sole object of the Kauravas was to stop Arjuna from penetrating their lines to reach Jayadratha. The Pandavas, on their part, were trying to penetrate the enemy ranks where they could, in an attempt to clear Arjuna's passage. The first to attack Arjuna was Drona, who challenged him to a fight. With a rapid volley of arrows, Arjuna threw him into confusion and rode forward laughing, 'I am not going to fight you today'. Working with one mind, the horses, the charioteer and the warrior went forward, taking advantage of an open space in the enemy's momentary hesitation.

They fought on, till Krishna knew the horses needed rest. Unharnessing them, he pulled the arrowheads from their flesh, stroked them, and let them rub their backs on the ground. While Krishna was busy thus, Arjuna stood by and fought off the enemy. Again Arjuna and Krishna mounted, and the refreshed horses surged forward. A little before the sun set, Krishna sighted Jayadratha in the distance and pointed him out to Arjuna. Arjuna shot, and his first arrow penetrated Jayadratha's throat.

Arjuna's impulsiveness had cost Krishna a sleepless night and a day of extraordinary effort. The next time, Krishna gave Arjuna no chance to be swayed by a momentary impulse. Arjuna was fighting Karna, who was now the commander of the Kauravas. When one of Karna's wheels sank in the soft earth, he dismounted and tried to free it. Appealing to the Kshatriya dharma, he asked Arjuna to stop fighting until he could get back in his chariot. The appeal was just the kind to move the chivalrous Arjuna. But Krishna immediately shouted, 'Who are you to expect dharma? Where was your dharma when Draupadi was disrobed? Where was it when all of you in chariots killed the boy Abhimanyu?' If there had been the slightest impulse of pity in Arjuna's heart, the reminder of Karna's wrongs put an end to it. Without hesitation Arjuna drew his bow and killed Karna.

When Duryodhana, the last of the Kauravas, was killed, Krishna was given the task of going to Hastinapura to console Dhritarashtra and Gandhari. As he sat with the aged couple, messengers came and reported the conversation between the dying Duryodhana and Ashvatthama. They reported Ashvatthama had got himself crowned as commander of the Kauravas, and had vowed vengeance on the Pandavas. The Kaurava army had been completely defeated and dispersed. The whole of the Kaurava camp was deserted. Krishna realized that Ashvatthama must be planning some treachery against the Pandavas. Cutting short his conversation, he hurried back to the Pandavas' camp.

The whole camp was in revelry. With victory, all discipline had been forgotten. Only the Pandavas themselves were anxiously awaiting Krishna's return. Without telling them his suspicions he took the Pandavas away, and had them spend the night in the deserted Kaurava camp. That night Ashvatthama and Kritavarma attacked the drunk and sleeping warriors. They killed Draupadi's brother and all her sleeping sons and set fire to the camp.

From the first day of the war to the last, Krishna had saved the Pandavas. In due time, the Pandavas were put on the throne of Hastinapura, and Krishna returned to Dvaraka. He had achieved all his life's aims: security for the Yadavas and for the Kshatriya class, the throne of Hastinapura for his friends, the Pandavas, and Vasudeva-ship for himself.

The next thirty-five years must have been the most tranquil period of Krishna's life. The end came suddenly and catastrophically.

The story of the end of Krishna and the Yadavas is confused. Part of it is probably historical, part of it is certainly overlaid with myth. It is said that some Yadava boys were playing when they saw many Brahmans approaching. To make fun of the Brahmans, they dressed one boy as a pregnant girl, brought 'her' solemnly to the Brahmans and had 'her' bow down to them. They asked them, 'Sirs, can you tell us what will be born, a boy or a girl?' The Brahmans saw through the trick and in anger at their disrespect said, 'This boy will give birth to an iron pestle which will destroy all the Yadavas except Krishna and Balarama.' The next day the boy delivered. The pestle was immediately pulverized and the powder was thrown into the sea. Then the king made a proclamation that henceforth no Yadava should be allowed to drink liquor. The city was frightened by all kinds of inauspicious omens. Krishna 'remembered how Gandhari had cursed him at the close of the war, 'In thirty-five years the Yadava clan will be destroyed.' Krishna and Balarama decided that all the Yadavas should go on a pilgrimage along the sea. Taking their wives, grown-up young people and immense quantities of food and drink, they went to Prabhasa. After eating they started on a great orgy of drinking. Suddenly a quarrel started. Satyaki sneered at Kritavarma, 'That wasn't very heroic, the way you killed poor Draupadi's sons in a night attack.' Kritavarma countered, 'I suppose it was heroic the way you killed Bhurishrava, cutting off his head after his arms had already been cut off.' From words they came to blows, and Kritavarma killed Satyaki. In revenge, Krishna's son Pradyumna killed Kritavarma. This triggered the old hostilities between rival clans and soon they were at one another's throats. Since they had no weapons, they pulled out handfuls of reeds growing by the shore, and the reeds turned to iron in their hands. These reeds had grown from the powdered pestle thrown back by the sea. All Krishna's sons were killed. In anger Krishna himself killed nearly all the Yadavas. Finally, two of the survivors, Daruka and Babhru, begged him to desist and seek out Balarama. They found Balarama sitting in an isolated spot under a tree. Krishna sent Daruka to Hastinapura to inform them that the

Yadavas had been killed by the curse of the Brahmans and that Arjuna should come to Dvaraka. Krishna then turned to Babhru and asked him to take the women and children into Dvaraka to protect them from the Dasyus. Babhru started to do his bidding when he was killed by an iron pestle thrown by a hunter. Krishna asked Balarama to wait while he took the women and children into the city. Telling his father what had happened, he asked him to guard the survivors till Arjuna came. Then he went out to rejoin Balarama. He found Balarama dead. Sitting down under a tree in melancholy contemplation, he was killed by an arrow from the hunter Jara.

The story above is full of contradictions and absurdities. Neither the *Harivamsha* nor the Jain versions of the story are any less confusing. That the Yadavas were destroyed in a drunken quarrel is the core of all the versions. The curses of Gandhari and the Brahmans seem to be obvious later interpolations, as does the ban on drinking among the Yadavas. One of the most improbable aspects of the story is that Krishna, who had worked all his life for the welfare of the Yadavas, killed most of them himself.

Apparently, the Yadavas were outside Dvaraka on an outing when a quarrel broke out and they started killing each other. It seems that there were also hostile bands of people that chose this opportunity to attack. The grass that changed to iron could well have been stiff iron-tipped reeds used as lances and arrows.

After the massacre of the Yadavas, Balarama, as usual, was sitting bewildered and ineffective. Even on their last day, Krishna had to take the initiative in providing for the safety of the others. He brought the women and children into the city and returned to stand by Balarama, to whom he had been loyal all his life. He found Balarama dead. He was free to go back into the safety of the city but he chose to remain outside. This deliberate choice of death rather than safety fits into the role he had played throughout his life. He was Krishna Vasudeva, the resplendent one, the one who lacked nothing, the one who gave magnificently. He could not remain with the women and children, awaiting rescue by Arjuna. He could not live under the protection of anyone, even of the Pandavas. He welcomed death, as all other actions of his life, with conscious deliberation.

Though Krishna had been primarily the giver in their life-long friendship, after his death he was more than repaid by Arjuna. Arjuna came and heard from old Vasudeva the account of the Yadavas' death.[1]

The Pandavas settled the sons of Satyaki and Kritavarma in small kingdoms, and gave Indraprastha to Vajra, Krishna's grandson and only survivor. Just as Krishna said he could not live in a world without Arjuna, Arjuna and the others could not live without him. Leaving Parikshit, Arjuna's gransdon, on the throne of Hastinapura, they set out to die.

Krishna had died. The Pandavas had died. But Krishna was reborn. The Abhiras, the very people who destroyed Dvaraka, brought Krishna back to life by making him their god. As they gradually established kingdoms in western India, like all other newly come rulers in India, they laid claims to Kshatriyahood. They took the name of their predecessors, the Yadavas, and made Krishna their god. The Abhiras were keepers of cows and they made their god a cowherd. Stories were elaborated about the child Krishna, stealing butter, playing pranks and making love to the milkmaids.

This transformation of Krishna is something of a paradox. The Krishna of the Mahabharata is wholly human, but his complexity and a kind of uninvolvement in his most intense action make him hard to grasp. We cannot feel close to the Mahabharata Krishna. The cowherds made Krishna a god. Krishna's teaching is contained in the first six chapters of the *Bhagavadgita*. Even in these chapters, about half of it is later addition. In these verses, Krishna talks as a man to his friend who is caught in a terrible mental crisis and needs guidance. But it is guidance given to an equal and not a devotee. The teaching is free of the later *bhakti* (devotion to god) principle. It does not contain the wealth of philosophical terminology seen in the later chapters of the Gita. In many ways it is a simpler philosophy and also a sterner one. It fully endorses the ritual of sacrifices. We have seen how all Kshatriyas were keen on these performances for the sake of this-worldly and other-wordly considerations. The concept of a conscious self as separate from a body was well known and the concept of an all-pervading consciousness, which is called *Atman* or just 'He', was also well known. This was coupled with a firm belief in rebirth according to one's merits and the possibility of not being reborn ever. Krishna told Arjuna, 'Do not be silly. All the people gathered here, including you and me, have been on the earth before and will be on the earth in future time. What dies is but the body, the self remains indestructible. Everything that *is* has death and everything that dies has birth, so you must not mourn because you are going to kill these warriors. For a person of the warrior class, to die or to kill in an open war is but the proper type of death. You cannot avoid bad actions by desisting from war. Other actions also have values. Nor can you desist from action as long as you live. The best way out is therefore to go on doing the actions which befall one because one is born into particular social circumstances, but the actions should be done without any desire for a selfish or other end. This is called *Yoga*. In this stage the mind is at one with the All-self, the body is doing actions without involvement, without an eye to their consequence. There is no joy at fulfilment, no fear or frustration because of failure. This ever-present awareness of the Atman, the All-soul, takes away values like goodness and badness from one's actions. You should always be aware of this, beyond all present miseries, joys and involvements.'

This advice given to Arjuna did not bear fruit, because the two people Arjuna did not wish to kill by his hands were not killed by him. His arrow threw Bhishma. his grandfather, from the chariot, who lived for a few months more, and Drona was killed by Dhrishtadyumna and not by him. This shows that the advice was to a friend and not to a humble devotee as is represented in the later chapters of the *Bhagavadgita*.

Krishna remains an elusive personality for this very reason. He worked, he thought intensely, he advised others, but we do not find him downcast or mourning because his actions, thought or advice did not bear fruit. He danced in joy, he killed in anger his own kinsmen as we are told in *Mousalaparva,* but we do not find him mourning even after the terrible end of his clan. He made arrangements that the old, the very young and the women be taken care of, and then met with his death. This is what he would have called Yoga, this calm, this noninvolvement. This is why Krishna remains a figure for thought and search, but never touches one emotionally as do the other figures of this great epic. It might have been for this reason that when at last he was made into a god, he became a god with the warmest human qualities: the naughty child, the playmate of simple cowherds, and the eternal lover of all the young women of India.

Note

1. Vasudeva died and Arjuna had the task of cremating him, Krishna and the other Yadavas. Then taking the women, children, and the treasure of the city, he started to return to Hastinapura. On the way, he was attacked by the Abhiras and robbed of some of the women and treasure.

Appendix

Yudhiṣṭhira-Yakṣa Dialogue

From the Āraṇyaka Parva

Yudhiṣṭhira-Yakṣa Dialogue

The Yakṣa said:

I stopped these brothers of yours time and again, king, when they tried to take water by force. Then I finished them off. This water is not to be drunk by anyone here who wants to live, king. Pārtha, do not commit violence! This is my old property. But answer my questions, Kaunteya, and you may drink and fetch.

Yudhiṣṭhira said:

I do not at all covet your old property, Yakṣa, for strict people
25 never approve of such coveting. As a person himself gives an
account of himself, I shall answer your questions according to
my lights, my lord. Ask me!

The Yakṣa said:

What causes the sun to rise, and what are its companions? What makes it set, and on what is it founded?

Yudhiṣṭhira said:

Brahman makes the sun rise, and the Gods are its companions. The Law makes it set, and on truth is it founded.

The Yakṣa said:

By what does one become learned, by what does one attain to great things, by what does one have a second, king, by what does one gain insight?

Yudhiṣṭhira said:

By learning one becomes learned, by austerities one attains

to great things; one has a second in perseverance, one gains insight by attending on one's elders.

The Yakṣa said:

30 What is the divine nature of the brahmins, what is their Law, like that of the strict, what is their human nature, what is their vice as of those without strictness?

Yudhiṣṭhira said:

Veda study is their divine nature, austerity their Law, as it is of the strict: mortality is their human nature, detraction their vice, as it is of those without strictness.

The Yakṣa said:

What is the human nature of the barons, what their Law, as it is of the strict? What is their human nature, what their vice, as it is of those without strictness?

Yudhiṣṭhira said:

Weaponry is their divine nature, sacrifice their Law, as it is of the strict; fear is their human nature, desertion their vice, as it is of those without strictness.

The Yakṣa said:

Which is the one sacrificial chant, which is the one sacrificial formula? What cuts down the sacrifice, what does the sacrifice not exceed?

Yudhiṣṭhira said:

35 Breath is the sacrificial chant, mind the sacrificial formula; speech alone cuts down the sacrifice, and the sacrifice does not exceed speech.

The Yakṣa said:

What is the best of the dropping, what is the best of the falling, what is the best of the standing, what is the best of the speaking?

Yudhiṣṭhira said:

Rain is the best of the dropping, seed the best of the falling, cows the best of the standing, a son the best of the speaking.

The Yakṣa said:

Who breathes, experiences the objects of the senses, is intelligent, honored in the world, and respected by all creatures—yet is not alive?

Yudhiṣṭhira said:

He who makes no offerings to the five, to wit Gods, guests, dependents, ancestors, and himself, may breathe but is not alive.

The Yakṣa said:

40 What has more weight than the earth, what is higher than heaven, what is faster than the wind, what more numerous than men?

Yudhiṣṭhira said:

The mother has more weight than the earth, the father is higher than heaven, the mind is faster than the wind, worries are more numerous than men.

The Yakṣa said:

What does not close the eyes when asleep, what does not stir when born, what has no heart, what grows by speeding along?

Yudhiṣṭhira said:

A fish does not close the eyes when asleep, an egg does not stir when born, a rock has no heart, a river grows by speeding along.

The Yakṣa said:

What is the friend of the traveler, what the friend at home, what the friend of the sick man, what the friend of the moribund?

Yudhiṣṭhira said:

45 The caravan is the friend of the traveler, the wife is the friend at home, the physician is the friend of the sick man, charity the friend of the moribund.

The Yakṣa said:

What travels alone, what once born is born again, what is the cure for snow, what is the great acre?

Yudhiṣṭhira said:

The sun travels alone, the moon is reborn, fire is the cure of snow, the earth is the great acre.

The Yakṣa said:

What in a word makes the Law, what in a word is fame, what in a word leads to heaven, what in a word is happiness?

Yudhiṣṭhira said:

Ability in a word makes the Law, giving in a word is fame, truth in a word leads to heaven, character in a word is happiness.

The Yakṣa said:

50 What is the self of a man, what is the friend made by fate, what is the support of his life, what is his highest resort?

Yudhiṣṭhira said:

A son is the self of a man, a wife is the friend made by fate, the monsoon is the support of his life, charity is his highest resort.

The Yakṣa said:

What is the greatest of riches, what is the greatest of possessions, what is the greatest of boons, what is the greatest of comforts?

Yudhiṣṭhira said:

Ability is the greatest of riches, learning the greatest of possessions, health the greatest of boons, contentment the greatest of comforts.

The Yakṣa said:

What is the highest Law in the world, what Law always bears fruit, what does not grieve when tamed, what bond never comes loose?

Yudhiṣṭhira said:

55 Uncruelty is the highest Law, the Law of the *Veda* always bears fruit, the mind does not grieve when tamed, the bond of the good never comes loose.

The Yakṣa said:

Abandoning what does one become friendly, abandoning what does one not grieve, abandoning what does one become rich, abandoning what does one become happy?

Yudhiṣṭhira said:

Abandoning pride one becomes friendly, abandoning anger one does not grieve, abandoning desire one does become rich, abandoning greed one becomes happy.

The Yakṣa said:

How is a man dead, how is a kingdom dead, how is a *śrāddha* dead, how is a sacrifice dead?

Yudhiṣṭhira said:

A poor man is dead, a kingless kingdom is dead, a *śrāddha* without a learned brahmin is dead, a sacrifice without payment is dead.

The Yakṣa said:

60 What is the right direction? What is called water? What is

food, Pārtha, and what poison? Tell me the time for a *śrāddha,* then you may drink and fetch.

Yudhiṣṭhira said:

The strict are the right direction, space is water, the cow is food, a request is poison; and a brahmin is the right time for a *śrāddha*—or do you think otherwise, Yakṣa?

The Yakṣa said:

You have answered my questions correctly, enemy-burner! Now tell me, who is a man, and what man owns all riches?

Yudhiṣṭhira said:

The repute of a good deed touches heaven and earth; one is called a man as long as his repute lasts. And he possesses all riches to whom the pleasing and displeasing are the same, and happiness and unhappiness, past and future.

The Yakṣa said:

65 You have explained man and the baronial man of all riches.
For that, one of your brothers shall live, whoever you please.

Yudhiṣṭhira said:

The dark one with the red eyes, shot up like a tall *śāla* tree, with the wide chest and the long arms, O Yakṣa, he shall live—Nakula!

The Yakṣa said:

You have Bhīmasena, you rely on Arjuna, then why, king, do
you want their rival Nakula to live? You give up Bhīma, whose
strength is the match of a myriad elephants, and want Nakula
to live? People say you hold this Bhīmasena so dearly, then by
70 what greater affection do you want his rival to live? All the
Pāṇḍavas rely on the strength of Arjuna's arms, yet you abandon
him and want Nakula to live?

Yudhiṣṭhira said:

Uncruelty is the highest of Laws, this I know as the final truth. And I will not be cruel, so, Yakṣa, Nakula shall live! "The king is by character always lawful." This do people know of me; and I shall not stray from my Law—Nakula shall live, Yakṣa! As Kuntī was, so was Madrī: I allow no difference. I want the same for both my mothers—Nakula shall live, Yakṣa!

The Yakṣa said:

Uncruelty you hold superior to profit and pleasure; for that all your brothers shall live, Bharata bull!

Bibliography

Adarkar, Aditya. "Karna in the Mahabharata." University of Chicago, 2001. Print.

Adluri, Vishwa, and Joydeep Bagchee, eds. *Reading the Fifth Veda: Essays by Alf Hiltebeitel.* Boston: Brill, 2001. Print. Studies in the Mahabharata.

Badrinath, Chaturvedi. *Dharma, India and the World Order: Twenty One Essays.* Bonn: Saint Andrew Press, 1993. Print.

Bharadwaj, Saroj. *The Concept of "Daiva" in the Mahabharata.* Delhi: Nag, 1992. Print.

Biardeau, Madeleine. *Hinduism: The Anthropology of a Civilization.* Trans. Richard Nice. Oxford: Oxford University Press, 1981. Print.

Bowles, Adam. *Dharma, Disorder and the Political in Ancient India/:The Apaddharmaparvan of the Mahabharata.* Leiden: Brill, 2007. Print.

Brockington, John L. *The Sanskrit Epics.* Leiden: Brill, 1998. Print.

Brodbeck, Simon, and Brian Black, eds. *Gender and Narrative in the Mahabharata.* London: Routledge, 2007. Print.

Chakravarti, Uma. "Beyond the Altekarian Paradigm: Towards a New Understanding of Gender Relations in Early Indian History." *Women in Early Indian Societies. Ed. Kumkum Roy.* Delhi: Manoharlal Banarsidass, 1999. Print.

Chana Reich, Tamar. "A Battlefield of a Text: Inner Textual Interpretation In the Sanskrit Mahabharata." University of Chicago, 1998. Print.

Dhand, Arti. *Woman as Fire, Woman as Sage: Sexual Ideology in the Mahabharata.* Albany: SUNY Press, 2008. Print.

Doniger, Wendy. *Karma and Rebirth in Classical Indian Traditions.* Berkeley: University of California Press, 1980. Print.

———. *On Hinduism.* Oxford: Oxford University Press, 2014. Print.

———. *Splitting the Difference: Gender and Myth in Ancient Greece and India.* Chicago, London: The University of Chicago Press, 1999. Print.

———, trans. *The Laws of Manu.* London: Penguin, 2000. Print.

Dumezil, Georges. *The Destiny of the Warrior.* Trans. Alf Hiltebeitel. Chicago: The University of Chicago Press, 1970. Print.

Fitzgerald, James. "India's Fifth Veda: The Mahabharata's Presentation of Itself." *Journal of South Asian Literature* 20.1 (1985): n. pag. Print.

———. *The Mahabharata, Vol. 7.* Chicago: The University of Chicago Press, 2004. Print.

———. "The Many Voices of the Mahabharata." *Journal of the American Oriental Society* 123.4 (2003): 803–18. Print.

Halbfass, Wilhelm. *India and Europe: An Essay in Understanding.* State University of New York Press, 1988. Print.

Hegarty, James. *Religion, Narrative and Public Imagination in South Asia Past and Place in the Sanskrit Mahgbhgrata.* New York: Routledge, 2011. Print.

Hill, Peter. *Fate, Predestination and Human Action in the Mahabharata: A Study in the History of Ideas.* Delhi: Munishiram Manoharlal, 2001. Print.

Hiltebeitel, Alf. *Dharma: Its Early History in Law, Religion and Narrative.* Oxford: Oxford University Press, 2011. Print.

———. "Draupadi's Garments." *Indi-Iranian Journal* 22 (1980): 97–112. Print.

———. "Draupadi's Hair." *Purushartha* 5 (1981): 179–214. Print.

———. "More Rethinking the Mahabharata: Toward a Politics of Bhakti." *Indo-Iranian Journal* 47.3–4 203–27. Print.

———. *Rethinking the Mahabharata: A Reader's Guide to the Education of the Dharma King.* Chicago: The University of Chicago Press, 2001. Print.

———. "The Burning of the Forest." *New Essays in Hinduism: Bardwell L. Smith, Ed.* Leiden: Brill, 1976. 208–224. Print.

———. *The Ritual of Batlle: Krishna in the Mahabharata.* New York: SUNY Press, 1990. Print.

———. *When the Goddess Was a Woman Essays by Alf Hiltebeitel, Volume 2.* Ed. Vishwa Adluri and Joydeep Bagchee. Leiden: Brill, 2011. Print.

Johnson, Williams J. *The Sauptikaparvan of the Mahabharata: The Massacre at Night.* Oxford: Oxford University Press, 1998. Print.

Karve, Iravati. *Yuganta: The End of an Epoch.* New Delhi: Sangam Press, 1974. Print.

Lingat, Robert. "Time and Dharma." *Contributions to Indian Sociology* 6

(1962): n. pag. Print.

Lothspeich, Pamela. *Epic Nation: Reimagining the Mahabharata in the Age of the Empire.* Oxford: Oxford University Press, 2009. Print.

McGrath, Kevin. *The Sanskrit Hero: Karna in Epic Mahabharata.* Leiden: Brill, 2004. Print.

Minkowski, Christopher Z. "Janamejaya's Sattra and Ritual Structure." *Journal of the American Oriental Society* 109.3 (1989): 401–20. Print.

Pollock, Sheldon. *The Language of the Gods in the World of Men: Sanskrit, Culture, and Power in Premodern India.* Berkeley: University of California Press, 2006. Print.

Rajagopalachari, C. *The Mahabharata.* Ed. Jay Mazo. Bombay: International Gita Society. Print.

Ramanujan, A. K. *The Collected Essays of A. K. Ramanujan.* Ed. Vinay Dharwadker. New Delhi: Oxford University Press, 1999. Print.

Scarf, Peter. *Ramopakhyana - The Story of Rama in the Mahabharata: An Independent-Study Reader in Sanskrit.* London: RoutledgeCurzon, 2003. Print.

Sharma, Arvind. *Essays on the Mahabharata.* Leiden: Brill, 1991. Print.

van Buitenen, J. A. B. *The Bhagavadgita in the Mahabharata: Text and Translation.* Chicago, London: The University of Chicago Press, 1981. Print.

———, trans. *The Mahabharata: Vol I.* Chicago, London: The University of Chicago Press, 1973. Print.

———, trans. *The Mahabharata: Vol II.* Chicago, London: The University of Chicago Press, 1975. Print.

Winternitz, Winternitz, and V. Srinivasa Sarma. *A History of Indian Literature.* Vol. 1. Motilal Banarsidass, 1996. Print.

Woods, Julian. *Destiny and Human Initiative in the Mahabharata.* New York: SUNY Press, 2001. Print.

Yaroslav, Vassilkov. "Kalavada (the Doctrine of Cyclical Time) in Mahabharata and the Concept of Heroic Didactics: Proceedings of the First Dubrovnik International Conference on the Sanskrit Epics and Puranas, August 1997." *Composing a Tradition: Concepts, Techniques and Relationships.* Ed. Mary Brockington and Petter Schreiner. Zagreb: Croation Academy of Sciences and the Arts, 1999. Print.